Soil Conservation

Soil Conservation

Norman Hudson

Cornell University Press
Ithaca, New York

First published 1971
Second printing 1973

International Standard Book Number 0–8014–0654–4
Library of Congress Catalog Card Number 76–160152

Printed in Great Britain

Contents

Acknowledgment

My grateful thanks are due to S. DURBACH for permission to publish his method for the design of open channels, to N. P. WOODRUFF for helpful advice on wind erosion problems, to the many friends and colleagues who have loaned photographs, and to the publishers from whose works I have taken diagrams or tables. I would also like to pay tribute to the memory of the late ROB CORMACK, who played a major part in laying the foundations upon which we have been able to build our knowledge of soil conservation in Africa. I am grateful to the Governors of the National College of Agricultural Engineering for permission to write this book while on the staff of the College.

Silsoe, Bedford 1971   NWH

The author and publishers thank the following for permission to include their material in this book:

Aerofilms Limited for plates 1.1, 2.5, 6.6 and 9.1; V. Austin for plate 6.1; Bemis Company Inc, St Louis, Missouri for plate 13.3; Penny Dix (NCAE) for plates 10.1 and 13.2; Fairchild Surveys (Aerofilm photograph) for plate 2.1; F. S. Greyvenstein for plate 12.3; Ministry of Agriculture, Forestry, and Wild Life, Tanzania for plate 6.3; National Institute of Agricultural Engineering for plate 2.2; G. Nicholas for plate 15.4; D. C. H. Plowes for plates 13.1 and 13.4; Philippine Tourist and Travel Association for plate 6.2; Prentice-Hall Inc, Englewood Cliffs, New Jersey for permission to reprint from J. H. Stallings, Soil Conservation 1957 the quotations on pages 26, 148, 150 and 151; J. Rau and Company, Salisbury, Rhodesia for plate 15.1; River and Sea Gabions (London) Limited for plates 12.4, 13.5 and 13.6; T. F. Shaxson for plates 6.4, 6.5 (also used on the jacket), and 15.2; Norris P. Swanson for plate 15.7, and A. Tewksbury for plate 8.1.

Preface

The theme of this book is that recently acquired knowledge not only makes easier the task of controlling soil erosion, but at the same time leads to more productive farming. Only in recent years have we been able to understand why one rainstorm causes more erosion than another apparently similar storm, to know why erosion is more severe in one province than another in the same country, to give numerical values to the factors which influence erosion, and to predict quantitatively how much erosion will occur under given conditions. Now we can do all these things, and the main result of this knowledge is that it shows how simple are the techniques by which we can control erosion. This does not mean that it is now an easy matter to stop erosion—there are many difficulties and hindrances—but the remedies are themselves simple if we learn how to apply them. What is equally important today is that the techniques of erosion control go hand in hand with more efficient farming—better yields, lower costs, and greater food supplies.

The book is intended to serve three purposes. First, soil erosion is as old as the earth, but the detailed study of it, and of how to prevent or control it, is very new. Only in this century has erosion been seriously studied and written about, and soil conservation as a quantitative science is barely twenty years old. As a result, much of our knowledge of the subject is very recent, and this book gives information about the significant advances which have been made in the last few years.

Secondly, the lead in both research and the methods of soil conservation has come mainly from the USA, and so has most of the teaching material. In the early days, soil conservation was mainly concerned with constructional works—building check dams and terraces—and these techniques required only minor modification to be as relevant in India as in America. But the new-style erosion control, which this book discusses, looks on these mechanical works as merely a foundation on which to build, and emphasizes those aspects of conservation which are important today—correct land use, and improved crop management. The developing countries of Africa and Asia need an approach based on their kind of land use and crop management, not the highly capitalized and mechanized agricultural industries of America and Europe. I have, therefore, attempted to translate the wealth of experience in the United States, and to show how it can be modified and applied in the developing countries.

Thirdly, the techniques of soil conservation have in the past been presented mainly by agronomists for other agronomists, or by engineers for other engineers. My purpose has been to present the engineering approach in such a way as to show students of all disciplines that the engineering of soil conservation is nothing more complicated than simple arithmetic and common sense. In this way I hope that it may serve as a useful text not only for agricultural engineers but also for students of agriculture, forestry, geography, geology, and ecology—indeed all the applied sciences which have a bearing on soil erosion.

The SI form of metric units has been used as far as possible, with imperial units in parallel. However, there are several cases where original concepts or design procedures have been developed entirely in imperial units, and to translate these would be artificial. Since soil conservation is so dependent upon American experience and literature the use of both systems of units will regrettably have to continue until the United States also adopts SI units. The Universal Soil-Loss Equation (Chapter 10) has been discussed entirely in its original imperial units, and the soil survey criteria in Chapter 9 have been reported in the units used in each country. Chapter 7, on estimations of run-off, and Chapter 8 on the design of protection works use both systems of units.

Throughout the book there are many references to the work of the Department of Conservation and Extension of the Federal Government of Rhodesia and Nyasaland, and in view of the present political climate a word of explanation is required. In 1953 the British territories of Northern Rhodesia, Southern Rhodesia, and Nyasaland joined to form the Federation of Rhodesia and Nyasaland in what has been described as an experiment in international multi-racial partnership. Ten years later the experiment was abandoned and the Federation dissolved into the independent countries Zambia, Rhodesia, and Malawi. Whatever the political results of federation, the sharing of knowledge, experience, and personnel resulted in great progress in many technical fields, and soil conservation was one of these. In 1964 the Federal conservation service was dispersed among the territorial governments, but I and many other specialist officers refused to transfer to the government of Southern Rhodesia. However, the effect of the technical leadership of the Federal service is still clearly seen throughout southern and central Africa where the conservation procedures, design specifications, and research programmes nearly all stem from the work of the Federal service.

The subject matter of the book draws extensively on my thirteen years' research into erosion control carried out in Africa, and owes even more to the interchange of new thoughts and ideas with other research workers throughout the world. The form of presentation follows the course of Soil Conservation taught to postgraduate students at the National College of Agriculture Engineering. These students have come so far from twenty-six different countries, and it is hoped that the experience of discussing their problems has resulted in a teaching text which will be of use in these and all other countries where soil conservation is a major consideration in agricultural development.

Chapter 1   Man and soil erosion

1.1   THE RELATION BETWEEN MAN AND THE EARTH'S RESOURCES

The balance between the demands which a community of plants or animals makes on its environment and the ability of nature to satisfy those demands is not the static equilibrium of a laboratory scale with equal weights on either side. It is more like the unstable balancing of a circus acrobat—a series of swings and overcorrections, resulting in an oscillation on either side of the true balance point. Thus a species of wild life increases in number according to the availability of its food supplies, but then goes beyond the optimum number. The natural correcting factors of starvation or migration reduce the population, but again there is an overcorrection, and soon the cycle starts again with increasing numbers.

1.1.1   The Malthusian Thesis

In primitive societies the human population also oscillates about a mean as the limiting factors of starvation, disease, and war, maintain an uneasy balance against the natural tendency to increase. A serious imbalance arises when man learns how to modify the limiting factors, but allows the natural increase to go unchecked. The essence of the *Malthusian Thesis* is that the resulting instability is the inevitable order for mankind. The thesis is named after the English political economist Thomas Malthus who first gave it formal expression (McCLEARY 1953). In an age when significant improvements in health, hygiene, and the standard of living were just becoming possible, Malthus aroused great argument when he pointed out that these very improvements could lead to misery through overpopulation. One of the key points in the argument is that populations tend to increase at geometric rates (1, 2, 4, 8, 16) while the supply of food and other essential requirements normally tends to increase at arithmetic rates (1, 2, 3, 4, 5). In the last century the opening up of extensive areas of the unexplored world disguised the normal growth rate, and, at a time when it appeared that the supply of new lands was inexhaustible, Malthus's ideas did not seem very relevant. Today, the tremendous expansion of population which accompanies the change from a simple agricultural community to a developed industrial society is now occurring on a world scale, as it did in Western Europe 100 years ago (figure 1.1). The problems arising from this increase are so serious that widespread concern is felt.

It is worth considering briefly the main causes of this increase. First, and probably the most important, are improvements in health and hygiene. Diseases which used to act as checks on the population of under-developed countries are being controlled. For example, in the case of malaria, the knowledge of how mosquitos spread the disease, together with new prophylactic drugs and the application of techniques such as aerial spraying, have reduced it from a scourge to little more than an inconvenience. Secondly, the spread of education and the teaching of simple rules of hygiene have greatly diminished incidence of diseases such as dysentery, hookworm, and bilharziasis. A third cause is that starvation is greatly reduced. Not that millions of people in the world are not hungry—they are, and the number increases daily (PEP Report 1955)—but international famine relief schemes, and the ability to move large quantities of food to famine areas, mean that populations are less frequently decimated by starvation than they have been in the past.

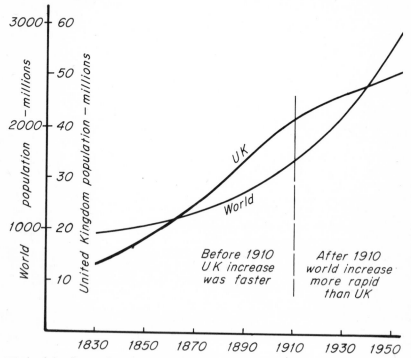

FIGURE 1.1   *Rates of increase in population*

Apart from these reductions in the factors which limit population increase, there are other influences positively helping the increase. Malthus recognized that when more jobs are available there will always be more people to fill them as surely, though not so directly, as better food supplies lead to more people to consume the food. The developing countries today have both increasing food supplies and increasing labour outlets. There is also another factor which did not occur in Malthus's time. This is the effect of aid from more affluent nations, which may have the side effect of stimulating population growth.

1.1.2   The exploitation of resources

The tremendous increase in the population of the world is well documented, and now generally accepted as fact (MUDD 1964). What is less recognized, and sometimes disputed, is the inability of the natural resources of the world to feed, clothe, and provide for the present and future population. Here too, as with population, a precarious balance has been turned by man into a serious imbalance. But while the graph of population shows an ever-increasing upward trend, the available natural resources mirror the trend with a disastrous fall (figure 1.2).

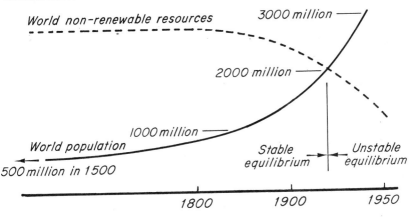

FIGURE 1.2   *Population and resources*

For countless centuries the world's capital of natural resources, the minerals, the forests and the soil, was only required to yield a very modest interest which was sufficient to provide for man's requirements. As the population grew, it became necessary first to extract ever-increasing interest, and then to start using up the capital resources.

The main impetus to the population expansion was given by the industrial revolution, which put into man's hand the tools, the machines, and the engines, which made possible the exploitation of natural resources on a scale previously unimagined. This exploitation or mining of non-renewable resources has continued to this day, and still continues. The wholesale exporting of cereals from North America, or beef from South America, or dairy products from New Zealand, or tobacco from Rhodesia, all represent the exporting of resource capital, achieved by the using up of fertility, and accompanied, of course, by a decrease in the long-term productivity of the land.

This is not a new concept. The appalling toll of soil erosion was demonstrated in great detail 25 years ago by JACKS & WHYTE (1939), and their conclusions have been confirmed and reinforced by numerous surveys since then (VOGT 1948, OSBORN 1948). The extent of the destruction of land resources may be estimated from the only detailed quantitative survey available, that carried out in the United States of

America in 1934, which showed that out of a total of 167 million hectares (414 million acres) of arable land

20 million hectares were ruined, (50 million acres)
20 million hectares were almost ruined, (50 million acres)
40 million hectares had lost more than half the topsoil, (100 million acres)
40 million hectares had lost more than a quarter of the topsoil, (100 million acres) (BENNETT 1939).

In other words, nearly 75% was seriously damaged. There is little doubt that equally devastating results would emerge from surveys in most countries of the world where agricultural development has been recent.

STALLINGS points out (1957 Chapter 11) that in America a big increase in productivity should have arisen from the introduction of improved crop management, better seed, better tillage implements, and increased use of fertilizers. In fact, the benefits of these have been so much offset by the decline in fertility due to erosion that the increase in national average yield of several crops has been disappointing. The problem in tropical and sub-tropical countries is particularly serious. BOSAZZA (1953) has shown that in Africa geological erosion has always been particularly severe owing to a combination of extremes of climate and steep river gradients. EDEN (1964) suggests that in spite of the relatively high resistance to erosion of sub-tropical and tropical soils in their natural state, they are particularly vulnerable to reduction in fertility and consequent degradation and erosion.

Today, many countries have Soil Conservation services and conservation programmes, but the unfortunate truth is that, even in those countries which are making the most strenuous efforts, the result is only a slowing down of the rate of destruction of the soil. The total wastage on a world scale is worse than ever. Two reasons may account for the lack of progress. First, the restrictions on soil exploitation are socially and politically unacceptable to people and to governments when such exploitation is adding to the immediate prosperity of individuals and of the nation. Secondly, in a hungry world it is hard to restrict the provision of badly needed food even if this does mean the reduction of long-term productivity.

1.2 THE POSSIBILITIES OF INCREASING FOOD PRODUCTION

There is a minority opinion that expansion of food production can meet the demands of the world. This optimistic view is usually linked with the wishful thinking that the extrapolation of present population trends gives an unduly alarming forecast, so that, by halving the estimate of demand and doubling the estimate of supply, the equation may be balanced (TIMMONS 1961). The mathematics of this approach seem particularly dubious when the possibility of increasing food supplies are analysed. The possibilities are

(*a*) to increase the acreage of food crops,
(*b*) to increase the yield per acre,
(*c*) to tap other food sources.

1.2.1 Increasing acreage

It is estimated that four-fifths of the potential arable land of 1600 million hectares (4 000 million acres) is already in use. But development to date has naturally been on the best and easiest land. That now remaining includes areas of dense forest, of desert, regions where development is unlikely until health hazards like malaria or trypanosomiasis have been cleared up, and areas presently unpopulated. A 10% increase in the world's arable land would do no more than make up the present food short-fall (PEP 1955). Furthermore, increases from this source would tend to be badly distributed, for there is little land available for new development in those countries with the worst problems of over-population and underfeeding.

1.2.2 Increasing yields

Here is the greatest opportunity. The average yield of maize in many parts of Africa is below 1 000 kilos of grain per hectare, while experimental stations consistently demonstrate that yields twice or three times greater can be achieved by applying elementary techniques, and intensive production can give 8 000 kg/hectare. Similarly, much of the world's rice is produced at yields only a fifth or a quarter of those which could be obtained. In order to achieve increased yields, the primary requirement is not research into new methods, but the increased application of techniques and practices which are already known. Other requirements are improved strains, more research into local conditions, more use of fertilizers, more capital, more mechanization, and the reduction of wastage from pest and disease. But the immediate problem is to double the yield of peasant agriculture by the application of elementary agronomy. Theoretically, this should be simple. But from the evidence available it appears to be more difficult to achieve this increase of peasant productivity than to raise production in the highly developed and capitalized agriculture of the United States of America and Europe.

1.2.3 Other sources of food

Man is a resourceful creature, particularly when his survival is threatened, and there is a strong possibility that hitherto untapped sources of food will be sought out and developed. The chemical food-pill of science-fiction writers is still impractical, but two possible sources, both being seriously investigated today, are the large-scale exploitation of fish foods, and the processing of lower forms of marine life, such as algae and plankton.

Fish, when produced in artificial ponds as a crop which is established, grown, and harvested, can give a higher yield in terms of kilograms per hectare than an irrigated vegetable crop, and further provide the animal protein which is the main deficiency in the diet of most under-fed people. In natural streams, rivers, and lakes, 'fish farming' cannot be as precise as in artificial ponds, and the yields are correspondingly lower, but the inland waters of the world could yield much more than the 2% of the world's edible fish which they presently supply. Estimates of the potential yield of fish from the earth's oceans are really only guesses, but, since 71% of the earth's surface is covered by water, it is quite certain that even a minutely small increase in average yield from this area could make good all our present food deficiencies (GRAHAM 1956).

The idea of algae or plankton as a food is not attractive at present, but the growth of such forms of life is a highly efficient way of converting chemical nutrients and the sun's energy into edible substances, and the product might be made palatable in either of two ways: by treatment, including the addition of synthetic tastes, so that the origin was not recognizable, or by using it as a high-quality food for conventional food animals like pigs, poultry, or cattle.

The present position appears to be that there are limited opportunities for expanding conventional food supplies, and unproved opportunities for developing new supplies, but the enormous gulf between supply and demand focuses attention on the vital need to prevent any running down of the soil's productivity.

1.3 THE HISTORICAL BACKGROUND OF SOIL EROSION

Today soil erosion is almost universally recognized as a serious threat to man's well-being, if not to his very existence, and this is shown by the fact that most governments outside Europe give active support to programmes of soil conservation. But it is relevant, before making any assessment of present knowledge of erosion, to consider the development of this science which was almost unknown 80 years ago, and now enjoys world-wide attention.

Studies of the effect of erosion on early civilizations have shown that a major cause of the downfall of many flourishing empires was soil degradation (LOWDERMILK 1953). Although this is clearly evident throughout 7 000 years of history, an awareness of the problem developed very slowly. We have few records of the earliest middle-eastern civilizations, but in such as are available there is no evidence of any conscious association between erosion and the failure of these civilizations through starvation. Later, the Old Testament contains threats and prophecies of streams drying up and starvation, but few exhortations about good stewardship. A few Greek writers mention land improvement: Homer advocates fallows to rest the soil, and Plato associates floods and erosion with destruction of forests. The Romans had a slightly better appreciation, and Virgil and Pliny recommend what today would be called conservation farming. But right up to the end of the nineteenth century the overall position remained basically unchanged—there were a few lone voices crying in the wilderness but no general awareness of the problem.

Part of this reluctance to appreciate the significance of erosion may stem from the fact that the earliest civilizations all arose on irrigated alluvial plains, and were frequently dependent upon flood deposits of silt for continued fertility. The civilizations of the valleys of the Nile, the Tigris and the Euphrates, which owed their existence to erosion in the headwaters, could hardly be expected to see erosion in the same light as a modern agricultural community.

1.4 THE GROWTH OF EROSION RESEARCH

The first scientific investigations of erosion were carried out by the German soil scientist WOLLNY, between 1877 and 1895. Small plots were used to measure a wide range of effects, such as that of vegetation and surface mulches on the interception of rainfall and on the deterioration of soil structure, and the effects of soil type and slope on run-off and erosion. Apart from this pioneer work, the lead in erosion research has come mainly from the United States of America. Isolated cases of practical application by farmers of mechanical conservation works increased from the 1850s until, in 1907, the United States Department of Agriculture declared an official policy of land protection.

The first American quantitative experiments were laid down by the Forest Service in 1915 in Utah, closely followed by those of MILLER in Missouri in 1917, which led in 1923 to the first published results of field plot experiments. Other similar experiments followed, using essentially the same method, and were given added impetus by the allocation of funds by Congress in 1928. These enabled BENNETT to establish between 1928 and 1933 a network of ten field experiment stations. During the next decade this programme expanded until forty-four stations were operating, and included experiments on mechanical erosion control and run-off from small catchments.

Throughout this period the work was limited to applied research, in which problems were studied under field conditions; and, although it had been apparent from the earliest days of Wollny's work that the prevention of splash erosion was of vital importance, there was no coordinated research involving an analytical study of the processes of erosion. Pioneer work in this field was carried out in the 1930s by a few individuals such as BAVER, BORST, WOODBURN, and MUSGRAVE, and led to the first detailed study of natural rain by LAWS in 1940, and the first analysis of the mechanical action of raindrops on the soil by ELLISON in 1944. The implications of this are best described by STALLINGS (1957 Chapter 1) who says:

'The discovery that raindrop splash is a major factor in the water erosion process marks the end of one era in man's struggle with soil erosion and ushers in another which, for the first time, holds out hope for a successful solution to the problem. The exact nature of the effects of raindrop splash is the phase of the water-erosion process that escaped detection during the first 7 000 years of civilization. It explains why the efforts at protecting the land against scour erosion these 7 000 years have failed. It explains why there is little or no erosion on land with ample plant cover. It explains many things that have puzzled agricultural leaders and practitioners throughout this long and troublesome period. . . .

It remained for Ellison to recognize the true role of the falling rain-drop in the water erosion process. He was the first to realize that the falling raindrop was a complete erosive agent within itself and that little or no erosion occurred when the ground surface was protected by ample cover. He showed that the protective effect of plant cover was due to the fact that it robbed the falling raindrop of its kinetic energy. Ellison's discovery opened a new field of soil erosion science.'

The development of this new line of investigation was, however, not straightforward. Some of the pioneer workers were unable to accept the new ideas with scientific impartiality. For example Dr H. H. Bennett, the first Chief of the Soil Conservation Service, whose contribution to the knowledge and application of conservation practices is still un-equalled, was quite mistaken when he wrote:

Some recently published statements with respect to the effects of rain-drop splash have left the impression that this is the most important factor having to do with the erosion process. It is an important factor, but, as already pointed out, it is only one of several factors having to do with erosion of farm lands. As a matter of fact, the cutting and abrasive effect of run-off from rains and the melting of snow are of far more importance than raindrop splash, which makes its principal contribu-tion by hurling soil particles into suspension in the run-off. (BENNETT *et al* 1951).

Today we have ample evidence that splash *is* in fact the most im-portant factor. However, the need for research on splash erosion to support field experimentation was realized by most workers, and the majority of research in this new phase, like the earlier field work, is now taking place in the United States of America.

Analytical research was directed to more specific objectives by the setting up in 1954 of a national study, which used modern techniques of data analysis to correlate the results of all the field experiments (WISCHMEIER 1955). As a result of this study, the main features in the erosion process were identified and mathematically enumerated. This work ushered in the present phase of quantitative scientific investigation.

Research on erosion problems has not been confined to America.

Africa has been well to the fore, with the first run-off plots established at the University of Pretoria by PROFESSOR HAYLETT in 1929, and the work of STAPLES in Tanganyika in 1933. Today, a network of field stations is in operation in a dozen or more territories. A notable programme including both field experiments and detailed laboratory studies was carried out in Rhodesia at the Henderson Research Station. International liaison between research workers across this continent has been well maintained, previously by the various technical agencies of the Commission for Technical Co-operation South of the Sahara (CCTA), the Inter-African Bureau for Soils (BIS), and the Southern African Regional Council for the Conservation and Utilization of the Soil (SARCCUS) and, more recently, by the Scientific, Technical and Research Commission of the Organization of African Unity (OAU). Many field experiments have also been undertaken in Ceylon, India, Puerto Rico, Australia, Israel and Japan during the last 10 years, but detailed laboratory research on the mechanics of erosion has been limited outside America to a handful of workers.

To summarize, the history of erosion research extends back only 80 years, and the vast majority of the applied or field research has taken place during the last 40 years. Analytical studies are even more recent; they started with Ellison in 1940, and have been accelerated rapidly in the last 10 years. In a science as new as this the dissemination of the results of research is particularly important.

1.5 THE GEOGRAPHICAL DISTRIBUTION OF EROSION

The two main agents of erosion are wind and water, and by consideration of the conditions under which each will be active, a pattern can be built up of the areas of the world where either wind erosion or water erosion is likely to be particularly serious.

1.5.1 Erosion by water

The factor which most influences soil erosion by water is the mean annual rainfall, as shown in figure 1.3. In regions of very low rainfall there can naturally be little erosion caused by rain. Further, what little rain does fall is mainly taken up by a vegetation permanently short of water so there is little run-off. At the other extreme, an annual rainfall of more than 1 000 mm usually leads to dense forest vegetation. This affords protective cover to the soil and, as is shown in the next chapter, the presence of cover is the key factor in reducing water erosion. The most severe erosion will thus tend to be associated with the middle range of rainfall when the vegetation is largely undisturbed, and with higher rainfall when the natural forest is removed. The main features of world rainfall distribution are shown in figure 1.4.

However, it is not only the *amount* of rainfall that matters, but also the *kind* of rain. The intensive downpour common in the tropics has a

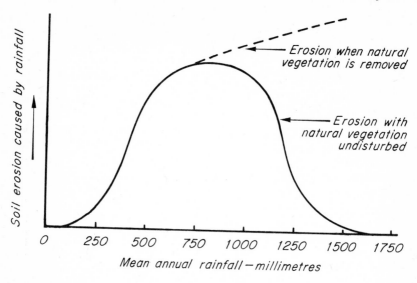

FIGURE 1.3   *The relation between rainfall and soil erosion*

very much more damaging effect than the gentler rain of temperate climates, and the approximate limits of the area of destructive rain are latitudes 40° North and 40° South. There are, of course, exceptions to this world-scale pattern. In semi-arid conditions, serious rain erosion often occurs because the rain, although low in quantity, comes in very severe storms (plate 1.1). In other cases, steep slopes and vulnerable soils can lead to quite serious erosion in temperate latitudes. In general, however, soil erosion by water can be expected to be most serious in areas between these latitudes, where the annual rainfall is neither very high nor very low. Figure 1.5 shows that, as a first approximation, this is in fact the case, the main areas being N. America up to about 40° N, parts of S. America, nearly all of Africa except the dry deserts and equatorial forest, Asia up to 40° N, and Australia excluding the dry centre.

1.5.2   Erosion by wind

There are also two main conditions which must exist before wind erosion can be a serious problem. First, only dry soil blows, so the vulnerable regions are those with a low mean annual rainfall, particularly less than about 250 or 300 mm. Secondly, large-scale movements can occur only where there are steady prevailing winds at all levels from the upper air down to ground level, and these are associated with large, fairly level, land masses. Naturally, there exist local exceptions, but on a continental scale, wind erosion is found to be most serious where it would be expected from consideration of these two requirements.

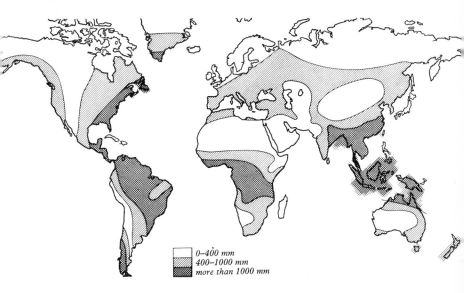

FIGURE 1.4 *Generalized map of mean annual rainfall*

Legend:
- 0–400 mm
- 400–1000 mm
- more than 1000 mm

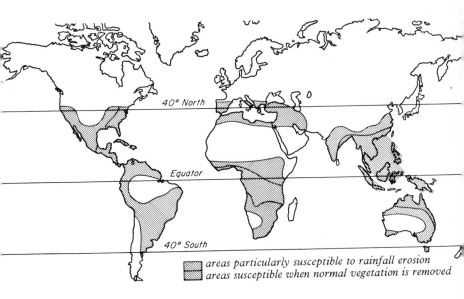

40° North

Equator

40° South

areas particularly susceptible to rainfall erosion
areas susceptible when normal vegetation is removed

FIGURE 1.5 *Generalized map of the geographical distribution of rainfall erosion*

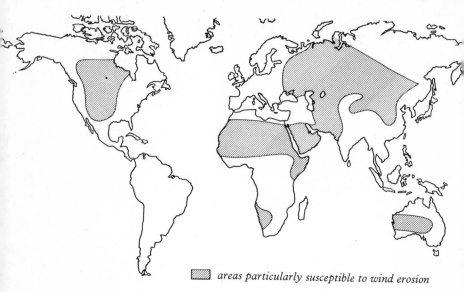

areas particularly susceptible to wind erosion

FIGURE 1.6   *Generalized map of wind erosion*

The main areas, shown in figure 1.6, are N. America (the Great Plains, famous as the Dust Bowl), the Sahara and the Kalahari deserts in Africa, Central Asia (particularly the Steppes of Russia), and central Australia.

PLATE 1.1   *Rainfall erosion is greatest when heavy rainstorms fall on land un-protected by vegetation*
                                                    Copyright Aerofilms Limited

References

BENNETT, H. H. 1939 *Soil Conservation*, McGraw-Hill, New York and London

BENNETT, H. H., F. G. BELL and B. D. ROBINSON 1951 Raindrops and Erosion, *Circular 895, United States Department of Agriculture*

BOSAZZA, V. L. 1953 On the Erodibility of Soils, *African Soils* 2, (3 and 4) 337

EDEN, T. 1964 *Elements of Tropical Soil Science*, 2nd Edition, Macmillan, London

GRAHAM, M. 1956 Harvests of the Seas, in *Man's Role in Changing the Face of the Earth*, University of Chicago Press

JACKS, G. V. and R. O. WHYTE 1939 *The Rape of the Earth—a World Survey of Soil Erosion*, Faber, London

LAWS, J. O. 1940 Recent Studies in Raindrops and Erosion, *Agricultural Engineering* 21, 431–433

LOWDERMILK, W. C. 1953 Conquest of the Land through Seven Thousand Years, *Agricultural Information Bulletin* 99, *United States Department of Agriculture*

McCLEARY, G. F. 1953 *The Malthusian Population Theory*, Faber, London

MUDD, S. (ed.) 1964 *The Population Crisis and the Use of World Resources*, Junk, The Hague

OSBORN, F. 1948 *Our Plundered Planet*, Faber, London, and Little, Brown, Boston.

P E P (POLITICAL & ECONOMIC PLANNING) 1955 *World Population and Resources*, Allen & Unwin, London

STALLINGS, J. H. 1957 *Soil Conservation*, Prentice-Hall, Englewood Cliffs, New Jersey

TIMMONS, J. F. 1961 Population Growth, Resources Productivity and Soil Conservation, *Journal of Soil and Water Conservation* 16, 207–213

VOGT, W. 1948 *Road to Survival*, Sloane, New York, and Gollancz, London

WISCHMEIER, W. H. 1955 Punched Cards Record Runoff and Soil Loss Data, *Agricultural Engineering* 36, 664–666

Chapter 2   The mechanics of erosion

2.1   GEOLOGICAL AND ACCELERATED EROSION

Erosion always has taken place, and always will. The surface of the earth is constantly changing with mountains rising, valleys being cut deeper and wider, the coast line receding here, advancing there. The physical pattern of the surface of the earth which we see today is not the result of some single cataclysmic sculpturing but the result of changes so infinitely slow that only after centuries is the effect noticeable. Erosion is simply one of the aspects of this constant process of change. It is fundamental to the formation of alluvial soils and sedimentary rocks. Man's activities seldom slow down or halt the process but frequently speed it up. We usually refer to 'geological erosion' or 'normal erosion' or 'natural erosion' when we mean that which results only from the forces of nature, and to 'accelerated erosion' when the process is influenced by man.

When trying to predict the probable severity of man-made erosion it helps to consider the rate of geological erosion. If the conditions of climate and topography are such that geological erosion is quicker than usual, then these same conditions will also lead to particularly severe accelerated erosion. Extreme examples of both kinds of erosion are shown in plates 2.1 and 2.2.

2.1.1   The agents of erosion

Erosion is essentially a smoothing or levelling process, with soil and rock particles being carried, rolled, or washed down by the force of gravity. The main agents which loosen and break down the particles are wind and water.

Wind does not by itself wear away rocks, but abrasion, even of hard rock, results from grains of sand or soil carried in suspension—rather like a slow-motion version of the process of sand-blasting used to clean metal surfaces before painting. The different aspects of wind erosion are described in section 2.2.4.

Water is probably the most important single agent of erosion. Rainfall, streams, and rivers all scour away or carry away soil, waves erode the shores of seas and lakes—in fact wherever water is in movement it is eroding its boundaries.

Temperature changes   When considering geological erosion the passage of time is hardly noticeable, and even minutely small or incredibly slow changes become significantly over a long period of time. Examples are the cracking and flaking of rocks by variations in temperature. Rapid variations between day and night affect only the surface of rocks, while the changes due to slower variations between summer and winter penetrate deeper. When temperature changes include frost the disruption is greatly increased by the expansion of water in cracks and crevices. Frost heave and contraction results in a progressive movement downhill in sloping ground as shown in figure 2.1.

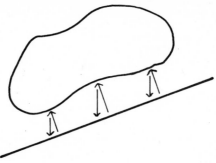

FIGURE 2.1   *Frost action. The expansion caused by freezing is at right angles to the soil surface. On thawing the particle sinks vertically. There is a net movement downslope*

Biological   Some actual destruction may be caused by living organisms, such as lichens and mosses on rocks, but the main effect of living things is the disturbance which speeds up the effect of other agents. Animals trampling on rocks or soil break it down and make it more easily carried away by wind or water, and at the other end of the biological scale earthworms and termites disturb the soil and increase the aeration and oxidation, and so speed up the processes of conversion from resistant rock to erodible soil.

2.1.2   Accelerated erosion

On a world scale man's non-agricultural activities which accelerate the erosion processes are hardly significant. We excavate mountains for coal and ores, we dig a hole here and fill in there, but this interferes with only a small part of the earth's surface. On the other hand, agriculture is so widespread that agricultural activities which materially alter the speed of the erosion processes are much more important. And nearly all agricultural operations do tend to encourage erosion. Whenever vegetation is cleared and the ground is more exposed, there are fewer trees to slow down the wind so wind erosion increases, less vegetation to absorb the energy of the falling rain and so more rainfall erosion, more surface run-off so streams and rivers become stronger, more cattle to crush the rock and soil. By ploughing and tilling the soil man disturbs and aerates the soil millions of times more quickly and effectively than the burrowing animals—in fact all the physical processes of

PLATE 2.1   *Geological erosion can be spectacular. This erosion is the result of highly erosive rain falling on soil with low resistance to erosion and with no vegetative cover*
Copyright Fairchild Surveys

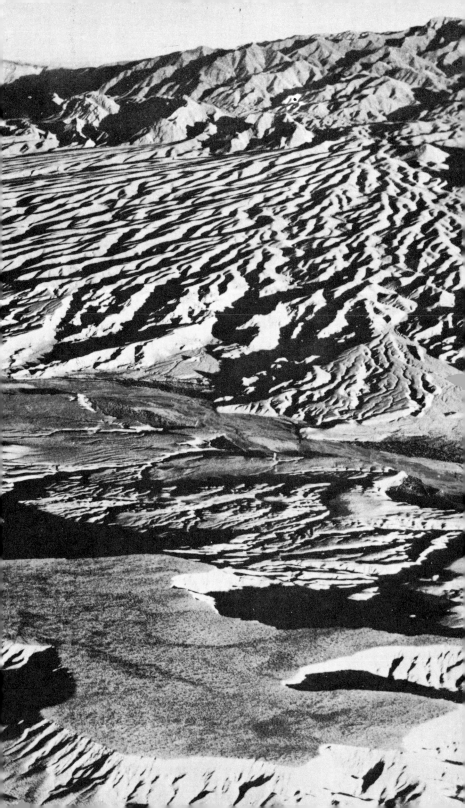

nature are accelerated, and so is erosion. Only in isolated cases is there a possibility of natural erosion being reduced, where desert areas are reclaimed, or arid regions made temperate by irrigation, or forests established, and these are infinitesimal compared with the areas where it is increased.

2.1.3 Acceptable limits of erosion

What then is the dividing line between geological erosion, a natural phenomenon we must accept, and accelerated erosion, a man-made destructive thing? Since it will be difficult if not impossible to draw this line, is another possibility to specify the limits of erosion which can be accepted as reasonable? The question then becomes 'What is the level of erosion at which we change from accepting it to feeling that something ought to be done about it?' The usual answer is that the object of soil conservationists is to ensure that land is only used in such a way that the use can be sustained indefinitely—that is, there is no progressive deterioration. This will be achieved when the rate of soil loss is no greater than the rate of formation of soil. The rate of formation cannot be precisely measured, but the best estimate of soil scientists is that under undisturbed conditions it will take of the order of 300 years to produce 25 mm of top soil (BENNETT 1939 Chapter 3), but that when the disturbances and aeration and leaching actions are speeded up by tilling the land, this will be reduced to something like 30 years. A formation rate of 25 mm in 30 years is approximately 12·5 tons m/hectare/year (5 tons/acre/year), and so this figure is frequently adopted as the target figure which erosion should not exceed. Naturally the acceptable loss will depend on the soil conditions—if the profile consists of a deep soil whose fertility is the same at all depths, then to lose 25 mm of soil in 30 years is much less serious than if the profile consists of a few centimetres of soil overlying hard rock. Target figures are therefore seldom higher than 1·25 tons m/hectare/year or 5 tons/acre/year, but frequently lower. In the United States figures from 2·5 to 12·5 tons m/hectare/year (1 to 5 tons/acre/year) are common, and the Central African Federation used 10 tons m/hectare/year (4 tons/acre/year) for sandy soils and 12·5 tons m/hectare/year (5 tons/acre/year) for clay soils. These figures are related to recommended farming practices by the Soil-Loss Equation discussed in Chapter 10.

PLATE 2.2   *This field in Tanzania lost 50 mm of top soil over its whole surface with rills cut down 150 mm to the plough depth, during a storm of only a few hours*
Copyright National Institute of Agricultural Engineering

2.2 FORMS OF EROSION

2.2.1 Water erosion

The first classification of water erosion attempted by early conservationists was into stages corresponding with the progressive concentration of surface run-off. It started with sheet erosion (the washing of surface soil from arable lands), then rill erosion as the water concentrates into small rivulets in the fields, then gully erosion when the eroded channels are larger, and finally stream bank erosion when rivers or streams are cutting into the banks. This classification is no longer appropriate to our understanding, and may be misleading for it entirely omits the splash or impact effect of the raindrop which we now know to be the first and most important stage in the erosion process. Also, sheet erosion conjures up a picture of soil being removed uniformly by the even flow of thin sheets of water. This is wrong on all accounts. Laminar flow of water only scours at velocities much higher than usually occurs in arable land, and also run-off is seldom in flat sheets.

If however, we banish the description 'sheet erosion', and substitute 'splash erosion', there is no objection to continuing the sequence—rill, gully, and streambank. 'Rill' erosion can be defined as localized small washes in defined channels which are small enough to eliminate by normal cultural methods, and channels are usually considered to be gullies when they are so large and well-established that they cannot be crossed by farm implements. There is obviously no precise dividing line between the two. In other parts of the world gullies are variously known as *wadis* is N. Africa, *nullah* in India, *donga* in S. Africa and *arroyo* in S. America.

2.2.2 Specialized forms of erosion

Pedestal erosion (plate 2.3).

When an easily eroded soil is protected from splash erosion by a stone or tree root, isolated 'pedestals' capped by the resistant material are left standing up from the surrounding ground. The erosion of the surrounding soil is shown to be mainly by splash rather than by surface flow because there is little or no undercutting at the base of the pedestal. This type of erosion develops slowly over several years and is often found on bare patches of grazing land. It can occur in arable lands which suffer excessive erosion during exceptional storms. The main interest is that it is possible to deduce approximately what depth of soil has been eroded by studying the height of the pedestals.

It is important to differentiate between pedestals and stools of grass which frequently have a soil level above the surrounding ground. Such raised soil levels may show the original level with the soil between the grass clumps having been eroded, but it is more likely that the level in the grass clumps has been raised by catching soil splashed from the bare patches. On experimental plots the soil level in tufts of *Eragrostis curvula* (Weeping Love Grass) was 20 mm above the level between the tufts, and it might easily be assumed that this is evidence of considerable erosion. In fact measurements showed that the soil loss was negligible and this effect was solely due to the lateral movement of soil by splash.

PLATE 2.3   *Pedestal erosion results when a stone or tree root protects the soil from the splash erosion which removes the surrounding soil*

PLATE 2.4   *Pinnacle erosion often occurs in gullies as the result of deep vertical rills widening until pinnacles are left like islands in the bed of the gully*

Pinnacle erosion

The characteristic erosion pattern which leaves high pinnacles in gully sides and bottoms is usually associated with 'difficult' soils which are highly erodible (plate 2.4). This erosion is always associated with deep vertical rills in the gully sides, and these cut back rapidly until they join and leave the isolated pinnacles. A more resistant soil layer, or gravel or stones, often caps the pinnacle, as in pedestal erosion. Banks eroded in this form are usually severely undercut by either flowing or standing water, and pipe erosion is also frequent. The chemical or physical soil conditions which cause this severe erosion are not clearly defined, but it is usually found where there is some severe imbalance such as excessive sodium and complete deflocculation. Soils liable to this type of erosion are recognized by the fact that when dry they take up water very slowly and reluctantly, but once saturated they have no cohesion and flow like mud.

Gully control or any reclamation is always difficult when pinnacle erosion is evident. Adverse conditions of soil moisture and plant nutrients make it difficult to establish vegetation, and the soil is most unsuitable for earth structures, while masonry or concrete structures are readily undermined or outflanked.

Piping

The formation of continuous pipes or channels underground is most common in those soil types subject to pinnacle erosion, but not entirely restricted to such soils. It occurs when surface water infiltrates through the soil surface and moves downwards until it comes to a less permeable layer. If there is an outlet so that the water can flow laterally through the soil over the less permeable layer then the fine particles of the more porous soil may be washed out. This in turn allows a more rapid lateral flow, so the sideways erosion increases, and eventually the whole of the surface flow disappears down a vertical pipe and flows underground before reappearing, probably in the side of a gully. Fortunately pipe erosion is usually confined to 'bad lands' of little agricultural value, for no effective control measures can be applied.

Slumping

Slumping is usually a process of geological erosion, and although it may be accelerated as in the sides of gullies it can occur without any intervention of man. It becomes prominent in high rainfall areas with deep soils. In such areas it can become the main agent in the development of gullies. This is shown in cases where the head of the gully has worked back right up to the crest and beyond, where there can be no inflow at the head of the gully. These gullies probably often start due to flood flow in channels, but once the gully has started, erosion can continue by slumping alone. The other main cases of slumping are river bank collapse, and coastal erosion.

2.2.3 Degradation

If soil erosion is defined in the widest possible terms it includes any degradation of the soil which reduces its ability to grow crops. Such degradation can occur in several ways without there being any physical removal of soil.

Fertility erosion is the loss of plant nutrients by erosion and can be comparable in magnitude with the removal of the same elements in the harvested crop. The manner of the loss varies for different elements. Phosphorous is mainly lost along with the colloidal particles on whose surface it is adsorbed, but nitrogen in the nitrite or nitrate forms is soluble, and so can be lost in solution in the run-off without any physical soil movement occurring.

Puddle erosion A comparable physical deterioration without net loss has been called puddle erosion because it can take place in a puddle. This is the physical breakdown of structure by rain, and the washing into depressions of the fine soil fractions resulting in a structureless soil and choked soil surface whose productive ability is much lowered (plate 2.5).

Vertical erosion Another physical translocation is the washing down of fine clay particles through a porous sand or gravel to accumulate at some less pervious layer lower down the profile. There are two effects possible; the loss of fine particles at one point and their increase at another point. In coarse sand soils an appreciable reduction in colloids and clays can result from vertical erosion with a consequent reduction of fertility. The effect where the fine material accumulates is also likely to be undesirable when the result is the formation of a layer less permeable to both roots and water.

2.2.4 Forms of wind erosion

Five different forms of wind erosion are recognized, although there is some overlapping, and several of the processes will usually occur at the same time.

Detrusion is the wearing away of rocks and soil projections by fine particles carried in suspension. The large rocks carved into grotesque shapes in deserts are formed by this process. A similar action takes place close to the ground where the moving particles are larger and bouncing along over the surface. This is known as *abrasion*. The three other forms relate to the way the material is carried away. The removal of very fine particles, carried off in suspension is *efflation*, and the rolling away of large particles is *extrusion*. Particles of intermediate size move off downwind in the bouncing action called saltation, and removal in this manner is termed *effluxion*. The mechanics of particle movement are discussed in section 14.2.1.

2.2.5 The relative importance of types of erosion

The question is often debated as to which form of erosion is the most serious, and this is important if a conservation programme has limited resources which are insufficient to tackle the whole erosion problem and must therefore be used against a selected part. However, there is no single answer, for it depends upon the reasons why the erosion needs to be controlled.

PLATE 2.5 *Puddle erosion is degradation of the soil by loss of structure without the soil being washed away*   *Copyright Aerofilms Limited*

If the problem is that the production of food crops is jeopardized by erosion then splash erosion and rill erosion on arable lands are the most important. If, however, the problem is that a high sediment load in streams and rivers threatens to silt up the storage dams required for an irrigation scheme, then the most important source of this silt will probably be gully erosion or streambank erosion. This is because the soil eroded by these forms goes immediately and wholly into the stream, whereas it is possible for soil to be lost in large quantities from arable lands but trapped in vegetation or deposited in ditches before it reaches the stream.

The importance of the different kinds of erosion, and the priorities given to their control, require an analysis of what the problem is, and what the objectives are of the remedial programme.

2.2.6 Phases in the erosion process

A similar situation arises when we consider the relative resistances to erosion of different soil types. Here different answers will be correct depending on what form of erosion is being considered. A soil might be resistant to surface erosion, but have a weak sub-soil which makes it vulnerable to undercutting of streambanks. This is probably best illustrated by considering the classic divisions of the erosion process as propounded by Ellison twenty years ago (ELLISON 1947). The three basic phases are detachment, transportation, and deposition and Ellison showed by laboratory experiments that different soils rate quite differently in each of these phases. For example the particles of a fine sand are more easily *detached* than those of a clay soil, but the clay particles are more easily *transported* than the sand particles. It is therefore necessary to define the nature of the erosion when referring to how easily or how much a soil is subject to erosion.

2.3 CALCULATING THE AMOUNT OF EROSION

2.3.1 Numerical estimations

Two of the essential qualifications of a science are the ability to define and measure the causes and effects of the natural phenomena related to the subject, and the ability to predict what will happen in given circumstances. Of these requirements, only a measurement of the effects was straightforward, and this has been done by measuring the weight of soil eroded, since Wollny's work in 1880. Attempts at predicting erosion came later, starting with the work of the United States Soil Conservation Service in the 1940s such as *The Quantitative Evaluation of Factors in Water Erosion—A First Approximation* (MUSGRAVE 1947), but subsequent refinements were hindered by the absence of the third factor—identification and measurement of the causes. However after Ellisons breakthrough on splash erosion, studies of the causative relationships have led to progressively more efficient mathematical models which allow the prediction of erosion from given facts. The latest and most efficient of these is the Universal Soil-Loss Equation described in detail in Chapter 10. This equation brings together in mathematical terms all the variable factors which influence erosion caused by rainfall. In subsequent chapters these factors will be separately considered in detail, but first we should establish a simple qualitative statement which puts into perspective the problems of erosion and erosion control.

2.3.2   Qualitative statement of the principles

The fundamental cause of soil erosion is that *rain* acts upon the *soil*, and the study of erosion can be divided into how it will be affected by different kinds of rain, and how it will vary for different conditions of soil. The amount of erosion is therefore going to depend upon a combination of the power of the rain to cause erosion and the ability of the soil to withstand the rain. In mathematical terms—Erosion is a function of the Erosivity (of the rain) and the Erodibility (of the soil), or Erosion = f (Erosivity) (Erodibility).

Erosivity can be defined as the potential ability of the rain to cause erosion, and for given soil conditions one storm can be compared quantitatively with another and a numerical scale of values of erosivity can be created. Erodibility is defined as the vulnerability of the soil to erosion, and for given rainfall conditions, one soil condition can be compared quantitatively with another, and a numerical scale of values of erodibility can be created. Erodibility of the soil can be subdivided into two parts. First the fundamental or inherent characteristics of the soil—its mechanical, chemical and physical composition—the things which can be measured in the laboratory, as discussed in Chapter 5. Secondly the erodibility will depend also on what treatment is given to the soil, ie, how it is managed. This management may in turn be subdivided into two parts, land management and crop management. The broad issues, which can be grouped under the heading land management, are the kind of land use—forestry, grazing, arable etc. These are discussed in Chapter 9. The subsequent decisions are more detailed. For arable land they include the kind of crop, the fertilizer treatment, the harvesting and so on. These all comprise 'crop management' and are discussed in Chapter 11. Some conservation management practices such as contour ploughing or terracing are bound up with both the broader issues of land management and the mechanics of crop management. Figure 2.2 shows this approach diagramatically, and, starting from the erosivity of the rainfall and the erodibility of the soil, leads to combining all the factors which influence erosion into the Soil-Loss Equation. In subsequent chapters the factors will each be analysed in detail.

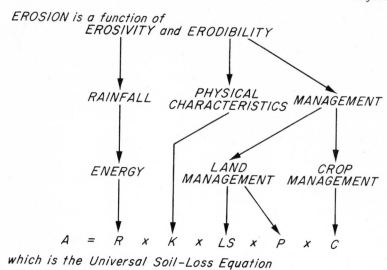

FIGURE 2.2   *The factors which affect rainfall erosion. The Universal Soil-Loss Equation $A = R \times K \times LS \times P \times C$ is discussed in Chapter 10*

References

BENNETT, H. H. 1939 *Soil Conservation*, McGraw-Hill, New York and London

ELLISON, W. D. 1947 Soil Erosion Studies Parts I to VII, *Agricultural Engineering* 28: 145, 197, 245, 297, 349, 402, 442

MUSGRAVE, G. W. 1947 The Quantitative Evaluation of Factors in Water Erosion—A First Approximation. *Journal of Soil and Water Conservation* 2: 133–138

Chapter 3   The physics of rainfall

3.1   PHYSICAL CHARACTERISTICS

There is obviously an association between the amount of rainfall and the amount of soil erosion, ie, more rain goes with more erosion, and less rain with less erosion, but in statistical terms the correlation between the two is poor. The same total quantity of rain can on different occasions result in widely differing amounts of erosion, and so other more specific measures are required to describe the ability of rainfall to cause erosion. In this chapter we shall establish the known facts about the main physical properties of rainfall, and then in Chapter 4 show how these properties are related to the erosive power of rainfall.

3.1.1   Quantity of rainfall

Any measure of rainfall amount is a sample, and so associated with the inevitable problems of sampling, namely, 'Is the sample representative of the whole?' and 'Is the sample measured accurately?' On both counts the data on rainfall which is usually available is of very doubtful reliability. Considering the size of the sample measured, a very intensive network of raingauges established in an experimental catchment might be as dense as one gauge per 25 hectares, but this corresponds (with a 125 mm diameter gauge) to a sample of about one in 20 million, which would for any other scientific measurement be considered totally inadequate. The density of gauges in a country which considered itself very well provided might be one gauge per 25 square kilometres—a sample of 1 in 2000 million, and in an undeveloped country a density of one gauge per 2500 square kilometres is a sample of 1 in 20 000 000 000! The siting of this remarkably small number of gauges is usually arranged primarily on convenience, eg, where they can be easily read and maintained, with little or no consideration of whether the site is representative of the whole. The accuracy of the measurement is usually unknown and studies have shown that variations in the shape and size of the instrument, and in the height at which it is mounted, and the way it is shielded from the wind, can seriously affect the recorded amount of rainfall. Clearly, even the apparently straightforward question of how much rain falls is not answered as precisely as might be imagined from a quick survey of the rainfall tables and maps.

In addition to the straightforward measurement of the quantity of rain there are a number of other questions to consider. If a rainfall map shows an average annual rainfall of say 700 mm this implies that if a given area, say a square metre, accumulated the year's rain it would rise to a depth of 700 mm over this area. But if the ground is sloping then what looks like a square metre on the map will be a considerably larger area of actual ground surface. The volume of water has to spread over the larger area and so the effective rainfall is considerably reduced. The problems of measuring rainfall on slopes and in remote areas are thoroughly presented by HAMILTON (1954).

Another aspect of the effectiveness of rain is how it is distributed through the year. The fairly uniform spread which is common in temperate climates is favourable for intensive agriculture and least conducive to erosion. In tropical climates it is more usual for the rain to be concentrated into part of the year. Erosion is more likely to result from both the heavier rain in the wet season and the dessication of plant life during the dry season. A single rainy season is described as a uni-modal distribution (figure 3.1). Another distribution pattern common in the sub-tropics is the bimodal—that is the rainy season is divided into two parts with a dry period between. These are often described as the little rains and the big rains and if the dry spell in between allows harvesting or tillage operations this distribution can be agriculturally desirable.

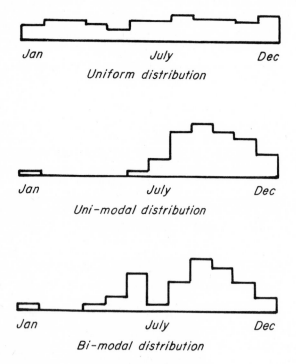

FIGURE 3.1   *Patterns of distribution of annual rainfall*

3.1.2   Intensity, or rate of rainfall

There is considerable evidence of a close association between erosion and intensity, and intensity is particularly important as a potential parameter of erosivity because it is the only feature of rainfall which, in addition to amount, is frequently recorded at conventional meteorological stations. Data on occurrence and frequency of intensities is nowadays recorded on most meteorological stations, and no erosion experiments would be properly equipped without some form of intensity recorder (plate 3.1). Any erosivity index based solely, or primarily, on some function of intensity has thus a greater scope for its application than an index based on any other characteristic. An index based on, for example, kinetic energy would still be extremely useful even if it required new instrumentation to measure the kinetic energy, but would only be applicable after the collection of new data, and so less useful than an index based on intensity.

PLATE 3.1 *A rainfall laboratory with measuring devices arranged round an underground room containing the recording apparatus. A Standard gauge, B Directional gauge, C Two intensity recorders, D Drop size sampling machine, E Momentum balances, F Soil trays. Not seen are the recording rain gauges, splash cups, acoustic recorder and energy wheel* (HUDSON 1965)

Measurements of intensity sufficient for meteorological purposes are normally obtained from recording raingauges where successive increments of rainfall are recorded as a cumulative total on a clock-driven chart whose speed varies according to the frequency with which the chart is to be changed, usually daily, or in remote or inaccessible areas, weekly or monthly. The intensity is computed from the rate of change in the quantity of rainfall recorded, ie, the gradient of the recorded line. This indirect measurement is suitable for averaging the intensity over fairly long periods, but when the time interval is short the method becomes very laborious, and is not very accurate (figure 3.2).

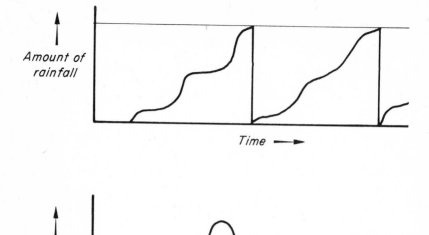

FIGURE 3.2   *Measurements of intensity (a) Indirect. The slope of the line on an autographic raingauge represents the rate of rainfall. (b) Direct. Intensity is measured directly, and the amount of rain is the area under the line*

Instruments which directly record the rate of rainfall rather than the quantity are available, and are often used in connexion with soil erosion experiments, but are seldom included in the equipment of ordinary meteorological stations.

In temperate climates the rainfall rate seldom exceeds 75 mm per hour, and then only in summer thunderstorms. In many tropical countries intensities of 150 mm per hour are experienced regularly. A maximum rate, sustained for only a few minutes, was recorded by the author in Africa at 340 mm per hour.

3.1.3   Raindrop size

The earliest recorded measurements of the size of raindrops were made by Lowe in 1892 who caught raindrops on flat sheets of slate which were ruled off into squares so that the size of the splashes could be measured. This method of calculating the size of a drop from the size of the splash which it makes on some collecting device is one of the most popular methods. One technique is to take an absorbent paper and lightly dust on to the surface a very finely powdered water-soluble dye. In the dry state the dye is invisible but on exposure to rain each raindrop makes a roughly circular stain which can be measured later. The drop size can be calculated from the formula $D = aS^b$, where D is the drop diameter, S is the stain diameter, and a and b are constants established by laboratory calibration for the paper used. The method is reviewed by HALL (1970).

Another popular approach is the 'Flour Pellet' method (HUDSON 1964 b). A sample of rain is caught in a dish containing flour. Each raindrop forms a small globule of wet flour and when dried in an oven these set into hard pellets which can be separated from the rest of the flour. A laboratory calibration has previously established the relationship between the size of a pellet and the size of the drop which formed it (figure 3.3).

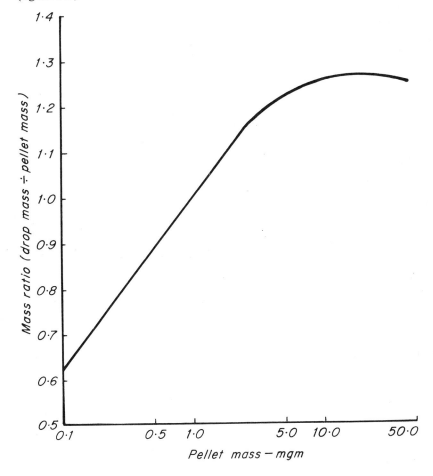

FIGURE 3.3   *Calibration for the flour pellet method of measuring the size of raindrops*

Using such methods (and some of the others described in HUDSON 1964 a) the range of raindrop sizes has been measured in many different countries and in many different types of rainfall. The upper limit appears to be about 5 mm diameter and drops bigger than this break up into a number of smaller drops. BLANCHARD (1950) showed in wind tunnel experiments that drops are stable up to 4·6 mm diameter, and unstable above 5·4 mm diameter, with a range in between where the drops may or may not disintegrate depending on the turbulence. High speed photographs show that the shape of falling drops is not at all like the conventional tear drop shape, but a sphere well flattened by the air resistance. Field observations agree with these sizes. Drops are only infrequently found larger than 5 or 6 mm diameter, but do occasionally occur. Probably this happens when two drops have collided to form a 'super drop' which reaches the ground before it has time to split up again.

3.1.4   Drop size distribution

Since the rain is made up of drops of all sizes, it is also necessary to determine the proportions of large and small drops—that is the size distribution—and how this distribution varies in different kinds of rain. It is clear from everyday observation that the low intensity rain which can last for days is mainly made up of small drops, whereas the high intensity rain from a thunderstorm has at least some drops which are much bigger. In both the drop-stain and the flour-pellet method of measuring drop size a sample of the rain is collected and so the distribution of drop sizes may be determined. The classical studies in this field of work were those carried out by LAWS and PARSONS (1943).

One of the difficulties of sampling rainfall is that of catching those storms which only occur infrequently, and for many years our knowledge on drop size distribution was limited to low intensity rain. Recent studies at high intensities have significantly changed the picture (HUDSON 1963).

It is not easy to describe a distribution by a single parameter. The 'average' drop size gives little indication of how it is made up, and probably the best index for drop distributions is the median volume drop diameter (D_{50}). This is the drop diameter such that half of the volume of the rain falls in the shape of drops with a smaller diameter, and half as bigger drops. It is obtained from a plot of cumulative volume against drop diameter (figure 3.6). Studies such as that of BEST (1950) showed that the relationship between D_{50} and intensity I is of the form $D_{50} = aI^b$ (a and b are constants), and there is no doubt that this form, implying increasing size with increasing intensity, is valid for low intensities. However, we know that there is a physical upper limit to the maximum drop size, and studies of high intensity rain (HUDSON 1963) showed that there is in fact a reversal of the trend at very high intensities. Figures 3.4 and 3.5 show drop size distribution curves for increasing intensity and it is clear that the modal value of drop diameter (ie, the peak of the curve) rises up to about 80 or 100 mm per hour but then decreases at still higher intensities. Plotting D_{50} against intensity (figure 3.7) shows that while a relationship of the form $D_{50} \propto I^b$ is valid for the low intensities from which it was derived it cannot be extrapolated to high intensity tropical rainfall. Even in tropical rainfall the intensity does not often exceed 150 mm per hour, but it is important to understand the nature of high intensity rain, and how it differs from temperate rain.

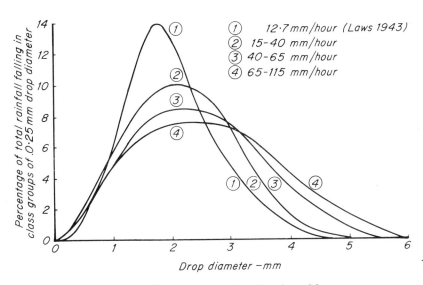

FIGURE 3.4   *Drop size distribution at low and medium intensities*

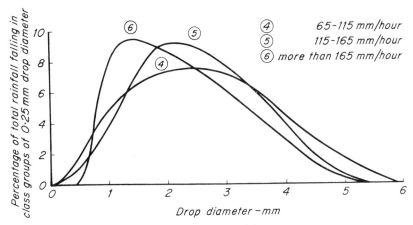

FIGURE 3.5   *Drop size distribution at high intensities*

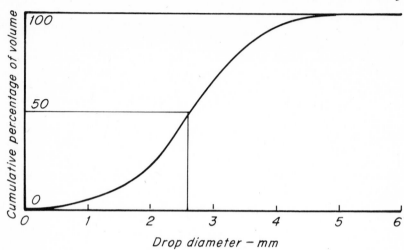

FIGURE 3.6   *Finding the median volume drop diameter (D50)*

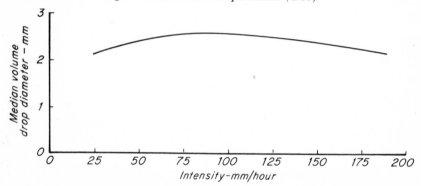

FIGURE 3.7   *The relation between median volume drop diameter and intensity*

3.1.5   Terminal velocity

A body falling freely under the force of gravity will accelerate until the frictional resistance of the air is equal to the gravitational force, and will then continue to fall at that speed. This is known as the terminal velocity and depends upon the size and shape of a body. A feather has a very low terminal velocity which is reached after a fall of a few centimetres, but a bomb dropped from an aircraft only reaches its very high terminal velocity after falling many thousands of metres. The terminal velocity of raindrops increases as the size increases, the largest drops of about 5 mm diameter having a terminal velocity of about 9 metres per second (figure 3.8).

Many laboratory measurements of falling drops of water were carried out by physicists at the beginning of this century, particularly by Mache, Schmidt, Liznar and Lenard in Germany, and Flower in England. All these early measurements agreed reasonably well considering the simple apparatus used, and so when LAWS (1941) obtained values 15% higher, using modern high speed photography, a very careful search was made for possible errors. Laws could find none in his own experiments, and must have been very pleased when his values were confirmed by the independent studies of GUNN and KINZER (1949). Their method was that water drops were given a slight electric charge and allowed to fall through induction rings which gave an electrical impulse when the drop fell through them. The impulses were fed through amplifiers to an oscillograph so that the time to fall the measured distance between the two induction rings could be measured very accurately. Gunn and Kinzer's results differed from those of Laws by less than 3%. Laws also measured the terminal velocity of raindrops in the open, and found that while turbulence and wind have some effect, nevertheless most raindrops reached the ground at 95% of their 'still-air' terminal velocity.

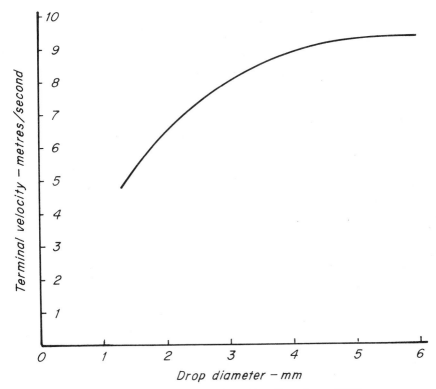

FIGURE 3.8   *The terminal velocity of raindrops* (data from LAWS 1941)

When rain is accompanied by wind there is an added sideways component of velocity, and the resultant vector may be greater than the still-air velocity. The effect will be greater on smaller drops falling slowly than on large drops with higher velocities. There is some evidence that in tropical rainfall the highest rates are less likely to be accompanied by wind (HUDSON 1964 c) and this may be connected with the wind patterns around the base of convective thunderstorms.

3.2   MOMENTUM AND KINETIC ENERGY

There is experimental evidence that the erosive power of rainfall is related to compound parameters derived from combinations of more than one physical property. The kinetic energy of the rain and its momentum are examples. If the size of raindrops is known and also their terminal velocity, it is possible to calculate the momentum of the falling rain, or its kinetic energy, by a summation of the values for individual raindrops. On the whole the indirect calculation method has given better results than attempts to measure directly the momentum or kinetic energy of falling rain. The forces involved are so small that any instrument sufficiently sensitive to record them mechanically is liable to be swamped by wind effects. This is particularly true of instruments attempting to measure the expenditure of energy in doing work, such as letting the rain drive round a vane or paddle-wheel whose rotation is used to wind up a weight against gravity. A more promising mechanical arrangement is to measure the average momentum over a period of time by in effect weighing the force exerted by the rain on the pan of a sensitive balance. Several models using this principle have been used for research purposes (ROSE 1958, HUDSON 1965) although the instrument is not in general use.

Another approach is to convert the kinetic energy into another form of energy which may be more easily measured. One such instrument is known as an acoustic recorder, because the rain falls on a diaphragm which emits sound. This is a convenient way of adding together the effect of the individual raindrops and the combined sound is picked up by a microphone and converted to electrical impulses which are fed into a chart recorder. Research on this line is continuing, (KINNELL 1968, FORREST 1970). Methods for direct measurement of momentum or energy may be promising, but the present state of knowledge rests on the indirect calculation from drop size and velocity. Studies have been carried out in widely separated countries and some of the main results are shown in figure 3.9. One of the difficulties is that very few measurements have been made at high intensities; another is that these studies were made by independent research workers and there is no way of telling how much of the variation is due to their different techniques and how much is real differences between the rain in various countries.

Both momentum and kinetic energy are shown in figure 3.10 to have very similar relationships with intensity, and the only question is which can be more easily and accurately measured.

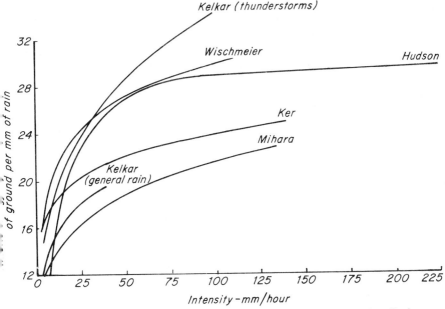

FIGURE 3.9   *The relation between kinetic energy of rainfall and intensity. Each curve extends to the highest intensity recorded. The studies were carried out in the following countries:* HUDSON—*Rhodesia,* KELKAR—*India,* KER—*Trinidad,* MIHARA—*Japan,* WISCHMEIER—*United States*

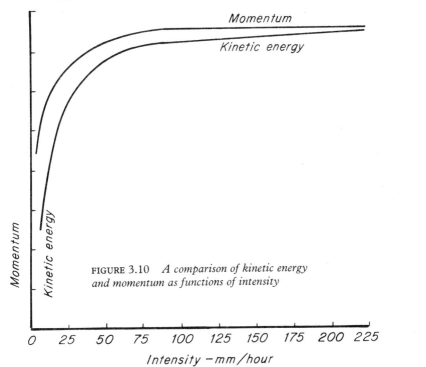

FIGURE 3.10   *A comparison of kinetic energy and momentum as functions of intensity*

Research in this subject is being stimulated by the knowledge that there is a strong connexion between the momentum or energy of rain and its power to cause erosion. The consideration of why some storms can cause more erosion damage than others, and ways in which this erosive power can be determined are the subject of Chapter 4.

References

BEST, A. C. 1950 The Size Distribution of Raindrops. *Quarterly Journal of the Royal Meteorological Society* 76, 16

BLANCHARD, D. C. 1950 Behaviour of Water Drops at Terminal Velocity. *Transactions of the American Geophysical Union* 31, 836

FORREST, P. M. 1970 *The Development of Two Field Instruments to measure erosivity: A simple rainfall intensity meter, and an acoustic rainfall recorder tested with a rotating disk simulator.* B.Sc. (Hons.) dissertation, National College of Agricultural Engineering

GUNN, R. and G. D. KINZER 1949 Terminal Velocity of Water Droplets in Stagnant Air. *Journal of Meteorology* 6, 243

HALL, M. J. 1970 Use of the Stain Method in Determining the Drop-Size Distributions of Coarse Liquid Sprays. *Transactions American Society of Agricultural Engineers*, 13, 1, 33–37, 41

HAMILTON, E. L. 1954 Rainfall Sampling on Rugged Terrain. *Technical Bulletin* 1096, *United States Department of Agriculture*

HUDSON, N. W. 1963 Raindrop Size Distribution in High Intensity Storms. *Rhodesian Journal of Agricultural Research* 1, 1, 6–11

HUDSON, N. W. 1964a A Review of Methods of Measuring Rainfall Characteristics related to Soil Erosion. *Research Bulletin* 1, *Department of Conservation, Salisbury, Rhodesia*

HUDSON, N. W. 1964b The Flour Pellet Method for Measuring the Size of Raindrops. *Research Bulletin* 4, *Department of Conservation, Salisbury, Rhodesia*

HUDSON, N. W. 1964c Bearing and Incidence of Sub-tropical Convective Rainfall. *Quarterly Journal of the Royal Meteorological Society* 90, 385, 325–328

HUDSON, N. W. 1965 *The Influence of Rainfall on the Mechanics of Soil Erosion.* M.Sc. Thesis, University of Cape Town

KINNELL, P. I. A. 1968 *An Acoustic Impact Rainfall Recorder.* Postgraduate certificate dissertation, National College of Agricultural Engineering

LAWS, J. O. 1941 Measurements of Fall-Velocity of Water-Drops and Raindrops. *Transactions of the American Geophysical Union* 22: 709

LAWS, J. O. and D. A. PARSONS 1943 The Relation of Raindrop Size to Intensity. *Transactions of the American Geophysical Union* 24: 452

ROSE, C. W. 1958 *Effects of Rainfall and Soil Factors on Soil Detachment and the Rate of Water Penetration into Soils.* Ph.D. Thesis, University of London

Chapter 4   The erosivity of rainfall

4.1   DEFINING EROSIVITY AND ERODIBILITY

Rainfall erosion is the interaction of two items—the rain and the soil. The amount of erosion which occurs in any given circumstances will be influenced by both, and our study of the processes of soil erosion is simplified by considering the two aspects separately.

We know from observation that one storm can cause more erosion than another on the same land, and we also know that the same storm will cause more erosion on one field than on another. The effect of the rain is called erosivity and the effect of the soil is called erodibility. The way they differ is best explained by examples.

Let us imagine an experiment station with a soil surface which is absolutely uniform as regards soil type, slope, and all other physical properties. Assume also that the whole of the station is covered by a completely uniform crop. If the amount of erosion taking place during each storm were measured, the amount would be influenced only by the nature of the rain. Comparing the effect of one storm with that of another storm would provide a relative measure of the power of each storm to cause erosion, and that is what is meant by erosivity. This will enable us to say that on this imaginary experiment station, storm A caused a soil loss of X kilograms per hectare and storm B caused a soil loss of Y kilograms per hectare. But we know that on a farm a few miles away the soil is different and during storm A the soil loss might be $2X$ kilograms per hectare. The difference is because one soil is more easily eroded than the other, and this vulnerability to erosion is what is meant by erodibility. It is thus the reciprocal of the soils resistance to erosion. This example is shown diagrammatically in figure 4.1. It is usual to assume that if one soil is eroded twice as much as another soil during one storm, it will lose twice as much in all storms, that is we are assuming that there is no interaction between erosivity and erodibility. This has not been proved, but it is unlikely that any error resulting from this assumption is significant.

The resistance of a soil to erosion depends on many factors and so to measure erodibility numerically an assessment has to be made of each factor. Some of these are the nature of soil (sandy soil is obviously more easily eroded than a hard clay), the slope of the land (a steep slope will erode more than a flat one) and the kind of crop (some crops will naturally protect the soil better than others). The evaluation of the factors affecting the erodibility of the soil will be considered in Chapter 5.

Formal definitions can now be stated as follows:
Erosivity is the potential ability of rain to cause erosion. It is a function of the physical characteristics of rainfall.

Erodibility is the vulnerability or susceptability of the soil to erosion.

It is a function of both the physical characteristics of the soil, and the management of the soil.

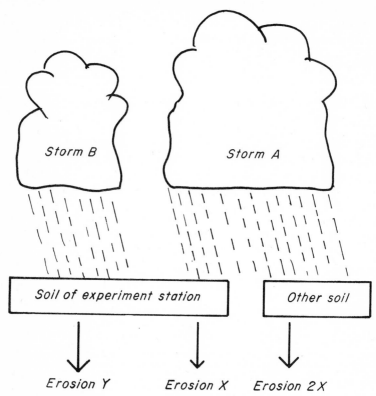

FIGURE 4.1   *The erosivity of rainfall and the erodibility of soil*

The relation between these two parameters can also be stated: A value on the scale of erosivity depends solely on rainfall properties, and to this extent it is independent of the soil. But a quantitative measurement of erosivity may only be made when erosion occurs, and this involves the erodibility of the eroded material.

Similarly relative values of erodibility are not influenced by rain, but can only be measured when caused by rain which must have erosivity. Thus neither is independently quantitative but each may be studied quantitatively while the other is held constant.

Figure 4.2 illustrates this diagrammatically. The erodibility of a soil corresponds with a particular step on the scale of erodibility. For this soil, the level of erosion in a storm depends upon how high is the erosivity, ie, how many rungs up the ladder which is the scale of erosivity. The same storm would cause more erosion if it landed on a field of higher erodibility, ie, if the ladder were resting on a higher step.

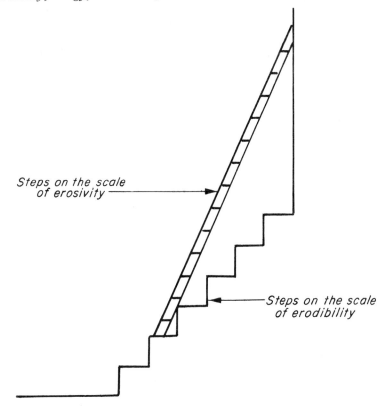

Steps on the scale
of erosivity

Steps on the scale
of erodibility

FIGURE 4.2   *The combination of erosivity and erodibility*

(Note however, that this analogy should not be pursued too far, for numerical values of erosivity and erodibility are expressed in units which have to be multiplied together, not added.)

These definitions of erosivity and erodibility are now generally accepted and used, but in some early literature erosivity is loosely used to refer to soil properties.

4.2   EROSIVITY, ENERGY, AND INTENSITY

4.2.1   Raindrop splash and surface run-off

Soil erosion is a work process in the physical sense that work is the expenditure of energy, and energy is used in all the phases of erosion—in breaking down soil aggregates, in splashing them in the air, in causing turbulence in surface run-off, in scouring and carrying away soil particles. If the available sources of energy are considered this explains why splash erosion is so vital in the erosion process. In table 4.1 the kinetic energy available from falling rain is compared with that from surface run-off. The exact figures used in this calculation are not important since they are based upon assumptions of the percentage run-off and assumed velocities but clearly the difference in the amounts of energy is very large, with rainfall energy dominating the picture.

TABLE 4.1   *Kinetic energy of rain and run-off*

Kinetic energy $= \frac{1}{2} \times$ mass $\times$ (velocity)^2

	Rain	Run-off
Mass	Assume the mass of falling rain is R	Assuming 25% run-off, mass of run-off is $\dfrac{R}{4}$
Velocity	Assume terminal velocity of 8 m/sec	Assume speed of surface flow of 1 m/sec
Kinetic energy	$\frac{1}{2} \times R \times (8)^2 = 32R$	$\frac{1}{2} \times \dfrac{R}{4} \times (1)^2 = \dfrac{R}{8}$

The rain thus has 256 times more kinetic energy than the surface run-off.

In this connexion it should be pointed out that the fairly recent appreciation of energy in the erosion process, coming at a time when reliable data was scarce, has led to the widespread quotation of some quite inaccurate facts. It is quite easy to show that there is an error of a factor of about 100 in estimates such as that 'the energy output of rain at 2 in. per hour on one acre is equal to that of six 40 horse power tractors'. However the literature already abounds with such statements (the present author was guilty in an early publication—HUDSON 1957), and since it has now been made almost official by inclusion in the *USDA Yearbook* (1955, page 127) it will no doubt continue as a popular misconception for many years.

Another approach to the part played by splash erosion and the role of surface run-off comes from Ellison's thought that erosion may be divided into detachment, or the tearing loose of soil particles from their moorings in the soil mass, followed by their transportation, and finally deposition. It follows that the principal effect of raindrops is to detach soil, while the principal effect of surface flow is the transportation of the detached soil. It is also clear that under conditions of heavy rain the detaching action of the raindrop splash is by far the most important part of the process. This was demonstrated practically in a simple field experiment (HUDSON 1957). Two 1/100 acre plots (0·004 hectare) of bare soil 1·5 metres wide by 27·5 metres long (5 feet by 90 feet) received identical soil treatment (weeding, digging, etc.) but over one there were suspended two layers of mosquito gauze which allowed the rain to pass through, but broke up the rapidly falling raindrops into a spray of fine drops at lower velocity. On the second plot the bare soil was exposed to the rain. The soil loss from the gauzed plot, where splash erosion was eliminated, was reduced to one hundredth of the soil loss from the unprotected plot.

There is of course an interaction between splash erosion and surface wash, in that splash impact seals the soil surface and increases the rate of run-off, but nevertheless under field conditions erosion is mainly dependent upon splash erosion.

4.2.2 Erosion and energy

There is a great deal of experimental evidence to suggest a link between erosive power and the mass and velocity of falling drops. In the early days of erosion research ELLISON (1944) in a laboratory experiment measured splash erosion for various combinations of drop size, velocity, and intensity. Analysis of his results gave the expression

$$S \propto V^{4.33} \times D^{1.07} \times I^{0.65}$$

where S is the grams of soil splashed in 30 minutes
$\quad V$ is the drop velocity in feet/second
$\quad D$ is the drop diameter in mm
$\quad I$ is the rainfall rate in inches per hour.

Another similar expression was obtained by BISAL (1960) who from similar laboratory experiments suggests $G = K D V^{1.4}$
where G is the weight of soil splashed, in grams,
$\quad K$ is a constant for the soil type,
$\quad D$ is drop diameter in mm and
$\quad V$ is impact velocity in meters/second.

In both these studies the combination of powers of drop velocity and drop mass are not very different from combining mass and velocity into the parameter kinetic energy. Indeed MIHARA (1959) found that splash erosion is directly correlated with kinetic energy, and FREE (1960) suggests that the relationship which best fits his experimental results was

for sand   Splash Erosion $\propto$ (Kinetic Energy)$^{0.9}$ and
for soil   Splash Erosion $\propto$ (Kinetic Energy)$^{1.46}$.

ROSE (1960) challenges the assumption that results such as these prove that splash erosion is dependent only on the kinetic energy of natural or artificial rain, and shows that if a relationship exists between erosion and energy, then an equally valid, though different, relationship will exist between erosion and momentum or any other function of mass and velocity. Since mass occurs in the same form in the formulae for both momentum and energy, it is necessary to vary velocity in order to resolve the problem of whether energy or momentum is the better index of erosivity, and this Rose did. After detailed experimental work, Rose concluded that the rate of detachment depends more closely on momentum than energy. However, it has been shown in the previous chapter that for natural rain the relationships between intensity and either momentum or kinetic energy are equally close and of the same pattern (figure 3.10).

The issue of whether momentum can be used instead of energy is therefore not important; the real question is can calculations of kinetic energy (or momentum) be used to estimate erosivity?

4.3   ESTIMATING EROSIVITY FROM RAINFALL DATA

4.3.1   The EI_{30} Index

The laboratory experiments by Ellison, Bisal, Rose and others certainly suggested that erosivity is related to energy, but it also had to be verified that the hypothesis holds for soil losses in the field caused by natural rain.

The confirmation came from the work of WISCHMEIER (1955) in the United States. At the Erosion Research Data Processing Laboratory at Purdue University, Wischmeier put on punch-cards all the data from the experimental plots of 35 conservation experiment stations; a total of 8 250 plot-years records. Using machine processing of punch-cards carrying the data, and computers to perform the calculations, a search was made for parameters which could be correlated with the recorded erosion. The results, summarized by WISCHMEIER *et al* (1958) showed that the correlation of soil loss in individual storms with rain amount was poor, and it was also poor with the maximum amount of rain falling in various time intervals such as 5, 15 or 30 minutes. The momentum of the rain was better, but the factor most closely related to erosion was the kinetic energy of the rain. However, there was still considerable unexplained variation and so multiple regressions were also tested in which several factors were combined in various arithmetical arrangements. After considering and testing all the reasonable possibilities the best estimator of soil loss was found to be a compound parameter, the product of the kinetic energy of the storm and the 30-minute intensity. This latter term requires some explanation. It is the greatest average intensity experienced in any 30-minute period during the storm. It is computed (see figure 4.3) from recording raingauge charts by locating the greatest amount of rain which falls in any 30 minutes, and then doubling this amount to get the same dimensions as intensity, ie, inches per hour or mm per hour.

This product term gave an excellent correlation. Wischmeier found that it was in fact possible to improve the relationship even further by taking account of other factors, such as the soil moisture at the beginning of the storm, but these further refinements added so little that they were felt to be not worth the extra complication. This measure of erosivity is described as the EI_{30} index. It can be computed for individual storms, and the storm values can be summed over periods of time to give weekly, monthly, or annual values of erosivity. The calculation procedure is shown in section 4.3.3. Numerical values computed in this way from rainfall figures will be subject to the same variation as the rainfall itself, and average values will only be as reliable as the rainfall data from which they are derived.

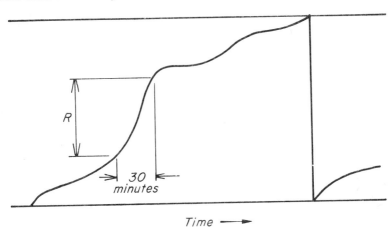

FIGURE 4.3 *Method of obtaining the 30-minute intensity. The 30-minute period with the greatest amount of rain R is found from the raingauge chart. Twice this amount is the 30-minute intensity*

4.3.2 The KE > 1 Index

Clearly erosivity can be found from rainfall records and the EI_{30} index is one way of doing this. However it was found in Africa that it was not as efficient as might be expected from Wischmeier's studies in America. An alternative method was therefore developed, and this centres upon the concept that there is a threshold value of intensity at which rain starts to become erosive. This idea arose from the observation that at low intensities there is little or no erosion. This is logical and to be expected. At low intensity, rain is composed mainly of small drops, falling with low velocity, and hence low energy. Even if a little splash erosion does occur there is usually no run-off to carry away the splashed particles. Experiments were carried out to see whether there is a recognizable point below which rain is non-erosive. Splash erosion was measured, using Ellison-type splash cups during periods of low intensity rain. This experimental method is described in section 4.4. The results showed that there is a threshold level of intensity and, although there is some variation from one storm to another, most rain falling at low intensities is not erosive and erosion is almost entirely caused by rain falling at intensities above this critical level. The value found in Africa was about 1 inch per hour or 25 mm per hour.

If in calculating erosivity we include the low intensity non-erosive rain this is bound to introduce a discrepancy, since the amount of non-erosive rain could vary greatly from one storm to another without affecting the erosive power. Even in severe tropical rainfall there is a high proportion of low intensity rain (usually more than half the seasonal total) and although the energy per mm is low, the total energy of this large amount of rain is still considerable. It was found that by leaving out the energy of the non-erosive rain an excellent correlation was obtained between splash erosion and the total energy of the rest of the rain.

We thus have another estimator of erosivity, which for convenience is written as $KE > 1$, meaning the total kinetic energy of the rain falling at intensities of more than one inch per hour. It can be used in exactly the same way as EI_{30} but appears to be more appropriate than EI_{30} for tropical and sub-tropical rainfall.

4.3.3   Calculation procedure

The calculation for EI_{30} and $KE > 1$ is similar, but another advantage of $KE > 1$ is that it can be used with less detailed rainfall records. For both methods it is necessary to know the amount of rain which falls at specified rates of intensity. In the sample calculation shown in table 4.2 only a few wide bands of intensity have been used and a more accurate calculation could be made using a greater number of intensity classes. The amount of rainfall in each class of intensity is multiplied by the appropriate energy value, and the energy is totalled for the whole storm. In the EI_{30} method this total energy is then multiplied by the 30-minute intensity to give the erosivity value. In the $KE > 1$ method the first line is omitted from the calculation and the index is simply the total energy of the remainder. The fact that the I_{30} value is not required may be a distinct advantage in countries with limited rainfall data, for it can only be obtained from autographic raingauge charts and is not ordinarily recorded by meteorological stations.

4.4   SPLASH EROSION AND WASH EROSION

Laboratory studies have usually compared estimates of erosivity with erosion measured as the amount of sand splashed out of small containers, whereas field experiments record the amount of soil washed into collection tanks at the lower edge of experimental plots. If an index of erosivity is set up to be an estimator of erosion it should be tested to see that it works as well for real field erosion as for small-scale laboratory experiments. The $KE > 1$ index was so tested in a series of experiments, starting with the special case of splash of sand and progressively adding the other variables.

TABLE 4.2   *Sample calculation of erosivity from rainfall records*

(*a*) Using the EI_{30} method

1 Intensity (in./hr)	2 Amount (in.)	3 Energy [1] (ft-tons/acre in.)	4 Total (Col 2 × Col 3)
0–1	1·5	816	1224
1–2	1·0	974	974
2–3	0·75	1048	786
> 3	0·25	1096	274
	3·5		3258 ft-tons per acre

I_{30} is derived from raingauge charts as shown in figure 4.3.
Using a typical figure of say 0·6 inches/hour

$$EI_{30} = E \times I_{30} = 3258 \times 0·6 = 1954·8 \text{ foot-tons per acre}$$

(1) Calculated from the expression

$$\text{Kinetic Energy} = 916 + 331 \log_{10} I$$

when kinetic energy is in foot-tons per acre and intensity in inches per hour (Wischmeier, Smith, and Uhland 1958)
This expression is shown in *SI* units in figure 3.9.

(*b*) Using the $KE > 1$ method
The Energy of the 1·5 inches of rain at less than 1 inch/hour is ignored and the remainder summed

$$KE > 1 = 974 + 786 + 274 = 2\,034 \text{ foot-tons per acre.}$$

Note on units
The EI_{30} method was developed in foot-pound-second units and all its applications have been in those units so there seems little point is converting it into *SI* units. The $KE > 1$ method converts readily to *SI* and becomes the $KE > 25$ method. A sample calculation follows:

1 Intensity (mm/hour)	2 Amount (mm)	3 Energy of rain (joules/m² per mm of rain) (from figure 3.9)	4 Total (Col 2 × Col 3)
0–25	30	—	—
25–50	20	26	520
50–75	10	28	280
> 75	5	29	145
Total	65		945 joules/m²

A first approximation may be made by assuming a single average value for the energy of all the rain at intensities over 25 mm/h. Thus

$$35 \text{ mm} \times 28 \text{ J/m}^2/\text{mm} = 980 \text{ J/m}^2.$$

First splash erosion was measured alone using Ellison-type splash cups (plate 4.1). These were first used by ELLISON (1944) and have been used subsequently by many research workers because they offer a simple but precise and reproducible measurement of splash. Brass cylinders 77 mm in diameter and 50 mm deep have a fine wire mesh soldered on one end to form a porous bottom. A thin layer of cotton wool rests on the wire and the containers are filled with fine sand. When placed in a shallow depth of water the cups are maintained at a constant moisture status of near saturation. The cups are oven-dried and weighed before and after exposure to rainfall and since the soil conditions have been standardized the weight of sand splashed out gives a relative measurement of the 'splashability' of the rain. With developments in experimental technique (BISAL 1950, HUDSON 1965), this method gives a simple but precise measurement. In the experiments to test KE > 1 groups of splash cups were exposed to every storm for two years, and the correlation between sand splash and KE > 1 was very good at $r = 0.96$.

PLATE 4.1   *Ellison-type splash cups measure the amount of a standard sand which is splashed out of the containers during a storm*

In the next stage surface run-off was introduced and soil used instead of sand in soil pans after the style of those used by FREE (1952). The pans were 1 metre long, 300 mm wide, and 100 mm deep, and set on a 5% slope (plate 4.2). They were filled with a seived clay loam soil which was maintained at constant moisture status by connecting each tray to a constant-head reservoir. The soil washed off the pan is collected in a trough at the lower edge. Again after two years of results the correlation between KE > 1 and the measured soil loss was still remarkably good at $r = 0.92$.

The next stage was to use a field scale plot 27·5 metres long by 1·5 metres wide on a 5 per cent slope (plate 4.3). The soil was undisturbed except for the minimum amount of weeding to keep the surface free of vegetation, and the soil moisture was not controlled. The soil loss was measured by catching the run-off in tanks at the bottom of the plot. In spite of having now re-introduced all the variables which occur in nature such as changes in the soil moisture when the storm starts, the correlation was still $r = 0.94$.

It is clear then that reliable estimates of the erosive power can be calculated from rainfall records, and in the EI_{30} index and the KE > 1 index we have two alternative methods, slightly different in approach but both tested and proved to be suitable for the purpose and efficient in operation.

PLATE 4.2 *Soil trays for measuring splash and wash erosion. The sixth tray in the background serves as a constant-head tank, maintaining constant moisture level in the other five trays. The porous tiles in the false floor are seen in the empty tray on the left*

PLATE 4.3   *The field plot whose soil loss was used to test the estimates of erosivity from rainfall records*

4.5   APPLICATIONS OF AN INDEX OF EROSIVITY

The ability to assess numerically the erosive power of rainfall has two main applications. In practical soil conservation it helps to improve the design of conservation works, and in research it helps to increase our knowledge and understanding of erosion. Some examples will illustrate these uses.

4.5.1   An aid to design

The soil conservation techniques used to combat and control erosion must be designed to do their job efficiently. If they are under-designed they will fail, if they are over-designed, ie, unnecessarily large or complicated, this is equally undesirable. The right balance can only be achieved if we know fairly accurately the severity of the problem which has to be faced, and a quantitative measure of erosivity makes it possible to identify the basic erosion risk in different areas. For example, if it is known that the erosivity of the rain in the northern part of a country is two and a half times as great as in the south, then it would be sensible to design terraces according to different specifications in the two regions.

In any country with sufficiently detailed rainfall data, maps of erosivity could be produced, as has been done in the United States of

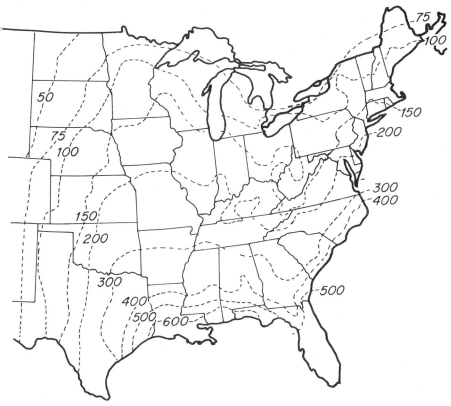

FIGURE 4.4 *Map of average annual values of rainfall erosivity* (from SMITH and WISCHMEIER 1962)

America. The total annual erosivity can be drawn on a map as in figure 4.4 and used to predict annual erosion losses. Information can also be tabulated on how erosivity varies during the year at any given location (figure 4.5) and this can be used for the detailed planning of conservation farming systems. These applications are considered in more detail in Chapter 10.

Another practical demonstration can be taken from an experience in Africa. When carrying out gully reclamation works which include the establishment of vegetation it is essential to have some rain to encourage growth, but highly erosive storms are likely to wash out the newly planted material. In tropical climates with a concentrated rainy season this means choosing either the beginning or the end of the rains.

Figure 4.6 shows how a monthly plot of values of erosivity gave the answer. Bulawayo has low values of erosivity at the beginning of the rainy season in November and December, but high values in March so the beginning of the season is evidently the best time for establishing

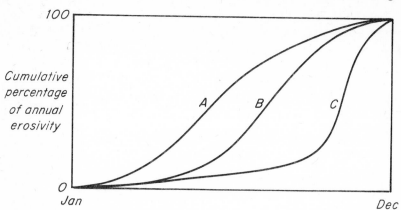

FIGURE 4.5 *Cumulative erosivity during the year. Curve A indicates fairly even distribution of erosivity, Curve B mainly summer rains, and Curve C heavy autumn rains*

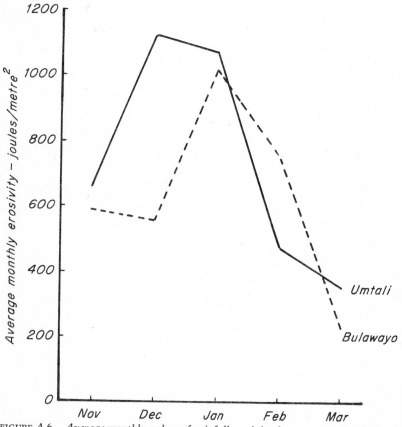

FIGURE 4.6 *Average monthly values of rainfall erosivity for two towns in Rhodesia*

anti-erosion vegetation. On the other hand at Umtali the season opens with high erosivity storms, and the better time would be in February and March when the erosivity falls away.

Any such calculations of erosivity must be based on average rainfall figures and a particular month or year could differ considerably from the average. The fluctuations of erosivity about the average will follow fluctuations in total rainfall, and so more reliable estimates of erosivity can be made where the rainfall is reliable, than where it is erratic. The length and accuracy of rainfall records will also affect the accuracy of estimates of erosivity.

4.5.2 An aid to research

Soil erosion research uses either natural rainfall or man-made simulated rain and in each case a quantitative scale of erosivity is a valuable asset. One of the drawbacks of using field plot experiments to measure the run-off and soil loss under natural rainfall is that it takes so very long to get reliable results. Experiments concerned with rotations are particularly difficult. A plot will have its particular treatment one year and the soil loss is recorded. The next year it moves to the next phase of the rotation and a different soil loss is recorded. The difficulty is to separate how much of this difference is due to the different cropping treatment and how much due to the different rainfall. Neither replications nor statistical techniques can completely overcome this problem, but if it is possible to numerically evaluate the erosivity then allowance can be made for the variations from year to year. This enables much more information to be obtained in limited time from field experiments. The same argument applies to the variations during one season. Suppose the measured soil loss is found to be different in the early part of the season from that later on. The question is 'does the difference arise from the change in crop growth or is the rain different during these two periods?' There is no answer without a means of measuring erosivity, but to measure the effect of crop growth on erosion is simple when the erosivity of each storm can be compared.

4.5.3 Is erosion cataclysmic or slow attrition?

An important question which occurs wherever there is a serious erosion problem is 'what kind of rain does the greatest amount of damage in the long term?' Is it the small storms which only cause a little erosion but happen very often? or is it the tremendous storm which only happens occasionally but does more damage than all the little storms? The experimental evidence differs widely. LITTLE (1940) quotes one extreme; a single storm at the experiment station at Bethany, Missouri, caused 50% of the total erosion in 5 years. Similarly, at the experiment station at Mazoe, Rhodesia it was found that in almost all seasons more than half of the total amount of erosion occurred in the one or two heaviest storms of the year. In one case three-quarters of the yearly loss took place in ten minutes (HUDSON 1957). On the other hand WISCHMEIER (1962) showed that the overall pattern in America is for the greater part of the total erosion damage to be done by the frequent small storms. There may be an explanation for these apparently irreconcilable results. The experiment stations both report the 'big bang' effect, and both experience tropical-type heavy rainfall from convective storms, whereas the data from the whole of America include a great deal of temperate rainfall. Whether this is the explanation or not, the main point is that here is an important erosion effect which differs widely according to the type of rainfall. The index of erosivity which can be calculated from rainfall records allows the effect to be evaluated for any climate.

4.5.4   Temperate and tropical rainfall

Probably the most important application of the measurement of erosivity is that it allows a simple explanation of why soil erosion is a serious problem in tropical and sub-tropical countries, but barely noteworthy in temperate climates. It was shown in section 4.3.2 that rain falling at low intensities is non-erosive and the threshold level of intensity at which it becomes erosive is about 25 mm per hour. Figure 4.7 shows the kind of distribution curve obtained by plotting the amount of rain falling at different intensities. (The data would be first plotted as a histogram showing the amounts for selected class groups of intensity, eg, 0 to 5 mm/hour, 5 to 10 mm/hour etc, and then a smooth curve drawn through the histogram.) The vital difference is that in temperate rainfall something like 95% of the rain falls at low non-erosive intensities, ie, only 5% is heavy enough to cause erosion, whereas in the case of tropical rainfall only 60% falls at intensities less than 25 mm/hour, and the remaining 40% contributes to soil erosion.

There are two further factors contributing to the difference. On the whole it is probable that the total quantity of rain will be greater in tropical climates so a comparison of the amount of erosive rain might be:

Temperate climate with 5% of the rain being erosive,
    5% of say 750 mm of annual rain = 37·5 mm of erosive rain
Tropical climate, with 40% of the rain being erosive,
    40% of say 1,500 mm of annual rain = 600 mm of erosive rain.

Another difference is that the average intensity of the erosive rain is higher in the tropical distribution—perhaps about 60 mm per hour as in figure 4.7 compared with about 35 mm per hour for the temperate rain. It was shown in figure 3.9 that the kinetic energy per mm of rain increased as the intensity increased, and so to calculate the total erosivity we would use a higher figure, perhaps 28 joules per square

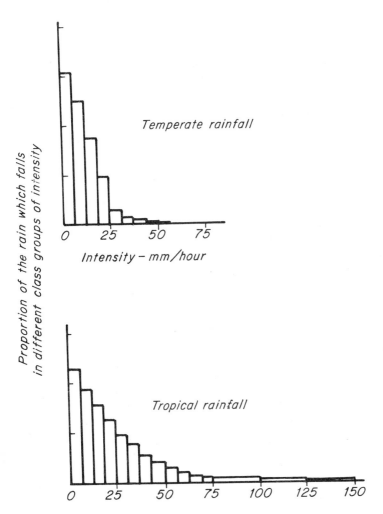

FIGURE 4.7 *The distribution of rainfall at different intensities for tropical and temperate rainfall*

metre per mm for tropical rain, compared with perhaps 24 for temperate rainfall. Using the same figures as in the example above, the annual erosivity values would be

Temperate rain $37 \cdot 5 \times 24 = \quad 900$ joules/metre^2
Tropical rain $\quad 600 \quad \times 28 = 14,400$ joules/metre^2

The erosive power of the tropical rain is therefore 16 times greater than that of the temperate rain. The actual numbers used in this example are not important. What is important is that this sample calculation shows how tropical rainfall is likely to have a very much greater power to cause erosion, and this is why erosion is so much more serious in countries with tropical or sub-tropical rainfall.

However the amount of erosion which takes place depends not only on the rain but also on the soil surface on which the rain falls. This aspect, the erodibility, will be considered in Chapter 5.

References

BISAL, F. 1950 Calibration of Splash Cup for Soil Erosion Studies. *Agricultural Engineering*, 31:621, 1950

BISAL, F. 1960 The Effect of Raindrop Size and Impact Velocity on Sand Splash. *Canadian Journal of Soil Science* 40, 242–245

ELLISON, W. D. 1944 Studies of Raindrop Erosion. *Agricultural Engineering*, 25:131–136, 181–182

FREE, G. R. 1952 Soil Movement by Raindrops. *Agricultural Engineering*, 33:491–494, 496

FREE, G. R. 1960 Erosion Characteristics of Rainfall. *Agricultural Engineering*, 41, 7, 447–449, 455

HUDSON, N. W. 1957 Erosion Control Research. Progress report on experiments at Henderson Research Station, 1953–1956. *Rhodesian Agricultural Journal*, 54.4. 297–323

HUDSON, N. W. 1965 *The Influence of Rainfall on the Mechanics of Soil Erosion*. M.Sc. Thesis, University of Cape Town

LITTLE, J. M. 1940 *Erosional Topography and Erosion*. Carlisle, San Francisco

MIHARA, Y. 1951 Raindrops and Soil Erosion. *Bulletin of the National Institute of Agricultural Science*, Series A, 1

ROSE, C. W. 1960 Soil Detachment caused by Rainfall. *Soil Science* 89, 1, 28–35

SMITH, D. D. and W. H. WISCHMEIER 1962 Rainfall Erosion. *Advances in Agronomy* 14, 109–148

WISCHMEIER, W. H. 1955 Punch Cards Record Runoff and Soil Loss Data. *Agricultural Engineering*, 36, 664–666

WISCHMEIER, W. H. 1962 Storms and Soil Conservation. *Journal of Soil and Water Conservation* 17.2, 55–59

WISCHMEIER, W. H., D. D. SMITH and R. E. UHLAND 1958 Evaluation of Factors in the Soil-Loss Equation. *Agricultural Engineering*, 39.8.458

UNITED STATES DEPARTMENT OF AGRICULTURE 1955 *Water*. Yearbook of Agriculture

Chapter 5   The erodibility of soil

5.1   DEFINITION

The erodibility of a soil is its vulnerability or susceptibility to erosion, that is the reciprocal of its resistance to erosion. A soil with a high erodibility will suffer more erosion than a soil with low erodibility if both are exposed to the same rainfall. Whereas the erosivity of rainfall was shown in Chapter 4 to be a fairly straightforward measure of the rain's physical properties, the assessment of erodibility is more complicated because it depends upon many variables.

5.2   FACTORS INFLUENCING ERODIBILITY

There are two groups of factors. First the actual physical features of the soil, ie, what kind of soil it is, and secondly the treatment of the soil, ie, what is done with it. The part concerned with treatment has much the greater effect, and is also more difficult to assess.

5.2.1   Soil physical characteristics

For many years soil scientists have attempted to relate the amount of soil erosion as measured in the field to various physical characteristics of the soil which can be measured in the laboratory. In fact work in this field has included either singly or in combination almost every soil property which is capable of quantitative measurement and BRYAN (1968) reviews more than thirty studies of this type. Pioneer work was done in America in the nineteen thirties when attempts were made to explain the results of early field erosion experiments in terms of soil properties LUTZ 1934). BOUYOUCOS (1935) suggested that erodibility is proportional to the ratio

$$\frac{\% \text{ sand} + \% \text{ silt}}{\% \text{ clay}}$$

and MIDDLETON (1930 and 1932) used a 'dispersion ratio' based on the changes in silt and clay content before and after dispersion in water. PEELE (1937) included a measure of the rate of water percolation through the soil, and YODER (1936) developed a technique later adopted in studies of soil structure, for measuring the stability of soil aggregates when mechanically agitated in water. Other methods based essentially on mechanical analysis have been used in Russia by VOZNESENSKY and ARTSRUUI (1940), in India by BALLAL (1954) and by MEHTA et al (1958), in Japan by NISHIKATA and TAKEUCHI (1955), and in France by HENIN (1963). Chemical properties were also investigated by WALLIS and

STEVAN (1961). Some of these studies have been partly successful in that they have given some indication of the relative resistance to erosion inherent in different soil types, for example EPSTEIN and GRANT (1967), or have allowed a comparative assessment of the effects of alternative management practices on a particular soil. Until recently the approach was less successful in providing a quantitative estimate of the erosion which will occur when the soil is subjected to rain of known erosive power. The position changed when WISCHMEIER and others (1969) showed a good correlation between erodibility and an index containing 15 physical properties of the soil. Subsequently this was refined and simplified to a practical method using only 5 properties and this method shows much promise (WISCHMEIER 1971).

Seeking a more direct line of approach, some research workers have sought measures of erodibility by subjecting the soil to tests more closely related to what happens in practice. ELLISON (1947 Part 1) suggested that resistance to splash erosion, and resistance to wash erosion should be measured separately, and this line has been recently revived by OVENS (1969). Other studies measuring resistance to a flow of water were carried out in Russia by GUSSAK (1946), who measured the volume and velocity of water required to wash away a given weight of soil in a specially designed flume, and ALDERMAN (1956) who measured the size of the crater formed by a jet of water playing onto submerged soils. However, these are still rather artificial tests, and also they have to be carried out on soil samples, with the attendant un-certainty as to whether the process of removing the sample may have destroyed or changed the very properties which should be measured.

Another line of approach has been to subject the soil to the action of rainfall and measure the resultant erosion. Natural rainfall is un-suitable since it is unpredictable and variable, and the search is for a measure of variations in the soil erodibility under constant erosivity. Artificial rainfall simulators have been widely used both in the laboratory on soil samples and in the field on undisturbed soil. The development of rainfall simulators as a major instrument for erosion research is described in more detail in Chapter 15, but a few of the techniques should be mentioned here as they were developed specially for studying some aspect of erodibility. The simplest variation consists merely of allowing single drops to fall from a burette as used by McCALLA (1944) and by RAI *et al* (1954) in laboratory tests of structure. Large drops of the order of 5 or 6 mm diameter are formed, and usually fall only a few feet. VILENSKY (1945) used a combination of both single drops and a spray to measure aggregate breakdown. To measure the breakdown of structure under conditions similar to tropical rainfall PEREIRA (1956) required a high impact effect, and allowed drops of 6 mm diameter to fall through 2 metres onto soil samples, assuming that extra-large drops achieving 50% of their terminal velocity would have an effect comparable with that of smaller drops falling at terminal velocity. A similar principle, but using a variety of drop sizes, was used by

MOLDENHAUER (1965). In order to be able to carry out field tests of erodibility on undisturbed soil ADAMS *et al* (1957) designed a portable rain simulator. In this instrument 100 drop-forming nozzles gave drops of 5·5 mm diameter from glass capillary tubes in which a fine wire was inserted to give better control of drop size. The height of fall was 1 metre, and so each drop had a kinetic energy equal to that of a drop of 3·44 mm diameter falling at terminal velocity.

Using simulator techniques several erodibility studies have given useful results, those of ADAMS *et al* (1958) and MOLDENHAUER (1965) being particularly noteworthy. These studies give only a relative measure of how one soil compares with another and the results cannot be related directly to soil loss, but they have a useful application. At field experiment stations soil loss is recorded from those soils on which stations happen to have been sited, and a method for comparing erodibility by using rainfall simulator allows the results to be extended to soils for which field experimental data is not available.

5.2.2　Land management

The amount of soil erosion which occurs under given conditions is, however, influenced not only by the soil itself, but by the treatment or management it receives. A soil might lose say 400 tons per hectare per year when used for the cultivation of row crops with the rows running straight up and down the steepest slope, while identical soil under well-managed pasture would only lose as many kilograms per hectare. The difference in erosion caused by different management of the same soil is very much greater than the difference in erosion from different soils given the same management. In fact erodibility is influenced more by management than by any other factors, and management includes both the broad issues of land management and the detailed decisions of crop management. The best land management might be defined as the most intensive and productive use of which the land is capable without causing any degradation. It is perhaps worth stressing the constructive nature of this approach. Conservation policies of land use today must be positive and encouraging, not restrictive. There is no point in preserving soil and not using it—the demand of the world is for its resources to be used as efficiently as possible without waste.

The best aid to ensuring efficient land use is undoubtedly Land Capability Classification. This will be fully discussed in Chapter 9, but the essential features are that first the available facts about a piece of land are collected in a special survey. These include items like the soil type, depth, drainage characteristics, and the slope of the land, which can all be measured or assessed in the field. On the basis of these measured facts the land is then allocated into one of eight classes of land. These classes reflect the risk of soil erosion, and so indicate the combination of management practices which will be required if the land is to be used efficiently and productively. This system was pioneered by the United States Soil Conservation Service but has been successfully adopted, often with local variations, in other countries with such widely differing climatic conditions that there is no doubt that it can be applied anywhere where soil erosion is a problem.

5.2.3   Crop management

In the same way that erosion is greatly affected by different kinds of land use, so, within any particular land use, there can be large variations in the amount of erosion depending upon the detailed management of the crops. This will be explained in more detail in Chapter 10, but to give a simple example, the loss of soil from two identical adjacent experimental plots was found to be 15 times greater from the plot with a badly-managed crop of maize than from the plot with a good maize crop (HUDSON 1957). Such differences in erosion are probably most spectacular on arable land under row crops, but highly significant differences have also been recorded during experiments with natural grassland, established pasture, forest, woodland, and indeed every form of land use. The old-fashioned concept that crops can be classified as 'soil building' or 'soil robbing' was seriously challenged years ago as soon as scientific principles were applied to the application of fertilizers, and the idea has been refuted by erosion studies in recent years. These have shown that often the run-down in fertility associated with certain crops is due more to the erosion which they cause than the removal of plant nutrients by the crop. Naturally close growing crops like grass will tend to cover and protect the soil, and row crops like cotton or maize will tend to give less protection, but these general trends can be completely reversed by management. It has been shown by experiment that a well-managed well-grown crop of maize can minimize erosion and build up the soil, and that a badly managed pasture can run down the productivity when there are serious losses of soil and plant nutrients. In fact crop management for erosion control can be summarized in the statement 'Erosion depends not on what crop is grown, but on how it is grown'. This topic will be expanded in Chapter 10.

5.2.4   Control measures

This analysis of the factors influencing the erodibility of the soil has led the discussion to the question of how erosion can be controlled. Erosion is a function of erosivity and erodibility, and the erosivity depends entirely on rainfall and so is outside our control. Erodibility depends partly on the soil properties which again we cannot change, and to a greater extent on land use and crop management, both of which are entirely under man's control.

In section 2.3.2 an equation for soil loss was presented in which $A = RKLSCP$.

In this form R is the erosivity, and all the other factors are components of erodibility. K represents the influence of the physical soil properties and, like the rainfall erosivity R, is beyond control. The factors S representing slope, and L representing length of slope will not ordinarily be altered, although they could be by bench terracing (which would change S) or by contour terraces (which would change L). The conservation practices factor P is affected by a combination of land management and crop management and so a considerable degree of control is exercised at this point in the equation. The cropping practices factor C depends solely on the crop management and this is the point where the most effective control measures are brought to bear. The numerical effect of these different aspects of erosion control will be discussed in Chapter 10.

5.3 THE RELATION BETWEEN MECHANICAL AND BIOLOGICAL CONTROL

The two broad divisions of management, land management and crop management, correspond fairly well with the two kinds of erosion control measures, mechanical protection works which are earth moving and soil-shaping measures, and the non-mechanical measures. These are all the practices which influence and reduce erosion by the management of growing crops and animals. The terms biological control measures, or bionomic control are sometimes used although neither is completely appropriate. Mechanical protection works are closely linked with the choice of land use. For example, it often happens that land requires mechanical protection in the form of channel terraces when it is used for row crops, whereas under forage crops these mechanical works would not be required. In the Land Capability Classification the link between land use and mechanical control is particularly evident for the recommended practice for each class spells out both the recommended cropping system and the kind and degree of protection required.

The relationship between the two aspects of erosion control, mechanical protection and bionomic measures, may be illustrated by analogy. To use a military example, man is at war, and the enemy is soil erosion. Man is under heavy attack and has suffered severe loss in previous engagements. The immediate action which is required is to erect strong defence works to prevent any further inroads by the enemy. Behind the shelter of these defensive works, plans may be made and reinforcements built up until the counter-attack may be launched which will defeat the enemy. Mechanical protection works are this first line of defence and very necessary to prevent further damage. But a war cannot be won by defence alone, and the attack which is launched from the strength of a good defensive position, uses as weapons improved land use, better management, and sound scientific farming.

Alternatively, to use a more peaceful metaphor, the task of creating an improved agricultural industry in developing countries can be likened to erecting a great new building. With any big building the first step is to excavate suitable holes in the ground and pour in masses of concrete to give a solid foundation. Only after the foundation is secure do we start raising the useful part of the building—the part that will be shops, offices or dwellings. The analogy is very apt—the new agriculture with increased production to feed the starving millions of the world can only be raised up when it is based on the solid foundation of adequate mechanical protection works. There are other similarities. The foundations must come first, not the other way round, and so must the mechanical protection works come first, to be followed later by the better farming. Also, constructing the foundations is a once-only job with only routine maintenance required later. The mechanical protection measures are the same,—a big job to design and construct initially, but subsequently needing only maintenance.

The relative position of mechanical and bionomic erosion control measures is clear. Mechanical works are not in themselves constructive or productive, but they are nearly always necessary, and where they are required they must come first. Later the principles of correct land use, and the techniques of scientific agronomy can be applied, and these will reduce and control erosion while at the same time increasing production. The two kinds of control measures are not alternatives, but are complementary and to be used together although each serving a separate purpose. In subsequent chapters the details of conservation methods will be discussed, starting in the next chapter with the principles of mechanical protection works.

References

ADAMS, J. E., D. KIRKHAM and D. R. NIELSEN 1957 A Portable Rainfall-Simulator Infiltrometer and Physical Measurement of Soil in Place. *Proceedings of Soil Science Society of America*, 21, 5, 473–477

ADAMS, J. E., D. KIRKHAM and W. H. SCHOLTES 1958 Soil Erodibility and other Physical Properties of Some Iowa Soils. *Iowa State College Journal of Science* 32, 4, 485

ALDERMAN, J. K. 1956 The Erodibility of Granular Material. *Journal of Agricultural Engineering Research*, 1, 136–142

BALLAL, D. K. 1954 A Preliminary Investigation into Some of the Physical Properties Affecting Soil Erosion of Madhya Pradesh Soils. *Journal of Indian Society of Soil Science*, 1, 37–41

BOUYOUCOS, G. J. 1935 The Clay Ratio as a Criterion of Susceptibility of Soils to Erosion. *Journal of the American Society of Agronomy*, 27, 738–741

BRYAN, R. B. 1968 The Development, Use and Efficiency of Indices of Soil Erodibility. *Geoderma* 2, 1, 5–26

ELLISON, W. D. 1947 Soil Erosion Studies Parts I to VII. *Agricultural Engineering*, 28, 145, 197, 245, 297, 349, 402, 442

EPSTEIN, E., and W. J. GRANT 1967 Soil Losses and Crust Formation as Related to some Physical Properties. *Proceedings of the Soil Science Society of America* 31, 547–550

GUSSAK, V. B. 1946 A device for the rapid determination of erodibility of soils and some results of its application (In Russian with English Summary) *Pedology* 481–491 Abstract in *Soils and Fertilizers* 10, 41, 1947

HENIN, S. 1963 L'appreciation des proprietes physiques du sol. *Annales Gembloux* 3, 631–633

HUDSON, N. W. 1957 Erosion Control Research—Progress report on experiments at Henderson Research Station 1953–1956. *Rhodesian Agricultural Journal* 54, 4, 297–323

LUTZ, J. F. 1934 The Physico-Chemical Properties of Soils affecting Soil Erosion. *Missouri Agricultural Experiment Station Research Bulletin* 212

MCCALLA, T. M. 1944 Waterdrop Method of Determining Stability of Soil Structure. *Soil Science* 58, 117

MEHTA, K. M., V. C. SHARMA and P. G. DEO 1963 Erodibility Investigations of Soil of Eastern Rajasthan. *Journal of Indian Society of Soil Science* 11, 1, 23–31

MIDDLETON, H. E., C. S. SLATER and H. G. BYERS 1934 The Physical and Chemical Characteristics of the soils from the Erosion Experiment Stations. *Technical Bulletin* 430, United States Department of Agriculture

MOLDENHAUER, W. 1965 Procedure for studying soil characteristics by using disturbed samples and simulated rainfall. *Transactions of American Society of Agricultural Engineers*, 8, 1, 74–75

NISHIKATA, T. and Y. TAKEUCHI 1955 Relation between Physico-Chemical Properties and Erodibility of Soil Part 2. *Research Bulletin Hokkaido National Agricultural Experiment Station* 68, 49–54

OVENS, G. 1969 *A Study of Soil Erodibility by Separation of the Primary Stages of the Erosion Process.* M.Sc. Thesis University of Reading

PEELE, T. C. 1937 The Relation of certain physical characteristics to the erodibility of soils. *Proceedings of the Soil Science Society of America* 2, 97–100

PEREIRA, H. C. 1956 A Rainfall Test for Structure in Tropical Soils. *Journal of Soil Science* 7, 1, 68–74

RAI, K. D., W. A. RANEY and H. B. VANDERFORD 1954 Some Physical Factors that influence soil erosion and the influence of aggregate size and stability on growth of tomatoes. *Proceedings of the Soil Science Society of America*, 18, 486–9

VILENSKY, D. G. 1945 Methodology for Soil Tenacity and Soil Erosion Studies. Translated by D. B. Kringold in *Agricultural Engineering* 26, 465

VOZNESENSKY, S. and A. B. ARTSRUUI 1947 A Laboratory Method for determining the anti-erosion stability of soils. Problems of erosion resistance of soils. *Tiflis* 18–33, 1940 (in Russian). Abstract in Soils and Fertilizers 10, 289, 1947

WALLIS, J. R. and L. J. STEVAN 1961 Erodibility of some California Wildland Soils related to their Metallic Cation Exchange Capacity. *Journal of Geophysical Research* 66, 4, 1225–1230

WISCHMEIER, W. H. and J. V. MANNERING 1969 Relation of Soil Properties to its Erodibility. *Proceedings of Soil Service Society of America*, 31, 1, 131–137.

WISCHMEIER, W. H., C. B. JOHNSON, and B. V. CROSS 1971. A Soil Erodibility nomograph for farmland and construction sites. *Journal of Soil and Water Conservation*, 26, 5, 189–192.

YODER, R. E. 1936 A Direct Method of Aggregate Analysis of Soils and a Study of the Physical Nature of Erosion Losses. *Journal of the American Society of Agronomy*, 28, 337–351

Chapter 6   The principles of mechanical protection

6.1 Descriptions and definitions

The naming of the various kinds of earthworks and structures used to control erosion is complicated because in some cases the same structure is called by different names in different countries, in other cases the same name is applied to different things. In order to resolve this situation it is worth describing the most common structures and listing the various names by which they are known.

6.1.1 Stormwater diversion drain

This is the ditch (or drain or channel) which intercepts (or diverts) the stormwater (or flood water or storm run-off) which would otherwise flow down from higher ground on to the arable land which it protects (figure 6.1). It is the first line of defence and vital to the protection system since all the structures lower down will be designed on the assumption that it will effectively control all the run-off from outside the arable land. If it fails to do this the water released will almost certainly breach the lower works. It is called variously a *storm drain, storm water channel, diversion terrace, diversion ditch*—or other combinations of these words. *Stormwater drain* will be used in this text.

6.1.2 Channel terrace

If surface run-off is allowed to flow unimpeded down the slope of arable land there is a danger that its volume or velocity, or both, may build up to the point where it not only carries away the soil dislodged by splash erosion but also has a scouring action of its own. To avoid this, some form of earthwork at right angles to the steepest slope is used to intercept the surface run-off. (Figure 6.1.) There are a variety of techniques and a host of names. In the United States these works are known as terraces, whereas in Commonwealth countries ridge or bund are more common names. In cross-section the features common to all types are an excavated channel (hence the name *channel terrace*) and a bank formed on the downhill side with the spoil from the excavation. They may be on a slight gradient (hence the name *graded terrace*) with the intention that the surplus run-off will flow gently off the arable land at non-erosive velocities to a place where it can be safely discharged. Or they may be on a true contour, ie, flat along their length with the intention of holding the water so that it infiltrates into the soil. This latter type are usually called *absorption terraces*, and may have the ends closed to increase the storage—hence the terms *open-end* and *closed-end terrace*. An early American name was the *Mangum terrace*

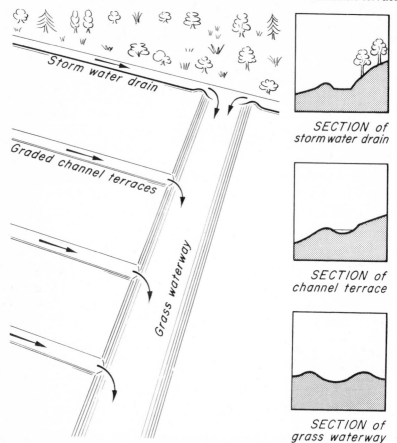

FIGURE 6.1   *The basic components of mechanical protection*
(a)   the stormwater drain which diverts storm run-off originating off the arable land
(b)   the graded channel terraces leading away the run-off from the arable land
(c)   the grass waterway into which both stormwater drain and channel terrace
discharge

after P. H. Mangum the N. Carolina farmer who introduced them in
the 1880s. This was a graded terrace with the bank built up from both
sides by repeated rounds with a disc plough or disc harrow. (Figure 6.2.)
Variations on this kind of terrace are the most common type in America.
Soil taken from the uphill side and used for building the ridge serves a
double purpose—the channel is excavated and the bank is raised; but
soil from the lower side, although helping to raise the bank, adds nothing
to the channel. In fact a drain along the downhill side of the ridge is
definitely undesirable as it may concentrate water into a 'slack' or low
spot and discharge it there. To avoid this disadvantage, terraces are

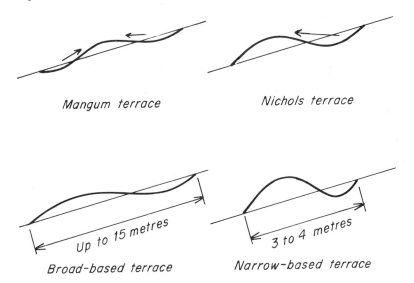

FIGURE 6.2 *Types of channel terrace. The difference between the Mangum and the Nichols is the direction of ploughing the soil. The difference between broad and narrow based terraces is the total width*

sometimes built solely by moving soil from the upper side, and this type is sometimes called the *Nichols terrace* after the Soil Conservation Service engineer who developed this method. A disadvantage of this form of construction is that there is an empty or unproductive run in one direction unless a reversable plough is used.

In the territories of the former Federation of Rhodesia and Nyasaland, where the design and construction of protection works is at an advanced level, and in the Republic of South Africa, the term *contour ridge* is most common, and means a graded open-end channel with raised bank. Two variations are used (figure 6.2) the *broad-based contour ridge* which is a wide, shallow, gently-sloping terrace which can be easily crossed by tractors and implements, so that row crops continue over them without interruption. The *narrow-based ridge* is also a graded channel terrace but with a steep-sided bank, often constructed using a road grader, and which cannot be crossed by tractors. In tobacco fields, particularly where short rotations are used, these narrow based ridges may be rebuilt each year (figure 6.2).

6.1.3 Artificial watercourse

Since the object of the protection system is to lead away the surface run-off the channels or drains must be able to discharge the water into a watercourse. Frequently there is no suitable natural watercourse and one must be artificially made. These are known variously as *grass waterways, sod waterways,* or *meadow strips.* They will normally run straight down the steepest slope and have a bank on each side to contain the water. The invert may be either undisturbed level ground surface or excavated to a shallow parabolic section (figures 6.1 and 6.3).

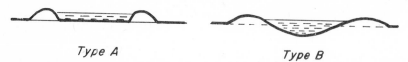

Type A   Type B

FIGURE 6.3   *Types of artificial waterway. Type A has a level invert of undisturbed soil and vegetation. Type B is excavated and then planted or seeded*

6.1.4   Bench terrace

Terrace is a case of a single name having two meanings, for the bench terrace is quite different from the graded terrace or channel terrace. Bench terracing is converting a steep slope into a series of steps, with horizontal or nearly horizontal ledges, and vertical or almost vertical walls between the ledges. To hold up the vertical face some structural wall is necessary, usually of stone or less frequently of brick or timber. In very stable soils the walls may be held only by vegetation. A prodigous amount of labour is required for the construction of bench terraces so, although they are commonly found in many parts of the world, it is more often as a legacy from the past than as part of present day development schemes. Plate 6.1 shows a famous example in Peru. Variations

PLATE 6.1   *The ancient bench terraces of Machu Picchu, in Peru*

are for the flat cultivated step to be quite horizontal, or to have a slight slope outwards, or a slope backwards towards the hill (figure 6.4). In the last case, sometimes called *reverse-slope terraces* there is some storage which assists infiltration. When the terrace also has a slight fall along its length it operates in a similar manner to a channel terrace, except that channel terraces are only spaced infrequently across the land, whereas with bench terraces all the ground is covered. A type of reverse-slope bench terrace on grade is used in modern tea plantation culture in Malawi, and called *step terraces*.

6.1.5 Irrigation terrace

Sometimes the flat bench terrace has a raised lip at the outer edge to retain irrigation water, extensively used for the production of rice, and to a lesser extent for tea, fruit trees, and other high value crops. For paddy, the terraces are also level along their length, so that each becomes a flooded shallow pond, but where intermittent water application is intended there can be longitudinal fall similar to that for border irrigation plots. The Banaue rice terraces in the Philippines are a magnificent example of irrigation terraces, a monumental engineering

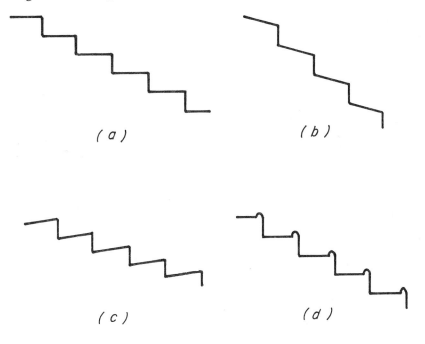

FIGURE 6.4   *Types of bench terraces*
(a) Level bench   (b) sloping bench   (c) reverse-slope or step terrace   (d) irrigation terrace

feat of great antiquity, but still maintained today (plate 6.2). This type of terrace is found in most regions where rice is a staple food, and is very common in Indonesia, Malaya, China, and Japan.

6.1.6 Contour bund

This is another term likely to cause confusion when ideas are taken from one country to another. In Africa this is often the name applied to a low bank thrown up by hand digging approximately on the contour, in fact a rudimentary type of channel terrace. In other countries the name bund is associated with various kinds of erosion-controlling bank which have grass or shrubs planted on them. The object of the grass may be either to trap silt from surface run-off water, or for the roots to help bind the bank together.

In India contour bunds have a quite different, but specific, meaning, being structures which attempt to serve as combined soil conservation and water conservation measures. They are like extra-large closed-end channel terraces with a storage capacity which is normally sufficient to impound all the surface run-off and hold it until it infiltrates. To cater for the exceptional storm there are emergency overflows, like dam spillways (figure 6.5).

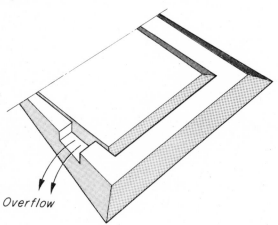

Overflow

FIGURE 6.5   *Diagramatic sketch of a contour bund*

PLATE 6.2   *The Banaue rice terraces of the Philippines, originally built many centuries ago, and still intensively used*   *Philippine Tourist and Travel Association*

6.1.7   Pasture furrow

This structure should be mentioned because it is similar in appearance, although its object is somewhat different. It is a small shallow drain whose function is to spread out surface water as evenly as possible and not allow it to concentrate in depressions or minor watercourses. The primary purpose is to conserve water by increasing infiltration, not to halt soil erosion, and the technique is frequently used on grassland, hence the name *pasture furrows*. In constructing this type of drain it is usual to take the excavated soil and, instead of using it to build a bank, it is spread evenly over a wide strip on the uphill side of the drain. The object is to leave a level sill along the downhill side of the drain so the run-off will spill evenly over the whole length of the drain.

6.1.8   Tied ridging

If all the rainfall can be held in place where it falls until it infiltrates into the soil, there will be no surface run-off and no wash erosion. Tied-ridging consists of covering the whole surface with closely spaced ridges in two directions at right angles so the ground is formed into a series of rectangular depressions (plate 6.3). The ridges and the cross-ties can be formed in a single operation by a specially designed implement (Boa 1966). A word of caution is necessary, for while the system can be very effective in the right conditions there are also situations where it is not suitable. It will work on level ground or if the amount of water which can be stored in the surface depressions, plus what infiltrates during the storm, is more than the worst storm likely to occur. If the soil becomes saturated and the depressions fill up and then overflow, the ridges will break. On sloping ground, once one ridge breaks it releases a small flood which bursts the next ridge releasing more stored water, and so on down the slope. A basic principle of mechanical protection works is that if they fail, the sudden release of surface run-off, concentrated at one point, is likely to cause more serious damage than if the works had not been built at all. The method has been used very successfully on deep permeable soils of East Africa, but has been unsuccessful on shallow soils in Central Africa. Two safety devices are essential. The ridges should be on grade with the ties lower than the ridges so failure and sudden release of run-off will be along each ridge not down the slope. Also a back-up system of conventional channel terraces should be provided to cope with flood run-off in exceptional storms which cannot be held.

Graded ridges without ties are used between large conventional channel terraces for the protection of tea in Malawi (plates 6.4 and 6.5).

6.1.9   Contour cultivation and grass strips

On gentle slopes, or whenever the erosion risk does not warrant major

PLATE 6.3 *Tied-ridges on maize lands in Tanzania effectively hold the rain until it can infiltrate*

earth-moving works, it may be sufficient to slow down surface run-off by carrying out all tillage operations on the contour. This avoids furrows and depressions running down the slope, and inviting run-off to concentrate in these with the result of causing scour erosion.

Another protection method which may serve when the erosion is not severe is the use of grass strips. Strips of grass or other close-growing vegetation are left unploughed between bands of cropped land. Surface run-off moving down the slope is intercepted by the strips, the velocity is slowed, and silt deposited in the grass strip.

The result which *is not* achieved by either grass strips or contour cultivation, and which *is* the primary function of channel terraces, is leading away the surface run-off so that the volume does not build up towards the lower end of the field.

PLATE 6.4   *Ridging on a tea experiment station in Malawi*

PLATE 6.5   *Ridges should be supported by channel terraces (at left with car on the ridge) and by waterways for safe disposal of run-off (in foreground)*

6.1.10 Ridge and furrow

This combines an element of erosion control with surface drainage. The ground is tilled into wide parallel ridges of the order of 10 metres wide, with intervening furrows about half a metre deep. Surface run-off moves across the ridge to the furrow and then down the furrow which is on a gradient of about 1 in 400. The method is particularly suitable for large areas of gently sloping land, which do not quite justify channel terraces, but need some controlled surface drainage (PHILLIPS 1963). A variation in East Africa, used on heavy black clay soils is called the camber-bed system (ROBINSON 1955 and BROOK 1959).

6.2 DESIGN PRINCIPLES

Before considering the detailed design of individual protection works, some general principles should be discussed, for mechanical protection is expensive and time consuming, and so deserves careful thought and planning. The following principles are developed from those of CORMACK (1951).

1   Mechanical protection works are usually confined to arable land for two reasons. The works are expensive and usually only the high value of arable land justifies the additional expense. It is not economic to construct mechanical protection works on rough grazing land when the construction costs are about as high as the purchase price of the land.

The second reason is that arable land is in general more vulnerable to erosion, and so it is more difficult to keep erosion under control without resorting to mechanical works.

This does not mean that mechanical protection should never be used except on arable land, nor that arable land automatically needs mechanical protection.

2   The primary objective of soil conservation protection works must be to control erosion. If, without reducing their efficiency as erosion control works, they can also conserve water by storage or improved infiltration so much the better, but if, in trying to achieve this second benefit the primary object is reduced, the result may be like a dual-purpose machine which does neither job well, and which is less efficient than two separate machines. A case in point is the slope of channel terraces, which are sometimes mistakenly put on a very flat grade with the idea of slowing down the run-off and so increasing infiltration. In fact when run-off is occurring the ground is saturated anyway so there is negligible increase in infiltration, but the risk of the channel over-topping is greater than if it were on the proper grade.

3   Mechanical works may not be necessary to the solution of an erosion problem. Or they may be one solution, but not necessarily the best. For example, arable land on a gentle slope may suffer serious

erosion if given no protection, but a system of contour ploughing or strip cropping might be a simpler and cheaper solution than channel terraces.

4   Mechanical protection works are potentially dangerous for two reasons. First, they concentrate surface water into channels where it is potentially more dangerous and likely to cause scour erosion than when dispersed. Secondly, as a result of this concentration, a protection system which fails nearly always results in more serious damage than if there had been no mechanical protection at all. There can be few conservation field officers not familiar with the pattern of broken contour banks illustrated in plate 6.6. As soon as any one bank is over-topped the flow from that channel pours down the slope in a concentrated stream. The next terrace down the slope is already loaded to capacity so it also fails, and adds its discharge, so that the next one fails, and so on to the bottom of the field. At this point the surface run-off from perhaps half the field is concentrated into a raging torrent tearing out the soil. Without any terraces the run-off would have flowed down unimpeded, but at least it would have been spread out over a wider area, and would have been slower moving and so cause less damage.

5   Maintenance. Man-made earthworks are subject to constant wear and tear, and their effectiveness will be short-lived unless they are adequately maintained and repaired. The natural agents of destruction are erosion and settlement, but more serious damage is done by cattle and humans making footpaths over earthworks, or by burrowing animals or by termites. In some parts of Africa a localized but quite serious problem occurs, for a species of field mouse likes to make its burrows in the raised banks of contour ridges. This alone would weaken the bank, but it is also a prized food delicacy among certain tribes, whose womenfolk dig out the nests, practically destroying the bank in the process. Whatever the likelihood or severity of the probable damage, some wear is inevitable, and regular maintenance at suitable intervals is essential.

6   Mechanical protection works must be designed to suit the construction methods which will be used. For example a scheme requiring a great deal of hand labour might be desirable in a country district where there is a problem of unemployment, but in a district where most of the able-bodied men are working in the industries of nearby cities then the scheme should be designed so that the work can be done by earth-moving machinery.

The kind of machinery should also be considered when the works are planned. A self-propelled road grader is efficient for building channel terraces provided there is a long run, but it is slow and awkward to turn, so for short runs or where turning space is restricted, it would be better to use a smaller more manoeuverable machine.

PLATE 6.6   *Mechanical protection works which fail are dangerous because the run-off is concentrated at the points of failure. This is a typical result of inadequate channel terraces*   *Copyright Aerofilms Limited*

As another example, it would not be much use designing a storm-water drain one metre wide if it is going to be excavated by a bulldozer whose blade is two metres wide. The design should start in this case with the assumption that the minimum width is two metres, and then decide an appropriate depth.

7   Similarly the choice and design of the works must be related to the particular site conditions. A storm-water drain two metres wide and one metre deep might be theoretically sound, but if the soil is half a metre deep over a hard rock, a better design could be found.

8   Integrated planning. The mechanical protection works for an individual piece of arable land will be designed specifically for that piece of land, but should be planned as part of an integrated plan for the whole area, not in isolation. Will the solution of today's problem fit in with future development? Will the waterways and drains now proposed

affect access to an adjoining farm? Does the road system fit in well with the drains? A system of mechanical protection against erosion will interact with most other aspects of land use and management, and so these questions must all be considered in the planning.

6.3 AGENCIES FOR CONSTRUCTION

The construction of mechanical protection works may be undertaken by the farmers themselves, or by private contractors, or by the Government, and each of these possibilities has advantages and disadvantages.

1   Construction by farmer. The main advantage of the construction being carried out by the occupier of the land is that he will then be personally involved and feel responsible. The job will probably be much better done and certainly better cared for afterwards than if it were done by someone from outside. The second advantage is that with careful planning of the timing of the construction the job can usually be done very cheaply by fitting it in with other farm work. The lorry which has just taken a load of produce to the market town can bring back a load of cement at little extra cost, the labour and machines needed for earth moving can be made available at times when there is no farm work required, and the work can be put off until a more convenient time whenever the weather or soil conditions are not suitable. This freedom from the necessity to stick to a time schedule can greatly reduce the cost of the job.

These arguments apply equally well to groups of farmers. When individual holdings are too small, or peasant farmers too poor, to be able to tackle jobs individually, the objective can usually be achieved by a joint effort by a village, or a district, or a co-operative.

2   Construction by private contractor. The main advantage of the private contractor is that he has, or should have, the most suitable equipment, and also the knowledge and experience of how to use it with maximum efficiency. The average farmer or group of farmers would not normally be expected to have either of these. The disadvantage is that since the contractor is in business his profit margin has to be added to the cost. His increased efficiency may or may not outweigh this factor.

3   Construction by Government machinery. Several advantages arise from the use of fleets of earth-moving machines owned and operated by the Government. Frequently it is only Governments which have the capital, or the credit facilities, to finance the fleet. Even for small earth-moving jobs the most efficient machine for the job is probably a very expensive one and in addition to the initial purchase price there is the capital required for the spares, workshops, and repair equipment required for maintenance. Also, being independent of the need to make a profit affords several advantages. Uneconomic but nationally desirable

schemes can be undertaken, or urgent jobs can be pushed through more quickly than the cheapest way of doing them.

One advantage of large groups of machinery is that they justify a resident engineer, and having an engineer to design the works, and supervise their construction is obviously more efficient than separating these two roles.

Work carried out and financed directly by the Government is completely under its control, but Government policies can also be indirectly assisted when the machinery is hired out, by preferential rates or priority treatment for selected types of work which a Government wishes to encourage. Similarly a region which a Government wishes to develop or which has suffered hardship like drought, can be assisted. Particular enterprises like irrigation, or fish farming, can be stimulated, if it is Government policy to do so, by making earth-moving machinery more readily available.

Another result of a flexible approach to costs is that Government machinery can undertake both profitable and non-profitable jobs and balance the costs so that they are spread evenly. The private contractor costs each job separately so the landowner whose land is less accessible, or whose site conditions are less favourable may be quoted such a high price that the work is not done. Government machinery can be charged at a uniform cost which evens out such differences and provides a service for everybody.

The main disadvantage of Government operated machinery is that the administrative costs always seem to be so high that the final cost is more than when done by private enterprise.

6.4 MAINTENANCE

After the initial construction, subsequent maintenance is essential. Ideally this should be done willingly by the land owners or occupiers, but it is often the case that Government adopts the policy of building mechanical protection works before their need or purpose has been understood and accepted by the local people. It is relatively simple for the Government to send in technicians and machines to design and build terraces, drains or bunds, but the subsequent maintenance can be a problem. Any element of compulsion may cause resistance and so reduce the chance of the policies ever being accepted. On the other hand if they are left unmaintained they will certainly fail, resulting in an 'I told you so' attitude. Equally, if building the works is delayed until the people can be persuaded that they are a good thing and worth looking after, the programme may be so slow that it is too late when finally implemented. The short-term answer to this problem is that when funds are allocated to a scheme a portion must be set aside for follow-up work. The long-term solution is to educate the people to the fact that the protection works are desirable and worth looking after.

References

BOA, W. 1966 Equipment and Methods for Tied-Ridge Cultivation. *Farm Power and Machinery Informal Working Bulletin* 28 FAO

CORMACK, R. M. M. 1951 The Mechanical Protection of Arable Land. *Rhodesian Agricultural Journal* 48, 2, 135–164

FAO 1963 Soil Erosion by Water: some measures for its control on cultivated lands. *Agricultural Development Paper* 81

PHILLIPS, R. L. 1963 Surface Drainage Systems for Farm Lands (Eastern United States and Canada). *Transactions of the American Society of Agricultural Engineers* 6, 313–317, 319

ROBINSON, J. B. D., T. R. BROOK and H. H. de VINK 1955 A Cultivation System for Ground water (Vlei) Soils—Part I. *East African Agricultural Journal* 21, 69

(Part II—Modification of the System, by BROOK, T. R. and J. B. D. ROBINSON ibid. 25, 192, 1959)

Chapter 7 The estimation of surface run-off

7.1 Quantities and rates of run-off

Before a start can be made on the design of the channels and ditches and other works which are to deal with surface run-off it is necessary to have information on the probable quantity of water. If the object is to impound or store the run-off then it may be sufficient to know the total volume of water to be expected, but the usual conservation problem is that of conveying water from one place to another, and in this case the rate of run-off is more important, and particularly the maximum rate at which run-off is likely to occur. This is the flow which a channel must be designed to accommodate.

In a hypothetical catchment area with an impervious surface and no losses the maximum rate of run-off would be directly proportional to the rate of rainfall. In natural catchments there are other factors; some of the rain is intercepted by vegetation, some infiltrates into the soil, some starts moving over the surface but is trapped in depressions, and some is lost by evaporation, but these and the many other factors are like alternative diversions from the main route which is the rainfall becoming surface run-off. Estimates of rates of surface run-off therefore all depend upon two processes; an estimate of the rate of rainfall, and an estimate of how much of the rainfall becomes run-off.

7.1.1 Intensity and duration of rainfall

It is common experience that the most severe rainfall only lasts for a short time. A storm which lasts for several hours will usually give a greater total amount of rain than a storm which lasts a few minutes, but the average rate of rainfall, expressed in inches per hour or mm per hour, will usually be less than the average rate for the short storm. The length of a storm is called its duration, and the relationship between intensity and duration is of the form shown in figure 7.1. The shape of the curve, and the numerical values of intensity will vary for different climates, but for all countries the general pattern will be the same, and can be constructed by drawing a trend line through a large number of points plotted from the records of individual storms.

This relationship can be expressed mathematically in several forms, one of the most common being

$$I = \frac{a}{t+b}$$

where I is the average intensity of the storm
t is the duration of the storm and
a and b are constants.

When intensity is in inches per hour, and the duration in minutes, values for *a* and *b* would be of the order of 120 and 40. For intensity in mm per hour corresponding figures would be 3 000 for *a*, and 40 for *b*.

For any given duration the graph or equation will indicate the highest average intensity which is probable for a storm of that duration. Having introduced the element of probability, the degree of probability must be specified. Does the 'highest probable intensity' mean the maximum which can ever occur?, or the greatest which is likely to happen over a period of one year, or two years? Given adequate records the maximum intensities can be calculated for various return periods (also called recurrence intervals) and the results shown as a family of curves similar in shape to figure 7.1 with separate curves for different return periods.

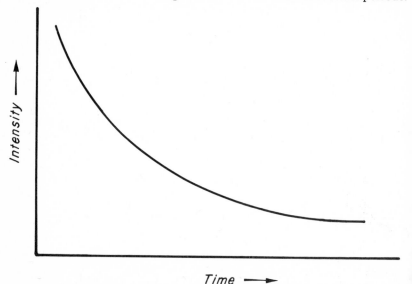

FIGURE 7.1   *The general relationship between intensity and duration*

Another variable is that the intensity/duration curve for one meteorological station will not be the same as the curve for a different part of the country with a different rainfall. In general the greater the mean annual rainfall, the higher the probable intensity for any given duration and return period. A family of curves can therefore also be drawn for different mean annual rainfalls, at any given probability.

Figure 7.2 shows examples of data presented in two graphical forms. In (*a*) the graph applies to a particular return period (in this case 10 years), and the different curves are for various mean annual rainfalls. In (*b*) the graph is for the rainfall at a particular station and the different curves are for various return periods. Data of this kind is broadly similar whether from Africa, America or Australia. Alternatively the information may be presented as contour lines on a map showing the maximum amount of rain for a given period of time (for example YARNELL 1935),

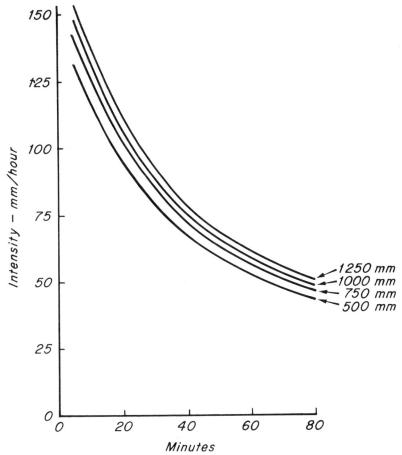

FIGURE 7.2 *Intensity-duration relationship*
(a) varying mean annual rainfall (from CORMACK 1951)

or the maximum rate of rainfall sustained for a given time (for example WILTSHIRE 1960). In both cases a set of maps is used, one for each of the selected return periods such as 1 year, 5 years, 20 years.

The effect of probability may also be derived mathematically from expressions of the form

$$I = \frac{KT^x}{t^n}$$

where I is intensity
T is the return period in years
t is the duration in minutes and
K, x and n are all constants.

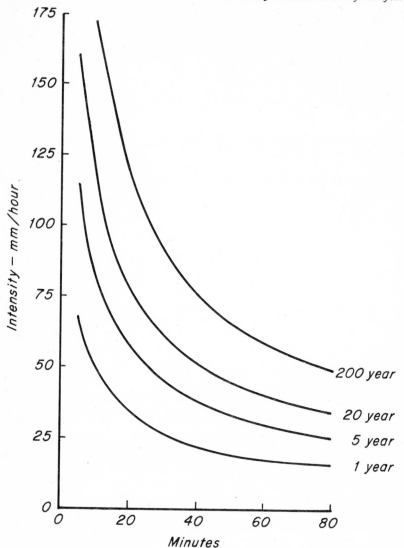

FIGURE 7.2   *Intensity-duration relationship*
(b) varying return period (from WILTSHIRE 1960)

However, some difficulty has been experienced in evaluating the constants and as a result the formula has not been widely adopted (SCHWAB *et al* 1966). In many countries detailed rainfall records have been maintained for a long time, but mainly in temperate climates, and there is less information on long-term patterns of rainfall in climates where erosion is serious. The source of information most likely to be useful to conservation planners is the *Rainfall Frequency Atlas of the United States* (HERSHFIELD 1961).

Intensity rates have been shown to be linked to storm duration, so the next step must be to consider the effect of this.

7.1.2 Time of concentration

The storm duration which will correspond with the maximum rate of run-off is known as the *time of concentration* or the *gathering time*. It is defined as the longest time taken for water to travel by overland surface flow from any point in the catchment to the outlet. The reason why this time corresponds with the maximum flow is best illustrated by considering the catchment shown in figure 7.3. If a severe but localized

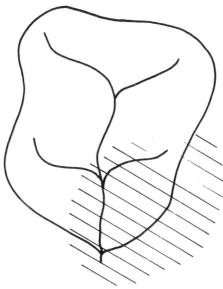

FIGURE 7.3   *A heavy storm on part of the catchment does not give the maximum flow*

storm falls in the lower shaded part of the catchment the run-off will be proportional to the product of the intensity and the area on which the storm falls. The intensity could be high but only a portion of the catchment area is receiving rain and yielding run-off. If a more widespread belt of rain covers the whole area the intensity will probably be lower, but the whole catchment area will be yielding run-off. It has been found that for normal catchments this second situation, of a storm covering the whole catchment, always gives a greater maximum rate of run-off. Maximum run-off will therefore result when the whole catchment is yielding run-off at the maximum rate it can do so. Since the intensity/duration curves show that intensity decreases as duration increases, the maximum rate of rainfall, and hence the maximum rate of run-off, will occur in a storm with the shortest duration which will still allow the whole catchment to contribute run-off. The shortest time for the whole catchment to contribute is the time it will take water to flow from the point in the catchment which is farthest away in time, hence the definition of concentration time. The longest time may not necessarily be that taken by run-off from the farthest point to reach the outlet, for there may be a nearer point which because of flatter grades or storage has a slower route to the outlet. This possibility is taken care of by the definition specifying the longest time for run-off to flow from a point in the catchment to the outlet.

The main variables affecting the time of concentration of a catchment are 1 *Size*: the larger the catchment the longer will be the gathering time. 2 *Topography*: steep topography will cause faster run-off and a shorter gathering time than a flatter catchment. 3 *Shape* of the catchment. In figure 7.4 the two catchments have the same area and both have a symetrical drainage pattern but the longest distance to the outlet is greater in one than in the other. The gathering time will therefore be longer, the corresponding intensity lower, and the maximum rate of run-off less. This is the explanation of the fact that, all other factors being equal, long narrow catchments tend to have less flashy floods than square or round catchments.

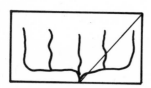 

FIGURE 7.4   *A short squat catchment has a shorter gathering time than a long narrow catchment*

An approximate estimate of the time of concentration can be obtained from area alone, and table 7.1 (from AYRES 1939) gives some suggested values.

TABLE 7.1

Area (acres)	(hectares)	Time of Concentration or Gathering Time— (minutes)
1	0·4	1·4
5	2·0	3·5
10	4·0	4·0
100	40·5	17·0
500	202·5	41·0
1000	405·0	75·0

A more accurate method is the BRANSBY-WILLIAMS formula

$$T = \frac{L}{D} \sqrt[5]{\frac{M^2}{F}}$$

where T is the time of concentration in hours
$\quad$ L is the longest distance from the outlet in miles
$\quad$ D is the diameter of a circle equal in area to the catchment area
$\quad$ in miles
$\quad$ M is the actual area in square miles
$\quad$ F is the average fall of the main watercourse in feet per 100 feet.
In SI units this becomes

$$T = \frac{L}{1 \cdot 5D} \sqrt[5]{\frac{M^2}{F}}$$

where T is in hours, L and D in kilometres, M in square kilometres, and F in metres per 100 metres.

Another formula, popular in America, is that of KIRPICH

$$T = 0 \cdot 0078 L^{0 \cdot 77} S^{-0 \cdot 385}$$

where T is the time of concentration in minutes
$\quad$ L is the maximum length of flow in feet
$\quad$ S is the average stream gradient in feet per foot.
In SI units this becomes

$$T(\text{minutes}) = 0 \cdot 02 L^{0 \cdot 77} S^{-0 \cdot 385}$$

where L is in metres, and S in metres per metre.

The average stream gradient does not always reflect the steepness of the land slopes in the catchment and figure 7.5 shows a graphical presentation by CORMACK (1951) which does allow for variations in slope.

7.2 THE RATIONAL FORMULA

The simplest method for estimating the maximum rate of run-off is the *Rational* formula which is $Q = C I A$
where Q is the rate of run-off in cubic feet per second
$\quad$ I is intensity in inches per hour
$\quad$ A is the catchment area in acres
$\quad$ C is a dimensionless constant.

The popularity of this method is enhanced by the fortunate numerical coincidence which makes C dimensionless in spite of the other three items being in various units. The mathematics of this are that for rain falling at one inch per hour on one acre

$43\,560$ (acre to sq ft) $\times \frac{1}{12}$ (inch per hour to ft) $\times \frac{1}{3600}$ (hours to seconds)

$= 1 \cdot 008$ cubic feet per second, which for all practical purposes can be taken as unity. C thus becomes a simple fraction expressing the ratio of the rate of run-off to the rate of rainfall. It is sometimes called the run-off coefficient.

The rational formula is equally applicable in metric units but an additional constant is required.

$$Q \text{ (cubic metres per sec)} = \frac{C I A}{360}$$

where C is the same dimensionless run-off coefficient
$\quad$ I is intensity in mm per hour
$\quad$ A is area in hectares.

The application of the formula consists of selecting appropriate values of C, I, and A. The area A can be measured, by survey or from maps or aerial photographs. The value of intensity I is the maximum rate of rainfall, determined as shown in section 7.1 from consideration of the time of concentration for the catchment, and the probability. Estimates of the coefficient C must be considered next.

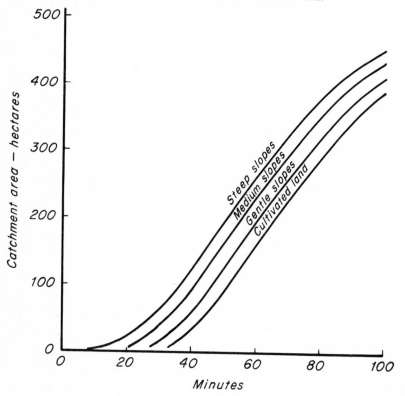

FIGURE 7.5 *The effect of land slope and catchment area on gathering time* (from CORMACK 1951)

7.2.1 The run-off coefficient

The proportion of rain which becomes run-off depends on many factors: the topography, the vegetation, the infiltration rate, the soil storage capacity, the drainage pattern, and so on. It is at the same time the virtue of the rational formula and its weakness that all these factors are combined into the single run-off coefficient C. Many tables of suggested values of C are available, for example, RAMSER (1927), a very early exponent of the rational formula, suggested the values shown in table 7.2 and empirically deduced from experimental catchments.

TABLE 7.2   *Run-off coefficients*

Rolling timber	0·18
Hilly timber	0·21
Rolling pasture	0·36
Hilly pasture	0·42
Rolling cultivated	0·60
Hilly cultivated	0·72

These coefficients are combinations of two topographical conditions—rolling and hilly, and three land uses, timber, pasture, and cultivated. All the other variables are ignored. The most that can be done to cater for different catchment conditions is to estimate the proportions of the catchment which have different coefficients and then to strike a weighted average. For example, if a catchment were 40% hilly timber and 60% hilly pasture, then using the figures of table 7.2 the calculation would be

$$\frac{4}{10} \times 0 \cdot 21 + \frac{6}{10} \times 0 \cdot 42 = 0 \cdot 084 + 0 \cdot 252 = 0 \cdot 336$$

and this figure would be used as the coefficient for the whole catchment.

The main advantage of the rational formula is that it can always be used to give an estimate of maximum run-off rates no matter how little recorded information is available. Naturally the precision of the estimate depends upon the precision of the information put in, but even in an undeveloped country with no rainfall or hydrological records at all, the method can be used to give an estimate which will be very much better than the only other alternative which is pure guesswork. The area can always be measured; there are several formulae for time of concentration, and this can be applied to the general formula for intensity if there is nothing better from local records; similarly if there are no measurements of local values of the run-off coefficient, then the published data of other countries will serve. As information on rainfall and run-off is obtained it can be fed in to the formula to give progressively more accurate estimates.

In countries where hydrological experiments have provided more detailed information, more sophisticated methods have been developed for estimating rates of run-off, and these make better allowance for variations in the catchment conditions than is possible in the rational formula.

7.3 COOK'S METHOD

This is also known as the $\sum$ W method (pronounced sigma W) because $\sum$ is the mathematical sign indicating the summation of several values, and the method consists of summing numbers, each of which represents the extent to which run-off from the catchment will be influenced by a particular characteristic. The letter W arises from the American use of the word *watershed*, which requires a word of explanation. In English, watershed is used as a geographical term for the highest point of ground from which water is shed on either side to different drainage systems. Other names are the interfluve, or the divide. In American usage the watershed is what in English is the catchment.

7.3.1 The United States Soil Conservation Service Procedure

The method used by the USSCS considers the effect of four features in the catchment: the relief, the soil infiltration, the vegetal cover, and the surface storage. Each of these is considered in turn, and the condition of the catchment is compared with 4 descriptions shown in table 7.3. The description is chosen which most nearly fits the catchment, and the corresponding number (shown in brackets) is noted. For relief, these numbers range from 10 to 40, for the other variables from 5 to 20. If the catchment conditions lie somewhere between two adjacent descriptions in the table, intermediate values may be interpolated. The arithmetic total of the four numbers is the catchment characteristic (U.S. *watershed characteristic*) and will lie between extreme values of 100 (if the highest number has been chosen for each of the 4 parameters) and 25 (if the lowest value has been chosen in each case).

It is important to differentiate clearly between this *catchment characteristic* and the *run-off coefficient* of the rational formula. The run-off coefficient is a fraction and indicates the fraction of rain which becomes run-off. Doubling the coefficient therefore doubles the run-off.

The catchment characteristic is a number which by reference to further tables or charts can be used to predict run-off. The run-off from a catchment whose characteristic is 80 will not normally be twice that from a catchment of the same size whose characteristic is 40. The tables are empirical, that is created from the measured run-offs from experimental catchments, and their form and use are explained in the next section.

7.3.2 A modification for African conditions

It is not necessary to use the same variables and scale of values which were adopted from use in the United States. Table 7.4 shows the system

TABLE 7.3 *Catchment characteristics for estimation of maximum probable run-off by Cook's method*

	(100) Extreme	(75) High	(50) Normal	(25) Low
Relief	(40) Steep, rugged terrain, with average slopes generally above 30%.	(30) Hilly, with average slopes of 10–30%.	(20) Rolling, with average slopes of 5 to 10%.	(10) Relatively flat land, with average slopes of 0 to 5%.
Soil infiltration	(20) No effective soil cover, either rock or thin soil mantle of negligible infiltration capacity.	(15) Slow to take up water; clay or other soil of low infiltration capacity, such as gumbo.	(10) Normal, deep loam with infiltration about equal to that of typical prairie soil.	(5) High; deep sand or other soil that takes up water readily and rapidly.
Vegetal cover	(20) No effective plant cover; bare or very sparse cover.	(15) Poor to fair; clean-cultivated crops or poor natural cover; less than 10% of drainage area under good cover.	(10) Fair to good; about 50% of drainage area in good grassland, woodland, or equivalent cover; not more than 50% of area in clean-cultivated crops.	(5) Good to excellent; about 90% of drainage area in good grassland, woodland or equivalent cover.
Surface storage	(20) Negligible; surface depressions few and shallow; drainageways steep and small; no ponds or marshes.	(15) Low; well-defined system of small drainageways; no ponds or marshes.	(10) Normal, considerable surface depression storage; lakes, ponds and marshes less than 2% of drainage area.	(5) High; surface depression storage high; drainage system not sharply defined.

From *Engineering Handbook for Farm Planners; Upper Mississippi Valley Region III*, United States Soil Conservation Service 1953.

developed for the Federation of Rhodesia and Nyasaland and shows several variations. The surface storage element was found to be un-important and so was left out, but the severity of tropical storms makes the soil infiltration and drainage very important and so this was given greater weight. This scale has been used successfully for 15 years, and is probably more appropriate to most tropical and sub-tropical conditions than the USDA table, but local modifications can always be made to cater for particular problems or circumstances.

TABLE 7.4　*Catchment characteristics for African conditions*

Cover		Soil type and drainage		Slope	
Heavy grass	10	Deep, well drained soils	10	Very flat to gentle	5
Scrub or medium grass	15	Deep, moderately pervious soil	20	Moderate	10
Cultivated lands	20	Soils of fair permeability and depth	25	Rolling	15
Bare or eroded	25	Shallow soils with impeded drainage	30	Hilly or steep	20
		Medium heavy clays or rocky surfaces	40	Mountainous	25
		Impervious surfaces and waterlogged soils (add 5 for t_1 and 15 for t_2 where soils have a factor of 30 or less)	50		

Select the most appropriate factor from each of these three tables and add them together.

Another variation was that for African conditions it was found un-necessary to make any allowance for different conditions of mean annual rainfall. In the USSCS procedure, the tables give figures for the run-off in a particular region, and these are modified for other regions by multiplying by a rainfall factor. In Africa, although there are wide variations in the annual rainfall amount, even in low rainfall areas there are many severe storms and the differences in run-off are far more influenced by variations in the surface conditions than by variations in rainfall intensity, so that it was found that a single set of tables could be used for the whole country.

On the other hand, the high rates of run-off made it advisable to introduce another factor—the shape of the catchment. Separate tables are used for each of three catchment shapes, square, or broad and short, or long and narrow (tables 7.5, 7.6, and 7.7) and the user selects the table for the shape which is nearest to that of the catchment.

Any calculations involving rainfall probability must be related to a return period, and the period usually chosen for the design of conservation works is 10 years. The data is therefore presented for a 10 year return period, and may be converted to other recurrence intervals by factors shown in table 7.8.

TABLE 7.5   *Run-off from a square catchment*

A˙ is the area of the catchment in acres.
C   is the catchment characteristics (from table 7.4)
The run-off (in cusecs) is for a 10 year frequency.

To use tables 7.5, 7.6 and 7.7 in SI units, let A be the catchment area in hectares, and the figure in the table multiplied by 0·07 will give the run-off in cubic metres per second.

A \ C	25	30	35	40	45	50	55	60	65	70	75	80
5	3	5	7	9	11	13	15	17	19	21	25	30
10	5	8	11	14	17	21	25	30	35	40	46	52
15	7	11	15	20	25	30	35	42	50	58	66	75
20	10	15	20	25	30	38	46	55	65	75	85	95
30	12	18	25	33	42	52	64	76	90	105	120	135
40	15	20	30	40	50	65	80	95	110	130	150	175
50	17	25	35	50	65	80	100	120	140	165	190	215
75	20	35	50	70	90	115	140	170	200	235	270	310
100	25	45	65	90	120	150	180	220	260	300	350	400
150	35	60	90	125	165	210	260	310	365	425	500	580
200	40	80	120	170	220	270	330	400	470	550	640	750
250	50	90	140	190	245	310	385	470	565	670	785	910
300	60	100	150	210	280	360	450	550	660	780	910	1050
350	70	120	180	240	330	430	540	640	760	890	1030	1160
400	80	140	200	280	370	490	600	710	860	990	1160	1280
450	90	150	220	300	410	540	660	780	940	1090	1280	1390
500	100	160	240	330	450	590	720	850	1030	1200	1390	1520

Cook's method differs from the rational formula in that it is empirical and requires some measured values to establish the scales. But this does not mean that its use is restricted to developed countries with long established programmes of experimental hydrology. All that is required as a starting point is a few carefully chosen experiments to establish reference points which will make it possible to make use of the published results from other countries.

TABLE 7.6 *Run-off from a broad and short catchment*

A is the area of the catchment in acres
C is the catchment characteristics (from table 7.4)
The run-off (in cusecs) is for a 10 year frequency

A \ C	25	30	35	40	45	50	55	60	65	70	75	80
5	4	6	8	10	12	15	18	21	24	27	31	35
10	7	10	12	15	20	26	32	38	44	51	58	65
15	9	14	19	25	32	40	48	57	66	75	85	95
20	12	18	25	32	40	50	60	70	80	95	110	125
30	16	25	35	45	55	70	85	100	115	135	155	175
40	19	30	42	55	70	90	110	130	150	175	200	225
50	23	35	50	65	85	110	135	160	185	210	240	275
75	30	50	70	95	120	150	185	220	255	295	340	390
100	35	60	85	120	160	205	250	295	345	395	450	510
150	45	85	125	170	220	280	340	410	485	560	640	725
200	55	100	150	205	280	360	445	535	630	730	830	935
250	65	125	190	260	340	440	550	665	780	900	1020	1145
300	80	145	220	300	390	490	600	720	850	990	1150	1350
350	100	170	260	340	460	580	700	830	980	1160	1340	1510
400	110	210	290	400	520	670	800	920	1120	1300	1500	1660
450	120	220	320	440	580	740	880	1020	1240	1420	1670	1810
500	130	230	340	470	630	800	960	1110	1350	1560	1800	1970

7.3.3 Run-off curve numbers

A further refinement of Cook's method should be mentioned although it is used for a different purpose. This is the run-off curve number method and used by the USSCS to estimate, not the rate of run-off, but the volume of run-off. The approach is similar in that for each of a number of variables a single value is selected from a range of possible choices. The extension is that Cook's method only allows for variations in the physical conditions of the catchment whereas the effect of management practices is now added. When the land is mainly arable the factors considered are:

TABLE 7.7   *Run-off from a long and narrow catchment*

A   is the area of the catchment in acres
C   is the catchment characteristics (from table 7.4)
The run-off (in cusecs) is for a 10 year frequency

A\C	25	30	35	40	45	50	55	60	65	70	75	80
5	3	4	5	6	8	10	12	14	16	19	22	25
10	4	6	9	12	15	18	22	26	30	35	40	45
15	6	9	12	16	20	25	30	35	41	47	53	60
20	7	11	16	21	27	33	39	46	54	62	70	80
30	9	15	21	28	36	46	56	66	76	88	100	115
40	12	20	28	36	46	58	70	85	100	115	130	145
50	15	25	35	45	60	75	90	105	120	135	155	175
75	20	32	45	60	80	100	120	145	170	195	225	255
100	25	40	55	75	100	130	160	190	220	255	290	330
150	32	55	80	105	140	180	225	270	315	360	410	470
200	40	70	100	135	180	235	290	345	405	470	540	615
250	45	80	120	160	215	280	345	415	490	570	660	760
300	50	90	135	190	250	320	400	480	570	670	780	900
350	60	100	150	200	280	370	470	550	660	770	890	1000
400	70	120	170	240	330	420	520	610	740	860	1000	1100
450	80	130	190	260	360	470	570	670	820	940	1100	1200
500	90	140	200	280	390	510	620	740	890	1040	1200	1320

TABLE 7.8   *Return period conversion factors*

2 years	0·90
5 years	0·95
10 years	1·00
25 years	1·25
50 years	1·50

1   *Land use*, which is split into 10 possible categories, such as Fallow, Row crops, Woods, etc.

2   *Conservation practice*—3 categories of arable land protection,
Up and down hill ploughing
Contour planting
Contour planting and terracing.

3 *Hydrologic condition of soil cover.* This is the only subjective assessment, and requires some experienced judgement to select from the 3 categories, *Poor, Good,* or *Fair.*

4 *Hydrologic soil group*   4 categories, whose full specification approximates to

A Deep sands
B Sandy soils with good drainage
C Shallow soils with poor drainage
D Clays and soils with severely restricted drainage.

In Cook's method the effect of each variable was reduced to a number, and the end product was the sum of the numbers, but the run-off curve number is derived directly as a single number from a table which lists all possible combinations (SCHWAB *et al* 1966, page 104).

When computing the run-off curve number for catchments under forest, only two variables are used; the Hydrologic Soil-Cover Condition, with 5 alternative classes, and the Hydrologic Soil Group, with the same 4 classes as for arable land.

For mixed forest and range land, three variables are used:

1 Type of vegetation, eg, herbaceous, sage-brush, oak-aspen, juniper.
2 Hydrologic condition of soil cover—as arable.
3 Hydrologic soil groups—as arable but omitting class A (deep sands) which would not normally be found on mixed forest/range land.

Having arrived at the run-off curve number, the maximum probable quantity of run-off is obtained from charts which for each curve number give the amount of run-off to be expected from different quantities of rainfall.

References

AYRES, Q. C. and D. COATES 1939 *Land Drainage and Reclamation.* McGraw-Hill, New York

CORMACK, R. M. M. 1951 The Mechanical Protection of Arable Land. *Rhodesian Agricultural Journal* 48, 2, 135–164

HERSHFIELD, D. N. 1961 Rainfall Frequency Atlas of the United States. *Technical Paper* 40, *United States Weather Bureau*

RAMSER, C. E. 1927 Run-off from Small Agricultural Areas. *Journal of Agricultural Research* 34, 9, 797–823

SCHWAB, G. O., R. K. FREVERT, T. W. EDMINSTER and K. K. BARNES 1966 *Soil and Water Conservation Engineering* (2nd Edition). Wiley, New York

WILTSHIRE, G. R. 1960 Rainfall Intensities in New South Wales. *Journal of the Soil Conservation Service of New South Wales,* 16, 1, 54–69

YARNELL, D. L. 1935 Rainfall Intensity—Frequency Data. *Miscellaneous Publication* 204 *United States Department of Agriculture.*

Chapter 8   The design of mechanical protection works

8.1   THE DESIGN OF HYDRAULIC CHANNELS

Most of the works used in the control of erosion are required to collect or divert or lead away streams of water, and the basis of their design is the application of the principles of the hydraulics of flow in open channels. There are four problems most frequently encountered.

1   Estimating the flow in a channel when the cross-section, gradient, depth, etc, are known or can be measured. This arises in irrigation canals, drainage ditches, and natural watercourses.

2   Estimating the depth of flow at which a given channel will carry a given rate of flow. This is the problem of forecasting how high a flood will rise, or how deep the flow will be in an irrigation canal.

3   Designing a channel which will carry away a given rate of flow as rapidly as possible. This arises when storm run-off has to be lead away from buildings or structures.

4   Instead of designing for maximum velocity (which is usually only possible for lined channels) the velocity may well be limited to non-scouring velocities in earth-lined channels. The problem then involves the choice of suitable cross-section and gradient, and this is the particular problem which most frequently occurs in the design of protection works.

8.1.1   The inter-relation of the variable factors

The basic formula for the rate of flow in a channel is $Q = V \times A$ where Q is the rate of flow,
V is the average velocity,
A is the cross sectional area of flow.
Many factors influence both the velocity V and the area of flow A, and they react upon each other in a complicated inter-relation.
The main factors are:

1   *Size*—obviously a large channel will carry more water than a small one.

2   *Shape*—channels of the same cross-sectional area, but different shapes, will carry different amounts of water. Water close to the sides and bottom of the channel is slowed by the friction effect, so a channel whose shape provides least area of contact with the water will have least frictional resistance and so a greater capacity. The unit used to measure this effect of shape is called the *hydraulic radius* of the channel. It is defined as the cross-sectional area divided by the *wetted perimeter*,

which is the length of the cross-section of the channel which is in contact with the water. Hydraulic radius thus has units of length, and in formulas it may be represented by either M or R. It is also sometimes called *hydraulic mean radius* or *hydraulic mean depth*. Figure 8.1 shows how channels can have the same cross-sectional area but different hydraulic radius, and figure 8.2 shows the relation between hydraulic radius and depth of flow for a rectangular channel. If all other factors are constant, then the lower the value of R, the lower will be the velocity.

FIGURE 8.1   *Hydraulic radius is a function of the shape of the channel*

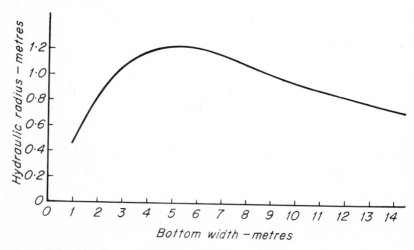

FIGURE 8.2   *The change of hydraulic radius for various bottom widths of a rectangular channel of area 12 square metres*

Earth channels are usually given a cross-section which is either trapezoidal, or a smooth curve which approximates to a part of a parabola. Channels originally excavated as trapezoidal sections tend towards a parabolic shape in time. V-shaped sections are most undesirable for earth channels because the lowest point is liable to scour. The basic dimensions of trapezoidal and parabolic sections are shown in figure 8.3.

3   *Gradient*—velocity is naturally affected by the gradient and increases when the channel gradient is steeper.

4   *Roughness*—the contact between the water and the channel exercises a frictional resistance, and this is affected, like any frictional effect, by

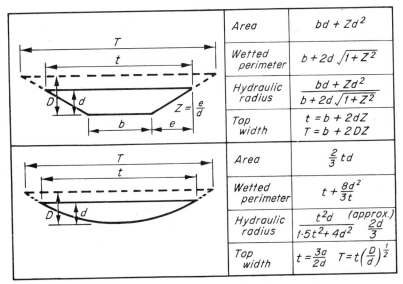

FIGURE 8.3 *Basic dimensions of common channel sections*

the smoothness or roughness of the channel. A concrete-lined canal naturally has less resistance than one whose sides are choked with vegetation. It may be desirable to minimize the roughness when it is required to pass as much water as possible, or to increase it when it is desired to slow the water down to non-scouring velocity.

The quantity or rate of water which will flow along an open channel is determined by all these factors, which are linked together in complicated relationships. The result is that there is seldom one unique solution to a problem in hydraulic design. More frequently the engineer is able to select from a number of alternatives the combination of size of channel, gradient, velocity, etc, which is most suitable for the job in hand.

8.1.2 Estimates of velocity

One of the earliest methods of estimating the velocity of flow in pipes and channels was developed in 1768 by the French engineer CHEZY in connexion with designing a canal for the water supply of Paris. It is written

$$V = C\sqrt{mi}$$

where V is the average velocity of flow in the channel

C is an empirical constant depending on the roughness and depth (often called the *Chezy coefficient*)

m is the hydraulic radius

i is the gradient.

It is not widely used owing to the difficulty of establishing values of the coefficient C, but a useful simple field formula has been derived from it. This is known as *Elliott's open-ditch formula*

$$V = \sqrt{m \times \frac{3h}{2}}$$

The Chezy coefficient has been taken inside the root, and the units come out very conveniently in fps units.

V is the average velocity in feet per second
m is the hydraulic radius in feet
h is the fall or gradient in units of feet per mile.

In *SI* units this becomes

$$v = 0{\cdot}3\sqrt{mh}$$

where v is in metres/second, m in metres, and h in metres per kilometre.

By far the most commonly used method for the estimation of velocity in open channels is the MANNING formula. Conveniently this can be used in both English and metric units. The original formula in metric units is

$$V = \frac{R^{\frac{2}{3}} S^{\frac{1}{2}}}{n}$$

where V is the average velocity of flow in metres per second
R is the hydraulic radius in metres (the letter M is also used to denote hydraulic radius)
S is the average gradient of the channel in metres per metre (The letter i is also used to denote gradient)
n is a coefficient, known as *Manning's n*, or *Manning's roughness coefficient*. Some values for channel flow are listed in table 8.1.

In English units the formula is usually given in the form

$$V = \frac{1{\cdot}486 \; R^{\frac{2}{3}} S^{\frac{1}{2}}}{n}$$

where V is the average velocity of flow in feet per second
R is the hydraulic radius in feet
S is the gradient in feet per feet
n is the roughness coefficient which has the same values as in the metric form of the equation.

The figure $1{\cdot}486$ arises because it is the cube root of $3{\cdot}28$ (the number of feet in one metre) and is more precise than necessary. Considering the accuracy of the values of n it would be more appropriate to use $1{\cdot}5$ instead of $1{\cdot}486$.

TABLE 8.1 *Manning's roughness coefficient*

		n
A	*Channels free from vegetation*	
	Uniform cross-section, regular alignment free from pebbles and vegetation, in fine sedimentary soils	0·016
	Uniform cross section, regular alignment, free from pebbles and vegetation, in stiff clay soils or hardpan	0·018
	Uniform cross section, regular alignment, few pebbles, little vegetation, in clay loam	0·020
	Small variations in cross section, fairly regular alignment, few stones, thin grass at edges, in sandy and clay soils, also newly cleaned, ploughed and harrowed channels	0·0225
	Irregular alignment, ripples on bottom, in gravelly soil or shale, with jagged banks or vegetation	0·025
	Irregular section and alignment, scattered rocks and loose gravel on bottom, or considerable weeds on sloping banks, or in gravelly material up to 150 mm diameter	0·030
	Eroded irregular channels, channels blasted in rock	0·030
B	*Vegetated channels*	
	Short grass (50–150 mm)	0·030–0·060
	Medium grass (150–250 mm)	0·030–0·085
	Long grass (250–600 mm)	0·040–0·150
C	*Natural stream channels*	
	Clean and straight	0·025–0·030
	Winding, with pools and shoals	0·033–0·040
	Very weedy, winding and overgrown	0·075–0·150

8.1.3 Nomograph solutions

The procedures used in the design of hydraulic channels call for maximum flexibility because so many different situations can arise. The gradient may be fixed if the channel must follow a particular route, or this may be one of the factors which the engineer can vary. There may be a maximum velocity because of the nature of the soil, or there may be a range of acceptable velocities. The roughness may be determined by the material of the channel, or there may be a choice of lining materials, or between bare soil and a vegetated channel. And the variables interact upon each other because if we change either gradient or roughness this will affect the velocity. The thought process of the design engineer may well run something like this:

If the sides of the channel are bare soil, the maximum velocity must not exceed x, and if the gradient is y and the hydraulic radius were z we would need a 10 metre channel—no—too wide—try hydraulic radius b, that brings it to 8,—still too wide—what about increasing the gradient to p?—that looks better. If we increased the depth a bit—no, that will increase excavation costs—what about a grass-lined channel?

—and so on, until the best of the alternatives is chosen. Graphical solutions of the various formulae are very often used to assist this process of trial and error selection. Two examples of solutions of Manning's formula are shown, in imperial units in figure 8.4 (from CORMACK 1951), and in *SI* units in figure 8.5.

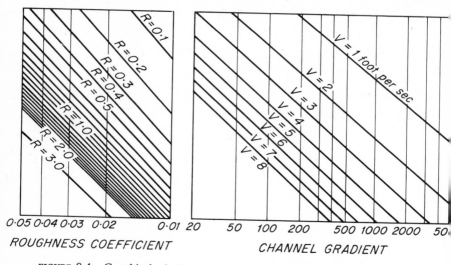

ROUGHNESS COEFFICIENT   CHANNEL GRADIENT

FIGURE 8.4   *Graphical solution of Manning's formula* (from CORMACK 1951)

Although the Manning formula assumes that the roughness of the channel can be described by a particular value of n, it has been shown that for channels lined with vegetation the value of n can vary according to the flow in the channel (REE 1949). At low flows grass remains upright and exercises a slowing down force, whereas at high flows it is flattened and offers much less resistance. The effect will depend on the length and density of the vegetation, and the velocity of flow, and the shape of the channel. The relation of the roughness coefficient n to these factors has been established by field experiments of the USSCS (PALMER *et al* 1954) and is shown in simplified form in figure 8.6. Another way of allowing for this variation in roughness is to incorporate it into a graphical solution for each type of vegetation. The grasses and plants commonly used in America for channel lining have been classified into 5 degrees of *hydraulic retardance* and a partial solution of Manning prepared for each (PALMER *et al* 1954, and SCHWAB *et al* 1966 Appendix C). Some care is required in adapting this procedure for the vegetation of other continents, because it is not easy to know how a local grass compares with for example 'a fair stand of Kentucky bluegrass'.

Chart and nomograph design methods for particular kinds of channel are described in the appropriate sections later in this Chapter.

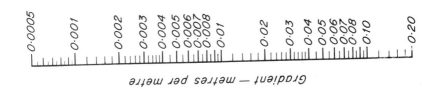

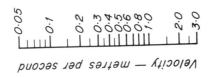

Example: Given **R**=0·3 metre, **n**=0·03, gradient—2/₀ or 0·02 metre per metre, find velocity V.

Solution: Join **R**=0·3 and n=0·03 and project to the pivot line. Join the point on the pivot line to gradient=0·02. Intersection of the velocity scale gives **V**=2·0 metres per second.

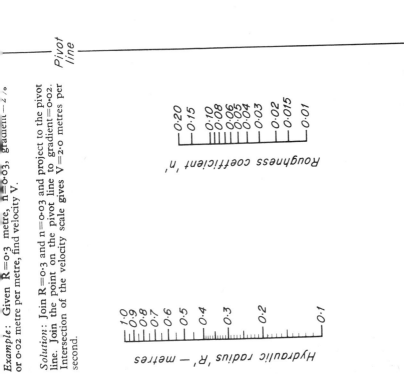

FIGURE 8.5 *A nomographic solution of Manning's formula*

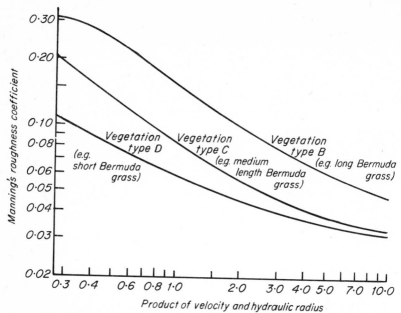

FIGURE 8.6 *The variation of roughness coefficient with flow conditions* (from PALMER and LAW 1954)

8.2 THE DESIGN OF STORMWATER DRAINS

The object of a stormwater drain is to intercept or divert the surface run-off from higher ground, when it is necessary to keep it off other land such as arable fields. The first step is to estimate the probable maximum rate of surface run-off, using one of the procedures discussed in Chapter 7, and then to design a channel or ditch which will carry this amount.

8.2.1 The Durbach method

While it is desirable for field officers to have some understanding of the hydraulic principles involved, it would be asking rather much to expect calculations in the field which involve sixth-roots or complicated charts. A design procedure was therefore evolved by S. DURBACH, Chief Conservation Engineer to the Government of Zambia, which, while based entirely on sound engineering principles, breaks down the operation to a number of small steps each of which does not require anything more than simple arithmetic. Since this method was developed in imperial units it does not convert easily to *SI* units, and the recommended procedure for designing metric channels is to work through the calculations using the tables, and apply a linear conversion at the end.

The sequence for the Durbach method is:

1 From table 8.2 select the maximum safe velocity. This is the fastest flow which will not cause scouring of the channel. The design is based on the velocity appropriate to the vegetative cover after two seasons, on the grounds that a small amount of scour during this period is preferable to overdesigning the channel for the rest of its life. If it is the intention to encourage a good grass cover by planting, sowing, and fertilizing, the permissible velocity is higher than for the same soil without vegetation.

TABLE 8.2 *Maximum safe velocities in channels*

			Maximum velocity on cover expected after two seasons			
Material	*Bare*		*Medium grass cover*		*Very good grass cover*	
	ft/sec	*m/sec*	*ft/sec*	*m/sec*	*ft/sec*	*m/sec*
Very light silty sand	1·0	0·3	2·5	0·75	4·5	1·5
Light loose sand	1·5	0·5	3·0	0·9	5·0	1·5
Coarse sand	2·5	0·75	4·0	1·25	5·5	1·7
Sandy soil	2·5	0·75	4·5	1·5	6·5	2·0
Firm clay loam	3·5	1·0	5·5	1·7	7·5	2·3
Stiff clay or stiff gravelly soil	4·5	1·5	6·0	1·8	8·0	2·5
Coarse gravels	5·0	1·5	6·0	1·8	unlikely to form	
Shale, hardpan, soft rock, etc.	6·0	1·8	7·0	2·1	very good grass cover	
Hard cemented conglomerates	8·0	2·5	—	—	—	—

Intermediate values may be selected

2 The probable gradient is chosen, and entering table 8.3 at this gradient, the channel factor X is obtained for the maximum velocity obtained from table 8.2.
(The formula for this table is $X = V\sqrt{S}$, and its origin derives from the Chezy formula $V = C\sqrt{mi}$).

3 The value of X is next carried forward to table 8.4 and the appropriate value of D obtained. This represents the *maximum* depth of flow which is allowable for the chosen gradient and velocity. It has been emphasized that there is always a choice of alternative designs, not any one unique solution, and some of the alternatives arise from the choice of this maximum value of D or any smaller depth.

4 The selected depth is transferred to table 8.5 which, from this value of D and the previously selected gradient, gives a value of F. This represents the discharge in cusecs per foot width of channel for the chosen conditions of velocity and gradient. The gradients most commonly used for diversion channels, are 1 in 200 or 1 in 250.

5   This value F (cusecs per foot width) is then divided into the maximum flow Q in cusecs to give the required width of channel. This width is for the top of shallow channels of trapezoidal or parabolic section. For rectangular channels the width may be reduced by one third.

Before considering alternative designs some examples will show how simple the method is.

Example 1   Design a channel to carry 75 cusecs on a gradient of 1 in 250 through a sandy soil. Low fertility of the soil and poor rainfall suggest that the grass cover after two years will only be of medium density.

Method

1   From table 8.2 $V = 4.5$ ft/sec.
2   Table 8.3 at $S = 250$ and $V = 4.5$, gives $X = 72$.

TABLE 8.3   *Channel factor 'X'*

$$X = V\sqrt{S}$$

where V = Velocity of flow in feet/sec (from table 8.2)
1 in S = Gradient of channel

% *Slope*	S \ v	1.0	1.5	2.0	3.0	4.0	5.0	6.0	7.0	8.0
2.0	50	—	—	14	21	28	35	42	50	57
1.0	100	—	15	20	30	40	50	60	70	80
0.66	150	—	18	25	37	49	61	73	86	98
0.50	200	14	21	28	42	56	71	85	99	113
0.40	250	16	24	32	48	64	80	96	112	—
0.33	300	17	26	35	52	69	87	104	—	—
0.25	400	20	30	40	60	80	100	—	—	—
0.20	500	22	33	45	67	90	112	—	—	—
0.17	600	24	37	49	73	98	—	—	—	—

Note 1   Figures in *Percentage Slope* column denote staff readings in feet per 100 feet intervals.
Note 2   Interpolate for intermediate values of V and S.
Note 3   From this table, select value nearest to those given in table 8.4 to obtain D.

3   From table 8.4 for $X = 72$, Depth $D = 1.75$ ft.

TABLE 8.4 *Values of 'X' for various values of 'D'*

Where X = Channel Factor (from table 8.3)
Where D = Depth of cut in channel in feet

D (feet)	X
0·25	20
0·50	32
0·75	42
1·00	50
1·25	58
1·50	65
1·75	72
2·00	79
2·25	86
2·50	92
2·75	98
3·00	104

Note 1 Values of 'X' selected above are those nearest to the values calculated from table 8.3.

Note 2 The depth of cut in the channel, as constructed, may be made *less* than 'D' as calculated above, provided this reduced value is used in calculating capacity in table 8.5. The actual depth should *never* be greater than 'D' calculated as above.

(Figures based on Manning $n = ·0225$)

---

4   Table 8.5 for $S = 250$ and $D = 1·75$, gives $F = 11$ cusecs per foot width.

5   Width $= \dfrac{Q}{F} = \dfrac{75}{11} = 7$ ft.

The channel design is 7 ft wide and 1 ft 9 in. deep.

Example 2   Design a channel to carry 100 cusecs on a gradient of 1 in 200 over soft decomposing granite.

Method

1   From table 8.2 the maximum permissible velocity is 6·0 ft/sec. or 7·0 ft/sec according to the vegetative cover. If information on this is not available, an experienced field officer can often make an esti-

TABLE 8.5 *Values of 'F'*

F = discharge in cusecs per ft width of channel for various values of 'D' and 'S' where
D = depth of cut channel in feet.
1 in S = Channel gradient

D \ S	50	100	150	200	250	300	400	500	600
0·25	1·0	0·7	0·6	0·5	0·4	0·4	0·3	0·3	0·3
0·50	3·1	2·2	1·8	1·6	1·4	1·3	1·1	1·0	0·9
0·75	6·0	4·3	3·5	3·0	2·7	2·5	2·2	2·0	1·8
1·0	9·7	6·8	5·6	4·8	4·3	3·9	3·4	3·0	2·8
1·25	13	10	8·0	7·0	6·3	5·7	5·0	4·4	4·0
1·50	16	13	11	9·5	8·5	7·7	6·7	6·0	5·5
1·75	19	17	14	12	11	10	8·6	7·7	7·0
2·0	21	21	18	16	14	13	11	10	9·0
2·25	24	24	22	19	17	15	13	12	11
2·5	27	27	26	23	20	18	16	14	13
2·75	29	29	29	26	23	21	18	16	15
3·0	32	32	32	32	27	25	22	19	18

Note 1 For maximum discharge values shown above, depth of flow in the drain is 2D ft (ie twice the depth of cut in the Channel)
Note 2 Values of F shown above are limited to a maximum velocity of 8 ft per second. (Values based on Manning n = ·035).

mate, but if this is not felt to be justified the lower value should always be used. In this case say V = 6·0 ft/sec.
2 Table 8.3 at S = 200 and V = 6·0 gives X = 85.
3 From table 8.4 for X = 85, D = 2·25 ft.
4 Table 8.5 for S = 200 and D = 2·25 gives F = 19 cusecs per foot width.

5 Width = $\dfrac{Q}{F}$ = $\dfrac{100}{19}$ = 5·3—say 5 ft.

The channel design is 5 ft wide and $2\frac{1}{4}$ ft deep.

The second point is the most suitable depth. The design indicates that $2\frac{1}{4}$ ft is the maximum depth, but it is probable that the rock will be harder as the depth increases and it may be easier to cut a wide shallow drain than one which is narrower and deeper.

In table 8.6 any depth less than $2\frac{1}{4}$ ft could be chosen, and the corresponding F values are those above 19 in the column for gradient 1 in 200. Some of the alternative F values are:

Depth 2·0 ft $F = 16$ cusecs per ft width
Depth 1·5 ft $F = 9·5$ cusecs per ft width
Depth 1·0 ft $F = 4·8$ cusecs per ft width
Depth 0·5 ft $F = 1·6$ cusecs per ft width

The F value divided into the flow Q gives the top width, with a one-third reduction for rectangular sections. The full range of alternative designs is set out in table 8.6.

TABLE 8.6   *Alternative designs for a Stormwater drain*

Depth	F	Width $\dfrac{Q}{F}$ (trapezoidal	Width (Rectangular)	Cross-sectional Area
2·25	19	5·3	3·5	7·9
2·0	16	6·3	4·2	8·4
1·5	9·5	10·1	7·2	10·8
1·0	4·8	20·8	13·8	13·8
0·5	1·6	62·5	41·5	20·8

Alternatives

The second example illustrates the point that the first solution may not be the most suitable. In the first place, what will be the shape of the channel? If it were to be excavated by plough or grader it will probably be parabolic, but soft decomposing granite suggests that it will either be dug out by hand or ripped and dozed with a crawler tractor. If this is the case the cross-section may well be rectangular, and since the tables are calculated for trapezoidal or parabolic sections, the reduction of top width by one third may be made. Figure 8.7 shows how the rectangular section of lesser width has approximately the same cross-sectional area.

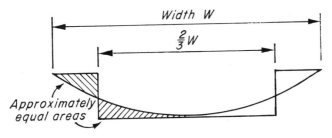

FIGURE 8.7   *The design width may be reduced by one-third if a rectangular section is used*

The figures of cross-sectional area show that the maximum permitted depth is most economical in volume of excavation, and experienced judgment or knowledge of site conditions is required to decide whether the greater excavation at shallower depth will be worth while.

8.2.2   The general solution of channel design

The Durbach method assumes that the channel will be of trapezoidal or parabolic section, and have a good vegetal cover. For other conditions the procedure is to select values of velocity, gradient, and roughness coefficient, then solve Manning's equation using figure 8.4 or 8.5, to determine the required hydraulic radius R. The cross-sectional area is obtained by dividing the velocity into the maximum flow Q, and then by trial and error a cross-section is found which combines the required area and the required hydraulic radius. As in the Durbach method, if the indicated design is not suitable for the site conditions, the procedure is repeated with different values of velocity and gradient.

The big influence of maximum permissible velocity on the size of the channel should be noted. Not only does an increased velocity give a greater flow for a given cross-section, but, more important, it allows a greater depth of flow, and this gives a more economical cross-section. It is often better economics to plant a good grass cover in a small drain than to use bare soil which requires a wide shallow drain to keep the velocity down.

8.3   THE DESIGN OF CHANNEL TERRACES

The design of a channel terrace is a special case of the general problem encountered in the design of stormwater drains, but there are fewer possible values of the variables and so the procedures can be much simpler. The channel is usually of parabolic section, so the hydraulic radius is fairly constant, and the soil is kept bare by cultivation, so roughness coefficient is uniform. The range of non-scouring non-silting velocities for bare earth channels is small, and the limits of suitable gradients less than for stormwater drains. The result is that, although it would be entirely possible to design terrace channels in the same way as stormwater drains, in practice a different approach is used. The flow of stormwater to be handled by each channel terrace is a function of its catchment area, which is the product of the distance between the terraces and the length of the terrace. These determine the run-off rate, and the channel cross-section must be able to lead it away on the chosen gradient. The four variable design factors are spacing between terraces, length of terrace, gradient, and cross-sectional area of the channel, and these will be considered in turn.

8.3.1 Spacing

The distance between channel terraces may be measured either as the difference in elevation between adjacent terraces (called the *vertical interval*, or VI), or as the distance between them on the ground. This is called the *horizontal interval*, or HI, but for convenience it is measured not horizontally but down the slope. For the slopes suitable as arable land the difference between the two measurements is negligible (figure 8.8).

Similarly, when the slope of the land is described as a percentage S, it is strictly the fall in metres (or feet) over a horizontal distance of 100 metres (or feet), but in practice it is usual to measure slope as the fall over 100 metres (or feet) measured down the slope. As figure 8.8 shows, this amounts to using the sine of the angle instead of the tangent, and again for the small angles of arable land the small difference does not warrant the conversion. However, for slopes steeper than 10°, the slope should only be calculated over the horizontal distance and at 45° the lazy way of calculating down the slope would give $S =$ approximately 70 per cent instead of 100 per cent (figure 8.8).

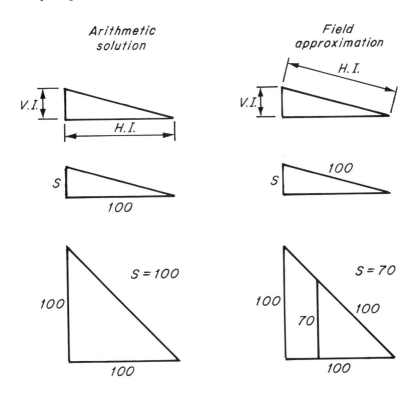

FIGURE 8.8 *Methods of measuring slope and the spacing of terraces*

For the field officer, lining in terraces with an engineer's level, it is convenient to set out the distance from one terrace to the next by measuring the vertical interval, and so formulae for terrace spacing usually give the vertical interval. The relationship between horizontal and vertical intervals is:

$$HI = \frac{VI \times 100}{S} \text{ where } S \text{ is the \% slope}$$

Some spacing formulae in current use are given in table 8.7.

TABLE 8.7   *Spacing of channel terraces*

United States Soil Conservation Service	VI feet $= aS + b$	(where a varies from 0·3 in the South to 0·6 in the North, and b is 1 or 2 according to soil)
Federation of Rhodesia and Nyasaland	VI feet $= \dfrac{S+f}{2}$	(where f varies from 3 to 6 according to the erodibility of the soil)
South Africa	VI feet $= \dfrac{S}{a} + b$	(where a varies from 4 for high rainfall areas to 1·5 for low rainfall areas and b varies from 1–3 according to the soil)
Israel	$VI \quad = \dfrac{S}{10} + 2$ metres	S is the slope of the land as a percentage

Figure 8.9 shows that all these formulae are of similar form, and give comparable results.

Although these design formulae are empirical, there is experimental evidence that the resulting spacing is suitable. Many experiments on the effect of different spacings have been carried out in the United States by measuring the soil loss from field plots of various lengths (WISCHMEIER *et al* 1958). The United States formulae were chosen as a result of the results of these experiments, and the author showed by experiments in Africa that under tropical rainfall too, this is a practical spacing (HUDSON 1958).

8.3.2.   Maximum length

After the spacing has been determined, the next design factor to consider is length. A survey of failed terraces in Africa showed that damage and failure were closely correlated with long terraces, and as a result the maximum lengths were considerably reduced to the values shown in table 8.8.

The necessity for designing the terrace layout so that these maximum lengths are not exceeded is of little consequence in some cases, but a major complication in others. In one example, shown in figure 8.10, the land to be protected is a large area of uniformly sloping land with no natural streams or watercourses. All the run-off from the terraces

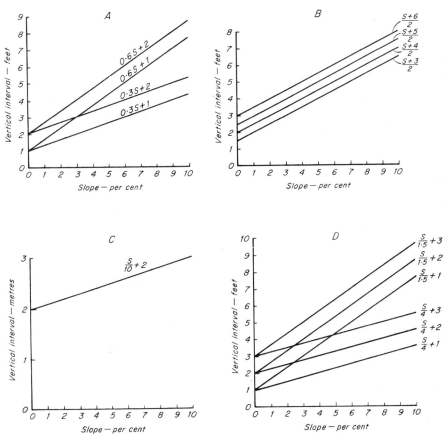

FIGURE 8.9 *Comparison of several formulae for the spacing of channel terraces.*
(a) United States (b) Rhodesia (c) Israel (d) South Africa

TABLE 8.8 *Maximum lengths of channel terraces*

| | Africa | | | | USSCS | |
| | Sandy soils | | Clay soils | | (Stallings 1957) | |
	feet	metres	feet	metres	feet	metres
Normal maximum	900	250	1200	400	1600	500
Absolute maximum	1200	400	1500	450	2000	600
Gullied land	—	—	—	—	1200	400

These distances all refer to the maximum length of flow. A channel which sheds run-off on both sides from a high point can have the maximum length on either side of the high point.

The metric figures are rounded off conversions of the lengths in feet.

must be discharged into artificial excavated waterways and the only effect of limiting the length is that the number of such waterways will be increased. In figure 8.10, if the maximum length is 400 metres, only 3 waterways are required, but if the maximum allowed is 250 metres, then 4 waterways are required. In this case the additional cost would be a small proportion of the total, and easily justified if it is going to mean a more efficient or long-lived system.

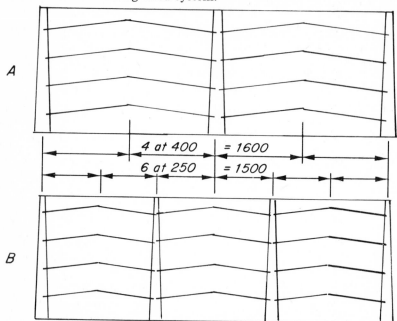

FIGURE 8.10   *The maximum permitted length of channel terraces influences the number of artificial waterways*

The second case is where the maximum length rule requires a major change in design. Figure 8.11 shows an example, with arable land on a ridge and a natural watercourse on either side. The obvious solution is to put in a ridge road on the crest and spill the terraces on either side from the road to the existing waterway. In this situation the normal maximum may be 'stretched' and this layout used with terraces up to the absolute maximum. If the absolute maximum length would be exceeded by such a plan, then an alternative layout must be adopted, such as inserting a single artificial waterway midway between the two natural ones. This would be unpopular and lead to questioning whether the maximum length rule is really necessary. The farmer naturally likes to have as few interruptions as possible to cultivation processes, and adding the cost of one waterway, where previously none were required, means a much bigger proportional increase in total cost than in the previous case of 3 waterways or 4, as shown in table 8.9.

TABLE 8.9   *Costs of protection schemes*

	Scheme A Figure 8.10	Scheme B Figure 8.10	Scheme A Figure 8.11	Scheme B
Diversion ditches	10 units of cost	10	10	10
Terrace construction	20	20	20	20
Waterways	9	12	—	10
Total	39	42	30	40
	Increase 3 units or $6\frac{1}{2}\%$		Increase 10 units or 30%	

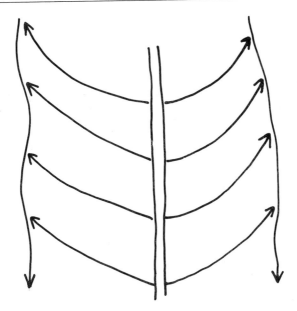

FIGURE 8.11   *Channel terrace layout on a ridge*

In this situation the temptation to exceed the maximum allowable length must be firmly overruled by the dictum that bad protection works are worse than no protection works. Experience has shown that the more difficult and more expensive scheme will work and the quick, easy, cheap way will fail.

8.3.3   Gradients

If the gradient of the channel is too steep it will scour, if too flat it will flow sluggishly and so will require a large cross-section and there will be the danger of silting. However, the choice of a grade which will result in non-scouring, non-silting velocities of flow under all conditions is not easy. A special feature about the flow of water in the channels of terraces is that the quantity of water increases along the channel. At the discharge point the flow in the channel is the run-off from the whole of the area served by the terrace, but half way along its length only half the area is contributing. Since the channel capacity must be sufficient to handle the maximum flow at the outlet, it follows that the same capacity would be more than necessary higher up the channel. This has led to two different approaches to the gradient of channel terraces—the variable gradient and the constant gradient.

Variable gradient   It is not practicable to cater for the increasing flow by making the cross-section of the channel bigger towards the outlet end. When the channels are built by machines operating along the length of the terrace it would be impracticable to vary the cross-section, and when they are built by hand labour it would be possible, but difficult to regulate. However, the capacity of the channel may also be varied by keeping the same cross-section, but increasing the gradient progressively as the required capacity increases. This approach is frequently used by the USDA and typical grades are:

First 100 metres   1 in 1000
Second 100 metres   1 in 500
Third 100 metres   1 in 330
Fourth 100 metres   1 in 250

This method partly fulfils the requirements in that greater capacity is provided towards the outlet end, but a possible disadvantage is that this increased capacity is only achieved by increasing the velocity. There is a danger that the range of velocities may go beyond the limits of non-silting and non-scouring flow, and the flatter grades may result in silting, or the steeper grades be liable to scour.

Constant gradient   The alternative is to use a constant cross-section, and a constant grade, accepting that this will mean considerable over-design at the beginning of the terrace. This method ensures a suitable velocity, and another advantage is that setting out the lines of terraces with a level is a little simpler when the grade is constant. This may be significant when this field work is carried out by unskilled staff. The recommended gradient for uniform grade terraces is 1 in 250.

8.3.4   Cross-sectional area

The cross-sectional area is usually less precisely defined and specified than the cross-section of other channels and drains. This is because, first, they are usually built with farm machinery and close control is not possible, and secondly because the cross-section will change when tillage and cultivation operations are carried out.

   In America recommended cross-sections vary in different regions, the specification usually being for a minimum area of 8 to 10 sq ft (about one square metre). In the Central African Federation the specification has three minimum sizes—channel width of 7 ft (2·1 metres), minimum channel depth 9 in. (0·23 metres), and bank height 9 in. (0·23 metres) above original ground level. For the design conditions for spacing and length previously discussed, this should cater for the run-off based on a 10 year return period.

8.3.5 Special-purpose channel terrace designs

For some crops it may be worthwhile to design the terrace layout to suit each individual field rather than to follow a standard design. An example is tobacco, where because of the production methods it is important that the terraces should be regularly spaced and of uniform length.

In such cases it is always possible to design the channel from first principles. The sequence would be to estimate the time of concentration, and the corresponding maximum intensity of rainfall, and hence the maximum run-off using the Rational formula as described in Chapter 7. Suitable values of the run-off coefficient C would be from 0·2 to 0·6 according to the soil and the cropping practice.

However the method can be simplified for the special case of channel terrace design. There is not much variation in the catchment area served by each terrace so a constant time of concentration can be assumed. (25 minutes is a suitable figure.) The corresponding maximum rainfall intensity, based on a 10 year return period, will for most tropical and sub-tropical climates be about $3\frac{1}{2}$ in. per hour. Instead of multiplying this by a run-off coefficient, the simplified method subtracts an amount which corresponds with the infiltration capacity of the soil. The figures adopted are:

$1\frac{1}{2}$ in./hour for well drained soil
1 in./hour for medium drained soil
$\frac{1}{2}$ in./hour for poorly drained soil

The coincidence of units shown in section 7.2 allows the net rainfall in inches per hour to be equated with run-off in cusecs per acre and so the design figures become

Well drained land   2 cusecs per acre
Medium drained land 2$\frac{1}{2}$ cusecs per acre
Poorly drained land   3 cusecs per acre

In *SI* units the corresponding figures are a rainfall of 90 mm/hour, less infiltration for well, medium, and poorly drained soils of 40, 25 and 10 mm/hour, leaving a net rainfall of 50, 65, or 80 mm/hour, corresponding to run-offs of 0·14, 0·18, or 0·22 cubic metres per second per hectare.

Knowing the maximum run-off to be accommodated by each terrace, the channel can be designed from first principles using the methods of section 8.2.2, but again a simplification is possible. It can be assumed that the channel cross-section will be parabolic, and that it will be kept clear of vegetation by cultivation, and that permissible velocities will be low. A partial solution of Manning's equation for these particular conditions can be presented for convenience as a table. Table 8.10 (adapted from CORMACK 1951) gives a range of alternative channel sections which will cover most situations.

TABLE 8.10   *Capacities of graded channel terraces*

The figures in the table show the capacity of graded channel terraces in cubic metres per second at upper and lower limits of gradient.

The gradients (right hand column) are the limits of gradient for velocities of 0·6 m/sec (upper figure) and 0·75 m/sec (lower figure). These limits should not be exceeded for clean-tilled channels of shallow parabolic section.

The capacities are based on a roughness co-efficient of $n = 0·0225$, a hydraulic radius of two-thirds of the depth, and a depth of flow of half the height from the invert of the channel to the top of the ridge.

Depth of channel (mm)	Width of Channel (metres)						Limits of gradient
	1·0	1·5	2·0	2·5	3·0	3·5	
50	0·022	0·033	0·044	0·055	0·066	0·077	1 in 40
	0·022	0·037	0·052	0·067	0·081	0·096	1 in 20
100	0·041	0·061	0·082	0·103	0·123	0·143	1 in 100
	0·050	0·077	0·103	0·130	0·157	0·182	1 in 70
150	0·060	0·092	0·122	0·152	0·182	0·213	1 in 220
	0·076	0·105	0·153	0·190	0·230	0·270	1 in 130
200	0·080	0·120	0·162	0·202	0·243	0·183	1 in 370
	0·102	0·153	0·204	0·253	0·304	0·353	1 in 220
250	0·103	0·154	0·205	0·254	0·305	0·354	1 in 420
	0·129	0·191	0·256	0·318	0·382	0·445	1 in 310
300	0·125	0·185	0·246	0·306	0·367	0·427	1 in 700
	0·154	0·230	0·306	0·382	0·455	0·530	1 in 430

8.4   THE DESIGN OF GRASS WATERWAYS

Two types of channel are used for artificially constructed waterways as shown in figure 8.12. Type A consists of raised banks which contain the water in a flat-bottomed channel. In Type B, soil is excavated to form a shallow dished drain and the excavated soil is either carted away or used to form low banks on either side. The advantage of Type A is that the natural vegetation is undisturbed in the bottom of the channel, and so it is particularly useful where water has to be discharged down the channel as soon as it is constructed, without waiting for grass to be sown or planted. The disadvantage is that the soil for the raised banks is not easily come by. If it is taken from outside the banks a channel down the slope results and is liable to gullying. To avoid this danger by carting in the soil is expensive.

Type B is preferable provided a good grass cover can be established before it has to carry water. The ideal solution is for the waterways to be established one or two seasons ahead of the construction of the drains and terraces which will discharge into it. Where this cannot be done it may be possible to divert the water into another temporary course while the waterway is prepared. Even if this results in some gullying of the temporary course, it may be justified if it is the only way that the permanent waterway can be established. The growth of the grass cover can be considerably accelerated by putting all the top soil on one side and spreading it over the channel when the shaping is finished, and by the use of compost, mulch, and fertilizer.

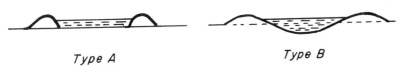

Type A   Type B

FIGURE 8.12 *Types of grass waterway*

8.4.1 Design as a hydraulic channel

The design of the cross-section is another specialized case of the design of hydraulic channels. The waterway must run straight down the slope, or the water would pile up on the lower side, and so the gradient is determined by the ground conditions. Since a good grass cover is required, the roughness coefficient is within narrow limits, and the only variables are the size and shape which, for the given slope, will pass the required rate of flow.

The trial and error procedure would be to assume a value for hydraulic radius and then determine the velocity from Manning's equation or a graphical solution of it such as figure 8.4. Provided this value of velocity is less than the permissible maximum (table 8.2) the cross-sectional area A can then be found from the relationship $Q = V \times A$, and a channel section can be designed to suit these values of area and hydraulic radius. If this section was not suitable or the velocity too high a different value of hydraulic radius would be chosen.

8.4.2 Simplified solutions

Again the labour of trial and error calculations can be avoided by graphical solutions of this special case. With the gradient fixed by the slope of the land, and assuming a roughness coefficient for the vegetation to be used, and assuming a velocity appropriate to the soil, then Manning's equation will give a required value of hydraulic radius. PALMER *et al* (1954) give graphical solutions for trapezoidal and parabolic channels. The charts are entered with the required hydraulic radius and area, and give the top width and depth. For trapezoidal channels a separate chart has to be provided for each side slope from 1:1 to 6:1, but parabolic sections are preferable for waterways and the single chart required for small parabolic sections is shown in figure 8.13.

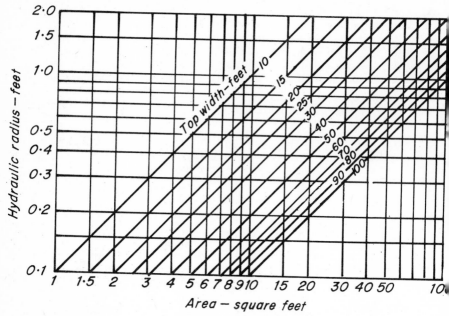

FIGURE 8.13   *Nomograph for the design of small parabolic channels* (from PALMER and LAW 1954)

Another partial solution for a special case is used by CORMACK (1951). A roughness coefficient of 0·04 is assumed, and a desired velocity of one metre per second. Manning's formula then reduces to $R^{\frac{2}{3}} \propto S^{\frac{1}{2}}$, that is for any gradient there is a corresponding hydraulic radius. At this hydraulic radius, for various top widths of a parabolic channel the cross-section area can be calculated and hence the flow. Table 8.11 shows the result in which the width required to pass a given rate of run-off can be read off directly. This particular solution is for erodible soils with a low permissible velocity and so gives wide sections. For more resistant soils a higher maximum velocity would be allowable.

The ultimate in simplification is to relate the width of waterway directly to the area of its catchment. This approach has been used in Rhodesia, the design figure being $1\frac{1}{2}$ ft of width for each acre of catchment (about one metre per hectare), but to make sure the waterway will be adequate for all conditions of slope, rainfall, and soil, a blanket design figure of this type has to contain such a big safety factor that in most cases it results in serious overdesign.

8.4.3   The Durbach method for grass waterways

This is similar to the Durbach design method for diversion drains in

TABLE 8.11 *Capacities of grass waterways*

The figures in the table show the capacity of grass waterways in cubic metres per second.
The capacities are based on a permissable velocity of 1 metre per second, and a good close-growing grass cover is assumed.

Depth of flow (mm)	Width of waterway (metres)					Gradient
	10	20	30	40	50	
150	0·92	1·84	2·76	3·68	4·60	1 in 20
200	1·20	2·40	3·60	4·80	6·00	1 in 40
250	1·50	3·00	4·50	6·00	7·50	1 in 60
300	1·75	3·50	5·25	7·00	8·75	1 in 80
350	2·05	4·10	6·15	8·20	10·25	1 in 110
400	2·31	4·62	6·93	9·24	11·55	1 in 140

that it establishes the flow per unit width, and this, divided into the maximum estimated flow, gives the design width.

The cross-section of the proposed channel is plotted so that the depth of flow is known for any given width of channel. A possible width is selected and the appropriate depth of flow and the average gradient of the channel applied to table 8.12, which gives the flow per foot of channel width. Multiplying this by the trial width gives the capacity of the channel. If it is too big or too small a different depth is tried. Although it is a trial and error method it is very quick and simple.

TABLE 8.12 *Values of discharge in grass waterways in cusecs per foot width of channel*

Depth of flow feet	S	50	100	150	200	250	300	400
0·25		0·3	0·2	0·2	0·2	0·1	0·1	0·1
0·50		1·0	0·7	0·6	0·5	0·4	0·4	0·3
0·75		1·9	1·4	1·1	1·0	0·9	0·8	0·7
1·0		3·1	2·2	1·8	1·6	1·4	1·3	1·1
1·25		4·4	3·1	2·5	2·2	2·0	1·8	1·6
1·50		6·0	4·3	3·5	3·0	2·7	2·5	2·2
1·75		7·0	5·5	4·5	3·9	3·5	3·2	2·8
2·0		8·0	6·8	5·6	4·8	4·3	3·9	3·4
2·5		10·0	10·0	8·0	7·0	6·3	5·7	5·0
3·0		12·0	12·0	11·0	9·5	8·5	7·7	6·7

1 in S = Average gradient of channel
Based on max. velocity of 6 ft per second, and $n = 0·035$

This method can also be used to estimate the carrying capacity of natural waterways, but since it assumes a maximum permissible velocity of 6 ft per second, and a roughness coefficient of 0·035, it should be used only for channels with a good cover of vegetation.

8.5   THE CONSTRUCTION AND LAYOUT OF PROTECTION WORKS

8.5.1   Construction sequence

Systems of mechanical protection need to be built in the right order. When water is going to be carried by a channel which has been designed as a vegetated waterway it will almost certainly erode if it tries to carry the water before the vegetation is established. Any grass-lined diversion drains or grass waterways should therefore be put in first, preferably the season before they have to start work in earnest.

The next point is that diversion drains should be put in before the channel terraces, and building the channel terraces should start from the top. The reason is that the channel terraces have been designed so that each can carry its own share of the run-off and no more. They cannot cope unless all the other protection works higher up the slope are in place. Even when it is the intention to build all the works within a short time there is always the possibility of tractors breaking down or sudden storms catching the job half done, so it is a good principle to always start construction at the top and work down hill.

8.5.2   Field layout

Whenever aerial photographs or large scale maps are available they should be used for the overall planning of the scheme and locating crests, watersheds, possible outlets, and natural watercourses.

In the field, the line of each drain or channel is staked out using a surveyor's level. Ordinarily stakes are set on grade at intervals of 100 ft or 50 metres, but extra stakes are required at local obstructions, especially depressions. If the staff man is unskilled, care is required to make sure that the staff is in a suitable place, not in a hollow or on a stone. Most levels used for this type of work are built for robustness rather than precision and long shots should not be taken, especially when there is heat haze.

It is a good plan to have a tractor and plough available at the time that the lines are staked out, so that the lines can be permanently marked. Stakes left in the field are liable to be blown down, knocked over by cattle, or taken for firewood. Also it is surprisingly easy to join up stakes in adjacent lines, and all these difficulties are avoided if lines marking the layout are made while the surveyor is still on the job.

8.5.3   Adjustments

Diversion drains or channel terraces if marked out strictly on grade will have many wiggles and irregularities at localized low or high points. Since these will be a nuisance both in construction and in later farming operations any straightening out will be desirable. It is quite in order to do some adjusting provided the changes are explained to and understood by whoever is going to construct the works. A contour-line passing through a small local depression will bend towards the uphill side, and the kink may be straightened provided the bank is specially raised and straightened at this point. When a staked line goes over a high area it will bend towards the downhill side. In this case the line can be straightened if the channel is cut extra deep at this point. In such cases a diagram and clear dimensioned sketches must be given to the person responsible for constructing the earthworks. Even on fairly even land it is sometimes desirable to move the stakes to give a better layout, and the distances which stakes can be moved laterally on different slopes are shown in table 8.13.

TABLE 8.13   *Lateral adjustment of stakes*

	Tolerance*		
Slope %	25 *mm*	50 *mm*	100 *mm*
1	2·5 m	5 m	10 m
2	1·25 m	2·5 m	5 m
3	833 mm	1·67 m	3·33 m
4	625 mm	1·25 m	2·5 m
5	500 mm	1·0 m	2·0 m
6	416 mm	833 mm	1·67 m

* For a carefully graded irrigation canal on gentle grade the maximum departure from grade would be 25 mm. The tolerance of 50 mm would be appropriate for a channel terrace, and 100 mm for a large diversion drain.

8.5.4   Parallel channel terraces

The adjustments just discussed will reduce minor local irregularities but unless the land is very even there will still be large variations in the distance between channel terraces. In the case of broad-based terraces which can be crossed by tractors and implements this is a minor disadvantage, but on steeper slopes, or when the ridges cannot easily be crossed, this becomes more serious. Short rows in the odd segments between terraces reduce the efficiency of mechanization, and the extra turning in limited space is likely to cause damage to the banks. If the odd areas are left uncultivated this is both a waste of land and a breeding ground for weeds. Plate 8.1 shows an Australian layout which demonstrates the awkwardness of a conventional layout.

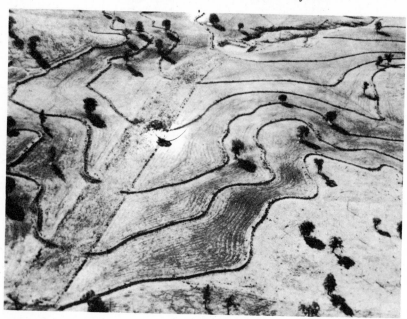

PLATE 8.1   *This protection scheme in New South Wales, Australia, is efficient, but makes tillage operations awkward*

In some cases it is possible to avoid these difficulties by constructing the terraces parallel to each other. This can be done if the channel gradient is allowed to vary from the design gradient in some places. In figure 8.14 a conventional uniform-grade channel terrace winds about when seen in plan, and the smooth curve is preferable. In section the smooth curve channel has a flatter grade in some places, steeper in others. The channel will have to be cut deeper between A and B, and between C and D, and the bank built up higher between B and C. If the cross-section of the uniform-gradient channel is the most economical design, ie, the smallest which will do the job, then it cannot be expected to work at other gradients, and it will probably overtop between C and D, and scour between B and C. But it could cope with the irregularities of grade if the channel were bigger, or the flow smaller. It is therefore possible to straighten out channel terraces into regular parallel patterns, but only at the sacrifice of having more terraces or larger terraces.

The layout of parallel systems is a trial and error process. It can be done in the field but it is usually easier and quicker to carry out a contour survey and to plan the layout in the office on the contour map. First a *keyline* is selected by eye and drawn in, and this is the smooth line of a

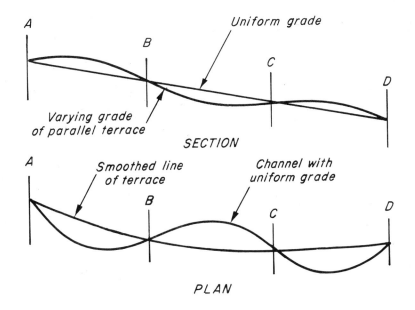

FIGURE 8.14 *Parallel terraces require some deviation from gradient*

channel terrace following a line thought to be typical of that part of the field. The distance between parallel terraces must be less than for normal layouts, and a commonly used figure is two thirds of the normal horizontal interval. Using this spacing another line is drawn, parallel to the keyline, and then checked to see that it has a fall over its whole length, and that the gradient is nowhere excessive. The maximum permissible gradient can be found from Manning's formula or from figure 8.4.

Further parallel lines are then drawn in and checked. When a line is unsatisfactory because it has an uphill grade at some point, or too steep a section, then it is rubbed out, and a new keyline drawn in its place. Next a new set of parallel lines are laid off from the new keyline, and checked as before.

The final result is several groups of parallel terraces, each group following its keyline (figure 8.15). Even with this system, short rows (called *point* rows in America) are only reduced, not eliminated, because there are still some odd shaped areas in between. One solution is to put these down to permanent pasture.

The design, layout, and construction of parallel systems is considerably more complicated than conventional uniform gradient channel terraces, but the advantages make them well worth while (DOMINY and WORLEY 1966).

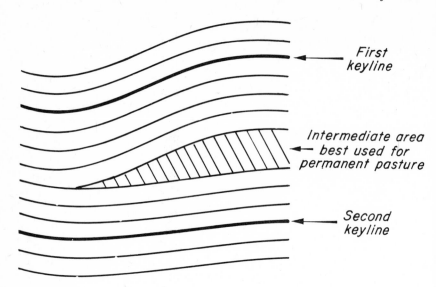

FIGURE 8.15   *The 'keyline' method of laying out parallel channel terraces*

References

CORMACK, R. M. M. 1951 The Mechanical Protection of Arable Land. *Rhodesian Agricultural Journal*, 48, 2, 135–164

DOMINY, P. F. and L. D. WORLEY 1966 Design and Construction Techniques for Parallel Terraces. *Transactions of American Society of Agricultural Engineers*, 9, 4, 580–582

HUDSON, N. W. 1958 Erosion Control Research—Progress Report on Experiments at Henderson Research Station 1953–1956. *Rhodesian Agricultural Journal* 54, 4, 297–323

PALMER, V. J., W. P. LAW and W. O. REE 1954 Handbook of Channel Design for Soil and Water Conservation. *Soil Conservation Service Technical Publication* 61, *United States Department of Agriculture*

REE, W. O. 1949 Hydraulic Characteristics of Vegetation for Vegetated Waterways. *Agricultural Engineering*, 30, 184–187, 189

SCHWAB, G. O., R. K. FREVERT, T. W. EDMINSTER and K. K. BARNES 1966 *Soil and Water Conservation Engineering* (2nd Edition) Wiley, New York

WISCHMEIER, W. H., D. D. SMITH and R. E. UHLAND 1958 Evaluation of Factors in the Soil-Loss Equation. *Agricultural Engineering* 39 458–462, 474

Chapter 9   Land management

9.1   LAND USE AND LAND CLASSIFICATION

The control of erosion by mechanical earth-moving techniques was likened earlier to establishing a solid foundation on which a sound agricultural industry can be built. Modern techniques such as mechanization, better crop varieties, and the scientific use of fertilizers can transform agriculture, but before they can be effective the basic use of the land has to be right. No techniques will make it possible to grow a good crop if the soil conditions are unsuitable for that particular crop, and no mechanical works can prevent erosion when the basic cause is trying to grow crops on land which is really unsuitable for arable farming. (Plate 9.1.) Correct land use is thus the first step towards both good agronomy and good erosion control, and a good definition of what the conservationist means by correct land use is to use every area of land according to its capability for sustained and economic productivity.

The technique which makes it possible to determine the most suitable use for any area of land is Land Classification. There are many different systems of land classification in use, each of which consists of classifying the land according to some special property. For example, classification maps have been drawn of the British Isles according to present land use. This is a single-purpose classification whose object is simply to record the facts as they are—which land is used for forestry, which for livestock farming, and so on. It does not attempt to record whether the land use is successful, or whether it is undergoing change, or what alternative crops could be grown.

Another kind of classification is that made according to suitability for a particular crop. A Government looking for expansion of say cotton might commission a survey of potential cotton growing areas. The classification might well be into categories *Very suitable* (for cotton), *Fairly suitable*, and *Not suitable*, and whether the land were suitable for rice or sugar cane would be irrelevant. Suitability for a particular form of land use is often the basis of a classification system, for example, suitability for irrigation.

Many other classification systems are discussed by JACKS (1946), and these examples have been mentioned to emphasise that there is nothing unique about the system used by conservationists and land use planners which is called the *Land Capability Classification*.

9.2   LAND CAPABILITY CLASSIFICATION

Like other kinds of land classification, this system also has a particular purpose, which is to record all the relevant data which will lead to a decision as to the combination of agricultural use and conservation measures which allow the most intensive agricultural use of the land without risk of soil erosion. The data required for this decision is described in section 9.2.3. Some of the key facts are the depth of the soil and its texture, the land slope, and the past erosion.

There is not one Land Capability Classification but many, for in every country or geographical region there are different factors which should be allowed for. The soils and climate will vary, and so will social customs, land tenure, economics—and all of these may affect the choice of the best land use. As the use of capability classification spreads (and it is highly desirable that it should be adopted wherever erosion is a problem) more modifications and variations will be added. All the methods stem however, from that developed in the United States (KLINGEBIEL *et al* 1961) so the logical pattern is to study that system first, and then consider some of the major variations.

9.2.1 The United States Department of Agriculture System

In this system land is allocated into eight classes, of which the first 4 are suitable for cultivation and the remaining 4 unsuitable. The following descriptions of the classes, and the type of use for which they are suitable are taken from *Soil Conservation* J. H. STALLINGS (1957).

Class I Soils in Class I have no, or only slight, permanent limitations or risks of damage. They are very good. They can be cultivated safely with ordinary good farming methods. The soils are deep, productive, easily worked, and nearly level. They are not subject to overflow damage. However, they are subject to fertility and puddle erosion.

Class I soils used for crops need practices to maintain soil fertility and soil structure. These practices involved use of fertilizers and lime, cover and green-manure crops, crop residues, and crop rotations.

Class II Class II consists of soils subject to moderate limitations in use. They are subject to moderate risk of damage. They are good soils. They can be cultivated with easily applied practices.

Soils in Class II differ from soils in Class I in a number of ways. They differ mainly because they have gentle slopes, are subject to moderate erosion, are of moderate depth, are subject to occasional overflows, and are in need of drainage. Each of these factors requires special attention. These soils may require special practices such as soil-conserving rotations, water-control devices, or special tillage methods. They frequently need a combination of practices.

Class III Soils in Class III are subject to severe limitations in use for cropland. They are subject to severe risks or damage. They are moderately good soils. They can be used regularly for crops, provided they are planted to good rotations and given the proper treatment. Soils in

PLATE 9.1 *On these steep slopes in Madeira, the erosion has been partly controlled by terracing, but the basic problem is that the land is too steep for arable farming*

this class have moderately steep slopes, are subject to more severe erosion, and are inherently low in fertility.

Class III soil is more limited or subject to greater risks than Class II. These limitations often restrict the choice of crops or the timing of planting and tillage operations.

These soils require cropping systems that produce adequate plant cover. The cover is needed to protect the soil from erosion. It also helps preserve soil structure. Hay or other sod crops should be grown instead of cultivated row crops. A combination of practices is needed to farm the land safely.

Class IV Class IV is composed of soils that have very severe permanent limitations or hazards if used for cropland. The soils are fairly good. They may be cultivated occasionally if handled with great care. For the most part, they should be kept in permanent hay or sod.

Soils in Class IV have unfavourable characteristics. They are frequently on steep slopes and subject to severe erosion. They are restricted in their suitability for crop use. They should usually be kept in hay or pasture, although a grain crop may be grown once in five or six years. In other cases, the soils may be shallow or only moderately deep, low in fertility, and on moderate slopes. These soils should be in hay or sod crops for long periods. Only occasionally should they be planted to row crops.

Class V Soils in Class V should be kept in permanent vegetation. They should be used for pasture or forestry. They have few or no permanent limitations and not more than slight hazards. Cultivation is not feasible, however, because of wetness, stoniness, or other limitations. The land is nearly level. It is subject to only slight erosion by wind or water if properly managed. Grazing should be regulated to keep from destroying the plant cover.

Class VI Class VI soils should be used for grazing and forestry, and may have moderate hazards when in this use. They are subject to moderate permanent limitations, and are unsuited for cultivation. They are steep, or shallow. Grazing should not be permitted to destroy the plant cover.

Class VI land is capable of producing forage or woodland products when properly managed. If the plant cover has been destroyed, the soil's use should be restricted until cover is re-established. As a rule Class VI land is either steeper or more subject to wind erosion than Class IV.

Class VII Soils in Class VII are subject to severe permanent limitations or hazards when used for grazing or forestry. They are steep, eroded, rough, shallow, droughty, or swampy. They are fair to poor for grazing or forestry, and must be handled with care.

Where rainfall is ample, Class VII land should be used for woodland.

In other areas, it should be used for grazing. In the latter case, strict management should be applied.

Class VIII   Soils in Class VIII are rough even for woodland or grazing. They should be used for wildlife, recreation, or watershed uses.

Reprinted by permission of Prentice-Hall Inc, Englewood Cliffs, New Jersey, USA.

It must be emphasized that this system of classification is primarily concerned with the risk of erosion, and not with productivity or fertility. Farmers instinctively classify land according to what is to them its most important characteristic—how well the crops yield, and it has to be very carefully explained that allocating land into Class II does not mean it can only grow second-rate crops. It might grow a particular crop better than Class I land, and an example of this is tobacco which does better on light sandy sloping land which would be Class II or III than on flat clays and loams which could be Class I. What the Capability Classification system does show (and all it shows) is what intensity of use is best for the land, and how carefully its conservation must be managed.

Within some of the main classes, smaller sub-classes are used to specify particular problems. In the American system these are applied only to classes II, III and IV and shown by the addition of the following letters added after the class.

e = erosion hazard—when vulnerability of the soil is the main problem in its use.

w = wetness—when excess water is the main problem.

c = climate—when climate (eg, temperature or lack of moisture is the main problem).

s = soil—when limitations of the soil (eg, salinity) are the main problem.

Among the countries using a capability classification system the United States is unique in the extent to which the soils of the country have been surveyed. This allows a further modification which is not possible in countries with less detailed soil survey information. When the soils of a State or County are well known it may be found that the land falling within a particular capability class usually consists of one of a group of soil types, each sufficiently different to be recognized and identified. These would then be called *land capability units*, and land would be classified into these smaller more precise categories as well as into the broad capability classes. The land capability unit is often the same as a soil series in the pedological sense, but need not necessarily be so. Even when soils have not been broken down into series, the principle of smaller divisions within capability classes can be applied whenever distinctive combinations of physical characteristics can be identified.

9.2.2 Modifications in other countries

A most encouraging feature of Capability Classification is that it is of almost universal application with little modification. A review of classification methods used in different countries up to 1962 was made by RAYCHAUDHURI *et al* (1962), but many other systems have been developed since then. A list of references to the classification methods of various countries is included at the end of this chapter. Three systems have been selected to show some of the possible variations and modifications, from Israel, the Philippines, and the Federation of Rhodesia and Nyasaland. Table 9.1 shows the main features of these systems, and the similarities are much more striking than the differences. The 4 classes of

TABLE 9.1   *A comparison of some land capability systems*

	United States Department of Agriculture	Federation of Rhodesia and Nyasaland	Israel	Philippines
Arable	I II III IV	I II III IV	I II III IV	A B C D
Non-arable	V (special problems) VI grazing VII forestry	V (wet land) VI grazing VII forestry	V VI	L M N
Non-agricultural	VIII	VIII	VII	X (water) Y (dry land)

arable land are common to all, with some sub-divisions in Israel. Class V, which in the USDA system is the best of the non-arable classes, is the main place where special variations can be introduced. In Rhodesia and Zambia there are large areas of broad flat valleys known as *dambos* in Zambia and *vleis* in Rhodesia whose soils are very wet for most of the growing season. These need a special class and it is provided by Class V with only a slight loss of flexibility. Similarly in the Philippines system the special condition of salinity is accommodated in their Class L, equivalent to Class V. In other countries special situations of major importance could similarly be taken care of in a special Class V. The other differences are (*a*) that Israel omits what in other systems is Class V and so only has seven classes, (*b*) the Philippines use letters instead of roman numerals for classes, and subdivides the land of no agricultural value into sub-classes wet and dry. Lakes, rivers, swamps and coastal areas are all class X, and dry non-agricultural land is Class Y.

Although the numbering of the classes is similar in each of these systems, this does not necessarily mean that land which is for example Class II in Israel would also be Class II in the United States, for this will depend upon how the capability class is determined from the physical characteristics of the land.

9.2.3   Soil coding for capability classification

Since capability classification attempts to relate the use of land to the attendant risk of erosion, all the factors and characteristics which influence the risk of erosion must be assessed and considered. This is done by first collecting all the relevant facts in a soil survey, and then assembling them in a convenient order known as a *standard soil code*. The code has two purposes—it serves as a filing system, so that a particular piece of information is always stored in the same place where it can be quickly found. It also provides a convenient way in which a great deal of information can be recorded in limited space directly onto a map or aerial photograph.

The code consists of a series of letters and figures, each of which denotes the value of a particular characteristic. For example, if the depth of soil is more than 1 500 mm this is represented by the figure 1, between 900 and 1 500 mm by 2, between 500 and 900 by 3, etc, and the figure representing soil depth is always placed in the same position at the top left-hand corner of the code.

A typical code would look something like this

$$\frac{2\,F\,5}{A\,1}$$

and the physical features described are in these positions

$$\frac{\text{Depth—Texture—Permeability}}{\text{Slope—Erosion}}$$

These are the main factors and are included in all coding systems, although each system has its own scale of values.

Effective depth

The effective depth is defined as:

The depth of soil that can provide a medium for root development, retain available water, and supply available nutrients. It is therefore, in most cases, the depth at which gravel, parent material, parent rock or other unconformable rock commences, or at which soil conditions are encountered that are unfavourable for satisfactory downward root development of normal crops.

Discretion should be used in interpreting the significance of layered horizons. For instance, if a gravel horizon occurs as a fairly narrow band and is underlain by soil that is suitable for root development special note should be taken of the effect that this gravel band will have on crop root development. If it will have no significant effect on roots it is disregarded. If on the other hand the gravel band will have a marked effect on the development of roots, special consideration should be given to reducing the overall effective depth.

Where gravel is sufficiently tightly held to offer a serious barrier to roots, or if it contains very little useful soil and is underlain by material that cannot contribute to effective depth as defined above, it is regarded as a 'limiting horizon' and is not included in the effective depth. Where gravel or soft weathering rock forms the limiting horizon and the depth of soil is marginal to a depth bracket the effective depth may be extended a few inches into this horizon.

The depth codes for four systems are listed in table 9.2 which shows that apart from the fact that the Israeli numbering system starts at the other end, the differences are slight. So slight indeed that there would appear to be a case for a single international standard.

TABLE 9.2   *Code symbols for effective depth*

Symbol	Description		Range
(a) Federation of Rhodesia and Nyasaland			
1	Deep	—	More than 60 in.
2	Moderately deep	—	36 to 60
3	Moderately shallow	—	20 to 36
4	Shallow	—	10 to 20
5	Very shallow	—	Less than 10
(b) Philippines			
1	Very deep	—	more than 150 cm
2	Deep	—	90 to 150 cm
3	Moderately deep	—	50 to 90 cm
4	Shallow	—	25 to 50 cm
5	Very shallow	—	Less than 25 cm
(c) Israel			
5	Very deep	—	More than 100 cm
4	Deep	—	75 to 100 cm
3	Moderate	—	45 to 75 cm
2	Shallow	—	20 to 45 cm
1	Very shallow	—	0 to 20 cm
(d) USDA			
1	Deep	—	36 in. or more
2	Moderately deep	—	20 to 36
3	Shallow	—	10 to 20
4	Very shallow	—	Less than 10

Texture

This refers to the mechanical composition of the top layer of soil. In undisturbed soils this is the topsoil, or in pedological terms the A horizons, and in arable land it is the soil in the plough zone. This will have a depth of from 150 to 250 mm and the lower limit is often recognizable by a change of colour. The texture of this layer is assessed in the field by working in the fingers a small ball of soil moistened to its 'sticky point'. Sufficient experience is very quickly acquired by field staff for them to recognize the characteristic feel of different textures such as *sandy clay loam* or *loamy sand*. Difficult or unusual soils are referred back for mechanical analysis in a soils laboratory. The symbols and textures are shown in table 9.3 but the terminology is confused by the fact that there are two scales for particle size grading—the International Scale, and the scale used by the United States Soil Survey.

TABLE 9.3 *Texture of surface soil*

Symbol	Texture	Description
(a) Federation of Rhodesia and Nyasaland		
A	Sand	More than 85% sand
X	Loamy sand	80–85% sand
B	Sandy loam	Less than 20% clay; 50–80% sand
C	Sandy clay loam	20–30% clay; 50–80% sand
D	Clay loam	20–30% clay; less than 50% sand
E	Sandy clay	More than 30% clay; 50–70% sand
F	Clay	30–50% clay; less than 50% sand
G	Heavy clay	More than 50% clay
(b) Israel		
1	Sand dunes, beach sand	Very light
2	Agricultural and heavy sands	Light
2/3	Sandy loams	Moderately light
3	Loam, silt loam, clay loam, sandy clay loam	Medium
3/4	Clay loam, sandy clay, silty clay	Moderately heavy
4	Clay and heavy clay	Heavy
(c) Philippines		
L	Loamy fine sand, loamy sand, sand, coarse sand, fine sandy loam, sandy loam	Coarse
M	Silt loam, loam, very fine sandy loam, silty clay loam, clay loam, sandy clay loam	Medium
H	Clay, silty clay, sandy clay	Fine
V	Fine clay	Very fine

A term like *fine sand* can be applied to particles of very different size according to which scale is being used. Also, while the names of textural classes such as *sandy loam* are usually the same in all countries, there is no agreement on the proportions of silt, clay, and sand which make up a particular class. The two particle size grading systems are listed in figure 9.1 and some of the textural definitions are shown diagrammatically in figure 9.2.

Permeability

Soil permeability is defined as the ability of the soil to transmit air and water. It should not be confused with the infiltration rate which is the rate at which water enters the surface of the soil.

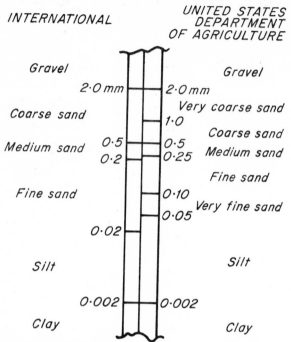

FIGURE 9.1 *Particle size grading according to the International (Atterberg) system, and that of the United States Department of Agriculture*

Quantitatively, permeability is the rate of flow through unit cross-section of saturated soil in unit time under a specified hydraulic gradient. A qualitative (subjective) assessment is made in the field, by observing the rate at which water soaks into a small lump of soil. Like the method of estimating texture, this sounds a crude test, but field staff who have been given training in the laboratory on soils whose properties have been measured, are able to make this field assessment quickly and accurately.

The classes of permeability defined by the United States Soil Survey and shown in table 9.4 are generally accepted, although some modifications are made in their application. The Philippines Soil Survey uses the United States 7 classes for detailed soil surveys, but for capability classification they are grouped into 4 classes. The Rhodesian system also has available the full 7 classes, but only the odd numbered classes are used in field survey work. In both cases the reason for this simplification is that the field test is sufficiently precise for allocation into one of 4 groups, but not to differentiate between all 7 classes. The wider range of 7 classes is available when special or difficult soils are referred for laboratory study.

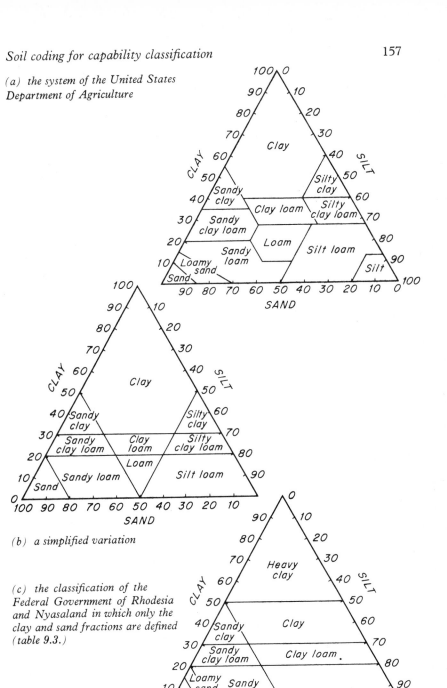

(a) *the system of the United States Department of Agriculture*

(b) *a simplified variation*

(c) *the classification of the Federal Government of Rhodesia and Nyasaland in which only the clay and sand fractions are defined (table 9.3.)*

FIGURE 9.2   *Some definitions of textural classification*

TABLE 9.4   *Classes of soil permeability*

Description	Rate of flow*	US Symbol	Philippine Symbol	Rhodesian Symbols used in field coding
Very slow	less than 0·5	1	} 1	1
Slow	0·05 to 0·20	2		
Moderately slow	0·20 to 0·80	3	} 2	3
Moderate	0·80 to 2·50	4		
Moderately rapid	2·50 to 5·00	5	} 3	5
Rapid	5·00 to 10·00	6		
Very rapid	over 10·00	7	4	7

* The rate of flow in inches per hour through saturated undisturbed cores under a head of $\frac{1}{2}$ in. of water.

Another variation is included in the Rhodesian system. The permeability of the upper subsoil, ie, material underlying the present topsoil, is coded and included in the code-description in every case. Where a significant change in permeability occurs in the lower subsoil and within the effective depth, it is recorded by a second symbol following the first in the code-description. The permeability of the topsoil is not coded.

The following schedule of the types of soil usually associated with each class of permeability has been compiled from Rhodesian experience, but is probably equally applicable for most tropical and subtropical climates.

Symbol 1: Relatively impermeable

(i) Heavy, stiff, sticky clays, with pronounced blocky prismatic, or columnar structure, and with shiny surfaces. Roots, if present, are flattened and occur entirely between structural elements. Dark yellowish, greyish, or black, usually strongly mottled with yellowish and bluish colours.
(ii) Severely deflocculated soils.
(iii) Massive laterite, cemented; not penetrated by roots.
(iv) Solid unfissured rock; not penetrated by roots.

Symbol 2: Severely restricted permeability
(i) Clays or heavy clays with very strong grades of blocky prismatic or columnar structures, and with shiny surfaces: very hard consistence.
(ii) Deflocculated soils.
(iii) Gravel or lateritic gravel, very compact and partially cemented, with only slight root penetration.
(iv) Highly weathered rock that is very clayey and dense, often cracking into large angular blocks when dry. Signs of waterlogging are often visible in this horizon.

Symbol 3: Moderately restricted permeability

(i) Clays or clay loams, greyish, yellowish or brownish sometimes slightly mottled, massive or angular blocky, hard consistence and

sometimes moderately compacted. Clay skins often conspicuous. (Includes many subsoils derived from sedimentary rocks.)
(ii) Sandy clay loams, and sandy clays tending to massive structure: moderately compacted and usually somewhat mottled or yellower than normal for the type.
(iii) Self-ploughing clays and heavy clays, dark brownish grey or black, with moderately strong grades of structure. (Typical 'black turf soils' or basalt and norite.)
(iv) Gravel or lateritic gravel, moderately compacted, but penetrated by roots.
(v) Soft highly-weathered rock, or relatively unweathered but well-jointed rock; slight penetration by roots.

Symbol 4: Slightly restricted permeability

Soils that are intermediate in permeability between 5 and 3 mainly by reason of somewhat heavy texture or slight compaction or denseness. Some clay skins are often visible.

Symbol 5: Good permeability

(i) Sandy loams, sandy clay loams, and sandy clays provided they are not compacted or deflocculated.
(ii) Clays and clay loams of good crumb, granular, or moderately blocky structure, readily permeable.

Symbol 6: Rapid permeability

Sands and loamy sands only.

Symbol 7: Excessively rapid permeability

Open gravel without soil, and very coarse and gravelly sands.

Slope

Considerable variations are found in the classes of slope and probably reflect to some extent the variation from one country to another of the availability of land, or the pressure on the arable land which is available. In some parts of Africa where there are large areas of land still undeveloped or only lightly used it is possible to rule out all land steeper than 12% as unsuitable for cultivation. In both Israel and the Philippines such limits would be much too severe, and the accepted figure for the steepest slope which should be classified as arable is 35% in Israel, and 25% in the Philippines. The other class groupings of slope are showed in table 9.5.

Previous erosion

All soil survey coding systems include some assessment of how much damage has occurred in the past, but again the definitions and scales vary in different systems. The common pattern is to use 4 degrees of

TABLE 9.5   *Slope categories*

Slope %	Codes		
	Central Africa	Israel	Philippines
1	A	A	
2			
3			a
4	B		
5		B	
6			
7	C		b
8			8
9			
10			
11	D	C	
12	Limit of		
13	arable		
14			c
15			
25		D	d
			Limit of
35		E	arable
		Limit of	
40		arable	e
60		F	f
			g

erosion from arable land, and in some cases additional elements are added for degrees of wind erosion and gully erosion. Some classifications are:

(a) USDA—water erosion
Class 1 slightly eroded phase
Class 2 moderately eroded phase
Class 3 severely eroded phase
Class 4 gullied phase.

—wind erosion
Class 1 blown phase
Class 2 severely blown phase
Class 3 blown-out land.

(b) Rhodesian classification for water erosion

Symbol	Description
1	No apparent, or slight, erosion.
2	Moderate erosion: Moderate loss of topsoil generally and/or some dissection by run-off channels or gullies.
3	Severe erosion, severe loss of topsoil generally and/or marked dissection by run-off channels or gullies.
4	Very severe erosion: complete truncation of the soil profile and exposure of the subsoil (B horizon) and/or deep and intricate dissection by run-off channels or gullies.

(c) Israel
1 Water: 0 no apparent erosion
1 slight erosion
3 moderate erosion
5 severe erosion, destroyed land or badland areas
7 moderate gully erosion
9 severe gully erosion
2 Wind: P slight wind erosion
S moderate wind erosion
U severe wind erosion

(d) Philippines
0 No apparent erosion
1 Less than 25% topsoil lost. Some rills may be present.
2 25% to 75% topsoil lost. Small gullies may be present.
3 More than 75% topsoil lost. Shallow gullies or a few big ones may be present.
4 All topsoil lost. Land truncated by gullies.
5 Soil profile destroyed.
6 Catstep—Small terraces like steps on slopes of overgrazed hills.
7 Gullies more than 30 metres apart.
8 Gullies less than 30 metres apart.

Subsidiary factors

So far the five main characteristics have been considered which are common to all capability systems. There are, however, a number of subsidiary factors which some systems use when they are thought to be relevant to local soil conditions. The layout of the code may be used to differentiate between broad groups of factors. Thus in the simplest code shown earlier,

$$\frac{2\ F\ 5}{A\ 1}$$

the symbols relating to *soil* characteristics are in the top line, and those relating to *land* characteristics in the bottom line. The difference is that the soil characteristics—in this case depth, texture and permeability—would be recognizable and measurable in a small sample, whereas the land characteristics, in this case the slope of the land and the past erosion, apply to where and how the soil occurs in relation to the land area as a whole.

A second division can be made between those factors which will determine the capability class of the land, and others which may be recorded because they are useful information, but do not affect the class. These are shown to the right of an oblique stroke, thus

$$\frac{2\ F\ 5\ /2G}{A-1/\ Gs}$$

The division of soil factors above and land factors below is maintained. In this example from the Rhodesian system the subsidiary information on the right of the oblique stroke is, on the top line the colour of the upper subsoil (2), the texture of the upper subsoil (G), and below the line the parent material (Gs—a code for Greenstone Schists). The symbols and descriptions of some of the subsidiary factors are:

1 Factors which may hinder cultivation

Where gravelly, stony, bouldery or rocky conditions in the plough-zone significantly affect the agricultural properties of the soil, that is they are sufficiently severe to hinder or prevent cultivation, they are described by symbols which are placed just before the surface texture symbol.

(*a*) Rhodesian system

Symbol	Description	Significance sufficient to :
g	Gravelly or stony	hinder cultivation
s	Very gravelly or stony	prevent cultivation
b	Bouldery	hinder cultivation
v	Very bouldery	prevent cultivation
o	Outcrops	hinder cultivation
r	Extensive outcrops	prevent cultivation

Gravel and stones are defined as fragments up to 10 in. in diameter; boulders are detached fragments of rock greater than 10 in. in diameter.

(*b*) Israel system
   Stoniness: 1   free of stones, or non-interfering stones
2   work interfering stones which can be easily removed
3   work interfering stones which can be removed with difficulty or great expense
4   work interfering stones and rock which cannot be economically removed—covering up to 50% of area
5   stones and rock covering 50% or more of area.

(*c*) The United States Soil Survey provides for five classes of stoniness from 0 (less than 0·01% of the area) to 5 (more than 90% of surface covered with stones), and the Philippine soil survey recognizes three classes, but in neither case is this factor normally shown in the code.

2 Nature of the limiting horizon

This factor is included at the moment only in the Rhodesian code, but its usefulness is such that it could well be introduced to other systems. It describes the material which limits the effective depth, that is it explains why roots are unlikely to penetrate beyond a certain depth. When the effective depth is more than 60 in. (1·5 metres) it is not recorded. As it is informative and does not affect classification it should be on the right of the oblique line although it is in fact recorded on the left of the line as shown earlier. The symbols used are:

Symbols	Description
C	Relatively impermeable clay which may or may not show signs of regular waterlogging.
H	A subsoil horizon that is sufficiently hard dense and compacted to prevent normal root development.
H1	Permeability not severely restricted.
H2	Permeability severely restricted, or relatively impermeable (generally deflocculated).
L	Laterite, wholly or partially indurated.
L1	Fractured, and permeability not severely restricted.
L2	Not fractured, and permeability severely restricted or relatively impermeable.
M	A horizon (soil, gravel, or weathering rock) that shows signs of regular waterlogging which is likely to prevent normal root development for significant periods during the growing season.
M1	Composed of material that is not itself of severely restricted permeability.
M2	Composed of material that is of severely restricted permeability or relatively impermeable.
Z	Gravel.

Z1	Loose and permeable with little or no soil; or moderately tight, but permeability not severely restricted.
Z2	Very tight and compacted, somewhat cemented and permeability severely restricted.
W	Weathered, or partially weathered rock; or relatively unweathered rock that is well fractured; permeability not severely restricted.
R	Rock, hard or unweathered and not well fractured; permeability severely restricted or relatively impermeable.

3 Soil reaction

Where the soil reaction (alkinity or acidity) is normal for the soil type it is not usually recorded, but where it is abnormal or is likely to present difficulties for particular crops it is shown by a symbol which indicates its pH rating. The scale is common to all systems.

Symbol	Description		pH Range
p0	Extremely acid	Below	4·5
p1	Very strongly acid		4·5–5·0
p2	Strongly acid		5·1–5·5
p3	Medium acid		5·6–6·0
p4	Slightly acid		6·1–6·5
p5	Neutral		6·6–7·3
p6	Mildly alkaline		7·4–7·8
p7	Moderately alkaline		7·9–8·4
p8	Strongly alkaline		8·5–9·0
p9	Very strongly alkaline	Above	9·0

4 Physical characteristics of the surface soil

Physical characteristics such as consistence, structure, structural stability, and porosity, may significantly affect the behaviour of the surface soil under cultivation. If these characteristics deteriorate, the soil will have an increasing tendency to compact and seal at the surface, with consequent reduction in aeration and penetrability by rain and emerging seedlings, and increased run-off and erosion. In the soils of sub-tropical Africa the physical condition of the soil can influence the capability classification and is recorded, when present, in two degrees.

Symbol	Description
t1	Slightly unfavourable physical conditions. The soil has a tendency to compact and seal at the surface and a good tilth is not easily obtained. With normal good management (including the return of plant residues), crops will not be severely affected.
t2	Unfavourable physical conditions. Compaction and sealing of the surface soil are more severe. A hard crust forms

when the bare soil is exposed to rain and sun and poor emergence of seedlings can severely reduce the crop. On ploughing, large clods are turned up which are not easily broken. Crops can be successfully grown only with the best management practices, including correct time of cultivation and the return of a considerable bulk of organic matter from crop residues or grass leys. Under natural vegetation, the grass cover is generally sparse and bare patches occur, particularly under grazing pressure.

5 Drainage

The permeability of the upper subsoil, recorded in the top line as a main feature in all systems but that of Israel, will usually give an adequate description of the drainage characteristics of the soil. But there can also exist conditions where the topography makes the *land* drainage different from the *soil* drainage. For example an alluvial sand might have a free draining nature as a soil, but if it were lying in an impermeable clay basin its major feature as agricultural land might well be that it was permanently saturated. Waterlogging arising from the topography of the land is less frequent in Europe or North America where the condition has usually been rectified by sub-surface draining, but it is more common in countries with less developed agriculture, and also more common in conditions of tropical or seasonal rainfall. The Rhodesian classification system has 3 degrees of wetness, according to how long the condition lasts after the end of the rainy season.

Symbol	Description	Significance
w1	Wet for relatively short and infrequent periods.	Choice of crop little affected; some interference with farming operations.
w2	Frequently wet for considerable periods.	Choice of crop limited; interference with farming operations.
w3	Very wet for most of the season.	Normal cropping precluded; sometimes suitable for rice or selected pastures.

6 Salinity

Soils which have a concentration of soluble salts or a degree of alkalinity sufficient to inhibit crop growth are not normally included in soil surveys for capability classification because the measurement and interpretation of salinity requires specialist knowledge and laboratory facilities. Where for special reasons the information is required in the soil code, a classification based on the salt content is used, as in the following examples.

(a) USDA

Class	Description	Percentage salt
0	Soils free of excess salt or alkali. Practically no crops are inhibited by or show evidence of injury from excess of salts or alkali.	0–0·15
1	Soils slightly affected by salt or alkali. The growth of sensitive crops is inhibited but that of salt-tolerant crops may not be.	0·15–0·35
2	Soils moderately affected by salt or alkali. Crop growth is inhibited and no crop does well.	0·35–0·65
3	Soils strongly affected by salt or alkali. Only a few kinds of plants survive.	above 0·65

(b) Rhodesian

Symbol	Description	Salt content per cent
s1	Yields of many crops restricted; unsuitable for sensitive crops.	0·1–0·2
s2	Suitable only for crops of high tolerance; yields may be restricted.	0·2–0·4
s3	Unsuitable for all except a few exceptionally tolerant crops.	above 0·4

7 Colour

The colour of soil can be a useful indicator of its origin, formation, or properties to a trained pedologist. But capability classification is intended to be a practical tool used by conservationists in the field who may have little knowledge of pedology, so colour is usually either omitted from both the survey and the code, or as in Rhodesia, recorded without comment. The universally employed system for recording colour is by use of Munsell colour charts. A fragment, or ped, of soil is taken from the upper subsoil horizon, moistened, and compared with standard colours on the charts. The full Munsell colour description consists of a number and letter description, eg, 10YR 4/3 or 5 RB 6 which identifies the precise shade, and a simplified code showing only the main colour group is often used when mapping.

Colour description	Symbol
All reds	1
Reddish brown	2
Yellowish-reds and reddish-yellows	3
Browns	4
Grey-Browns	5
Yellowish-Browns	6

Yellows and olive-yellows	7	
All greys except very dark and very light greys	8	
All very dark greys and dusky colours	9	
All very pale colours of whatever hue	0	

8 Parent material

It may be helpful to record the parent material from which the soil is derived, but this is usually, like colour, an optional extra not normally included. A simple letter code is usually formed from abbreviations of the name, eg, in the Rhodesian system, Gr for granites, Ga for gabbros, Ep for epidiorites, Hs for Hornblende schists etc. In the Philippines system it is A for acid igneous, B for basic igneous, basalt, L for limestone etc.

9 Natural vegetation

If the natural vegetation has not been disturbed it may be a useful indicator of soil characteristics, and therefore worth recording, particularly when the presence of certain species or associations of plants is known to be associated with physical properties. Drainage conditions, and particularly the boundaries of different drainage patterns, can often be accurately established from a knowledgeable assessment of the natural vegetation.

Where the land is best suited for livestock rather than arable farming, this identification and interpretation of natural vegetation may be more important in planning the most intensive land use than features like the depth and texture of the soil. A procedure for detailed surveys of the vegetation and for recording it in code form like a soil code has been developed for use in Africa (VINCENT 1962).

10 Available moisture capacity

The capacity of the soil to hold moisture influences land use in two ways. A large capacity is desirable, both as the reservoir of moisture for plant growth and also because more storage of rain in the soil means less surface run-off. Ordinarily the moisture holding capacity may be deduced from a combination of some of the factors already discussed, ie, depth, texture and permeability. Where more detailed information is required, the five-class code of the USDA could be used.

Symbol	Degree of available moisture capacity	Available moisture capacity in in. of water per 60 in. of depth	mm of water per metre depth
1	Very high	12 in. or more	20 or more
2	High	9–12	15–20
3	Moderately high	6– 9	10–15
4	Low	3– 6	5–10
5	Very low	Less than 3	Less than 5

11 Soil series

When the soils of a country are known well enough for the frequently recurring patterns of soil factors to be classified and identified, then it is simpler to code such groups of factors in one operation. A soil series is one example of such a grouping of separate factors, but is not the only way such capability units are defined. In the Philippines certain standard combinations of depth, texture, permeability, and parent material are called 'soil types' and given a single number. In America these sub groups are usually based on a series description, for example 9413 identifies 'a deep, well-drained, moderately light-textured soil with moderately permeable subsoils, and rapidly permeable substrata, found in Coastal plains, with low moisture-holding capacity, acid reaction, medium fertility, and low organic matter content'. This is the series description of *Sassafras sandy loam*, and in any district where soils of this nature occur, all this information is condensed into the code 9413 for mapping purposes.

12 Code formats

The usual form of the mapping code was discussed earlier, ie, the soil factors on top, land factors below, and information which does not affect the classification on the right of an oblique stroke. The way in which various subsidiary factors can be fitted in is best shown by example.

1 Rhodesian Standard Code

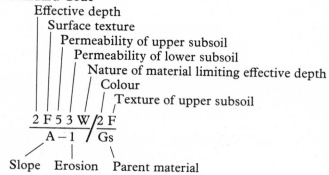

2 Subsidiary factors

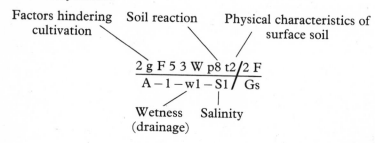

3 Philippines Standard Code

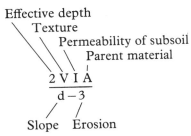

4 Philippines Soil Type Code $\dfrac{95}{d-3}$

95 denotes a particular soil type, which is a textural classification within a soil series.

5   USDA Series Code $\dfrac{3401}{B-2}$

3401 denotes Kalamazoo series sandy loam.

9.2.4   The criteria for capability classes

The allocation of a piece of land into one of the eight capability classes is determined by considering several of the soil characteristics which have been assessed in the survey and recorded in the standard soil code. Each capability class has specified limits for each factor, and to be rated as belonging to a particular capability class the specification for every factor must be met. The essence of the classification is the risk of erosion, and this danger will be increased if the soil is vulnerable in any one respect, so classification depends upon the weakest factor as the strength of a chain is that of its weakest link. The criteria for the four classes of arable land are usually much more detailed than for the non-arable classes, where a consideration of slope alone often determines the class. The criteria for the arable classes as used by the Soil Conservation Service of the Federation of Rhodesia and Nyasaland are quoted from their *Conservation Officers Handbook* as follows:

Class I
Maximum permissible slope
    Two per cent. (Symbol A only.)
Texture of surface soil
Clay loam or heavier. (In practice this excludes most soils except the typical 'red' soils on basic igneous rocks. Many clay loams and the heavier, darker, or more yellowish clays are unlikely to have satisfactory physical characteristics or permeabilities.)

Minimum effective depth
36 in. of clay loam or heavier.
Permeability
Adequate (symbols 5 or 4) to at least 36 in.
Physical characteristics of surface soil
Good (No *t* symbols are permissible).
Erosion
Nil, or very slight. (Symbol I only is permissible.)
Wetness
Not permissible. (Symbol wl will downgrade the soil to Class II and symbol w2 to sub-class IVw.)

Class II

Maximum permissible slope
5 per cent. (Symbols A or B.)
Texture of surface soil
In general sandy loam or heavier, but sands and loamy sands are permissible, provided that—
(i) the upper subsoil is a sandy loam or heavier, and
(ii) the slope does not exceed 2 per cent.
(Owing to the rapid deterioration in stability that occurs when sandy soils are cultivated, it is necessary to confine them to the less severe slopes in each class.)
Minimum effective depth
(i) If slope does not exceed 2 per cent: 20 in. of sandy loam or heavier.
(ii) If slope is greater than 2 per cent: 20 in. of sandy clay loam or heavier.
(The effect of this and the previous criterion is to permit sands with heavier subsoils in this class, provided that the slope is only slight, and to exclude all other sands completely.)
Permeability
Adequate (symbols 5 or 4) to at least 20 in. and not worse than moderately restricted (symbol 3) to 36 in. (This means that severely restricted permeability—symbol 2—is not permissible in the subsoil or limiting material above 36 in.)
Physical characteristics of surface soil
No more than slightly unfavourable. (Symbol tl, but not t2 is permissible.)
Erosion
No more than moderate erosion. (Symbols 1 or 2 only are permissible.)
Wetness
Wetness for relatively short and infrequent periods (symbols wl) is permissible. (Symbol w2 will downgrade the soil to sub-class IVw.)

Class III

Maximum permissible slope
8 per cent. (Symbols A, B or C.)
Texture of surface soil
(i) If slope does not exceed 5 per cent: no direct limitations.
(ii) If slope is greater than 5 per cent:
(1) Sandy loam or heavier, if more than 20 in. effective depth.
(2) Clay loam or heavier if less than 20 in. effective depth.
(Here again soils that are very sandy at the surface have been excluded on the steeper slopes.)

Minimum effective depth
    (i) If the slope does not exceed 5 per cent: 20 in. of sand or loamy sand, or 10 in. of sandy loam or heavier.
    (ii) If the slope is greater than 5 per cent: 20 in. of sandy clay loam, or 10 in. of clay loam or heavier.

Permeability
    In general, not worse than moderately restricted (symbol 3) to 36 in., but this requirement may be relaxed to 20 in. if
    (i) the slope does not exceed 5 per cent, and
    (ii) the texture of the surface soils and the subsoil is clay loam or heavier.
    (This means that severely restricted permeability—symbol 2—is not permissible above 36 in. except in the case of heavier soils with a greater water-holding capacity on gentle or moderate slopes.)

Physical characteristics of surface soil
    No direct limitations.

Erosion
    Severe erosion is permissible, but not very severe. (Symbols 1, 2 and 3 only.)

Wetness
    Wetness for relatively short and infrequent periods (symbol w1) is permissible. (Symbol w2 will down-grade the soil to sub-class IVw.)

Class IV

Maximum permissible slope
    12 per cent. (Symbols A, B, C or D.)

Texture of surface soil
    (i) If slope does not exceed 8 per cent: no direct limitations.
    (ii) If slope is greater than 8 per cent: sandy loam or heavier.
    Again soils that are very sandy at the surface are excluded on the steeper slopes—
    (i) If slope does not exceed 8 per cent: 10 in. of soil of any texture.
    (ii) If slope is greater than 8 per cent: 10 in. of sandy clay loam or heavier.

Permeability
    No direct limitations.

Physical characteristics of surface soil
    No direct limitations.

Erosion
    Severe erosion is permissible, but not very severe. (Symbols 1, 2 and 3 only.)

Wetness
    Soils may be frequently wet for considerable periods (symbol w2). Symbols w1 and w2 are permissible, but not w3 which invariably down-grades to Class V. When the requirements of a higher class are met in all respects except wetness, the sub-class IVw will be used.

These criteria are tabulated in table 9.6.

Since some factors are more important than others, the process of determining the class can be streamlined by considering the soil factors in a certain sequence, as shown in figure 9.3. First the section of the diagram is selected according to the degree of slope, then the lines are followed down to the appropriate texture, then effective depth, then permeability. This leads to the first assessment of class, but the additional requirements (in the left column) must also be checked, and failure to comply with any requirement means down-grading to a lower class.

TABLE 9.6   *Criteria for arable land classes of the federal classification*

Criteria for Classes I to IV for the normal cropping areas of natural regions II and III

Land Capability Class	I	II	
Permissible slope	0–2%	0–2%	2–5%
Minimum effective depth (Texture here refers to average textures)	36 in. of CL or heavier	20 in. of Sal. or heavier	20 in. of SaCl or heavier
Texture of surface soil	CL or heavier	Sal or heavier S, or LS if upper subsoil is Sal or heavier	Sal or heavier
Permeability 5 or 4 to at least – Not worse than 3 to –	36 in.	20 in. 36 in.	20 in. 36 in.
Physical characteristics of the surface soil. Permissible symbols	Not permitted	t1	t1
Erosion— Permissible symbols	1	1 and 2	1 and 2
Wetness criteria— Permissible symbols	Not permitted	W1	W1

S = Sand,

Sal = Sandy Loam,

LS = Loamy Sand,

CL = Clay Loam

SaCL = Sandy Clay Loam,

(From *Conservation Officers Handbook*, Dept of Soil Conservation, Federal Government of Rhodesia and Nyasaland)

III		IV	
0–5%	5–8%	0–8%	8–12%
20 in. of S or LS 10 in. of Sal. or heavier	(a) 20 in. of SaCL (b) 10 in. of CL or heavier	10 in. of any texture	10 in. of SaCl or heavier
No direct limitations	(a) Sal or heavier (b) CL or heavier	No direct limitations	Sal or heavier
No direct limitations 36 in. or 20 in. if average texture is CL or heavier	No direct limitations 36 in.	No direct limitations	
t1 and t2	t1 and t2	t1 and t2	t1 and t2
1, 2 and 3	1, 2 and 3	1, 2 and 3	1, 2 and 3
W1	W1	W1 and W2	W1 and W2

Additional
requirements

* FACTORS AFFECTING
  CULTIVATION

g
b   *Downgrade Class I to II*
o
s
v   *Class VI*
r

* PERMEABILITY

        3 to 20 – otherwise
               class IV
        Not applicable to
        basalts or norites

* EROSION

     Class: I   : 1
            II   : 1; 2
          III   : 1; 2; 3

* 't' FACTORS

     Class: II   : t1
         III   : t1; t2
        IV   : t1; t2

* WETNESS

     Class: II   : w1
         III   : w1
       IV   : w2
        V   : w3

*w2 downgrades Class II
and III to IVw unless the
land is already Class IV
on code, in which case it
remains as Class IV.*

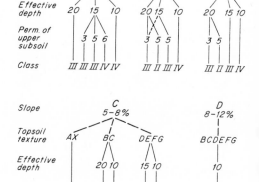

The effective depth is given in inches

* NOTE

     *Any land not meeting the
minimum requirements
shown on this sheet is
Class VI.*

FIGURE 9.3   *A chart for the systematic determination of Capability Class
Re-drawn from a chart of the Planning Branch, Department of Conservation,
Federal Government of Rhodesia and Nyasaland*

The minimum requirements for each class in the Israeli system are shown in table 9.7 and for the Philippines system in table 9.8.

TABLE 9.7 *Criteria for arable land classes in Israel*

Class (see table 9.1)	Slope (see table 9.5)	Erosion (see section 9.2.3)	Depth (see table 9.2)	Texture (see table 9.3)	Stoniness (see section 9.2.3)
I	Not steeper than 2%	Not more than category 1	More than 1000 mm	Sandy loam or heavier	Not more than category 2
II	6%	category 3	more than 750 mm	heavy sand or better	category 2
III	15%	category 3	more than 450 mm	do.	category 3
IV	35%	category 5	more than 450 mm	do.	category 3
V	—	category 7	—	do.	category 4
VI	—	category 5	—	do.	category 5
VII	—	category 5	—	do.	category 5

TABLE 9.8 *Criteria for arable land classes in Philippines*

Class (see table 9.1)	Slope (see table 9.5)	Erosion (see section 9.2.3)	Depth (see table 9.2)
A	Not steeper than 3%	Not more than category 1	More than 1500 mm
B	8%	category 2	1000 mm
C	15%	category 4	50 mm
D	25%	category 4	—

9.3 LAND USE PLANNING

An often quoted definition of planning is that 'Planning is the conscious process of selecting and developing the best course of action to accomplish an objective'. In the case of Land Use Planning the objective is the efficient intensive use of the land resources. It is difficult to imagine any field of human activity where some form of planning is not essential to achieve the objective. Consider going on holiday. Certainly it is possible to come home from work one evening, throw some clothes into a suitcase, go to the railway station and buy a ticket to the first holiday resort which comes to mind. Some fortunate people may indeed enjoy so unplanned a holiday but for most of us it would be disappointing to find oneself in a mountain holiday resort without climbing boots, or on a sunny beach with only winter clothing in the suitcase. No, one is more likely to achieve the objective of a happy holiday by a planned approach and this means going through a logical sequence of steps.

These are

1 Collecting the necessary facts
2 Analyzing the facts
3 Making decisions
4 Carrying out decisions
5 Assessing the results.

All five of these steps are essential both for our simple case of taking a holiday, or for planning the optimum use of thousands of hectares of land. Collecting the necessary facts for our holiday mean finding out how much leave we have due, how much money we can afford to spend, which holiday resorts are suitable, and a host of equally obvious items of basic data. Next we must analyze this data, sort it into groups of items which are related, like the cost per day, the number of days, and the total cost. This analysis will allow us to set up the alternatives— 10 days in an expensive hotel at one resort or 20 days in a cheaper hotel at another. Now we are in a position to take the third step—making the decision. In doing this we have to balance what is theoretically desirable, what is practically possible, and what is inadequate. The right decision is unlikely without the previous steps of collecting the data, and sorting it out. Next we carry out the decision by going on holiday, and finally we evaluate it. We consider 'was it worth it?' and 'would I go there again?', or perhaps only learn from the experience how to do it better next time.

In agricultural development also there is the unplanned approach of rushing in and starting schemes with no surveys, no pilot trials, and no data collection, or the planned approach to land use. In the planned approach the first step of collecting the information about the land is to carry out surveys and measure the soil properties. Next the data is sorted and analyzed into the soil codes and the capability classes which are like a filing system for the data. When the land has been investigated and classified the alternatives can be weighed up and the decisions made. Then comes the fourth step of carrying out the plan, and finally assessing the result to see if the objective has in fact been achieved. Governments seem particularly liable to forget that carrying out the plan does not automatically mean achieving the objective. The last stage of evaluation is as vital as any other, for there may have been some unknown factor which has prevented the plan from working.

Land Capability Classification is a tremendously valuable tool in land use planning for it ensures the logical and systematic collection of data about the soil, and presents the results in a form most useful to the planner. Of course it is not the whole story of land use—there are the economic, political and social spheres which must also be investigated, but it does provide what has been so badly needed in the past— a logical method for deciding the most appropriate agricultural use of land.

References

JACKS, G. V. 1946 Land Classification for Land Use Planning. *Technical Communication* 43, *Imperial Bureau of Soil Science*

KLINGEBIEL, A. A. and P. H. MONTGOMERY 1961 Land Capability Classification *Agricultural Handbook* 210, *United States Department of Agriculture, Soil Conservation Service*

RAYCHAUDHURI, S. P. and R. S. MURTAY 1969 Land Classification for Agricultural Development. *Indian Journal of Agronomy*, 7, 172–181

STALLINGS, J. H. 1957 *Soil Conservation*. Prentice-Hall, Englewood Cliffs, New Jersey

UNITED STATES DEPARTMENT OF AGRICULTURE 1951 Soil Survey Manual *Agricultural Handbook* 18

VINCENT, V. 1962 The Planning Procedures of the Federal Department of Conservation and Extension—Ranch Planning. *African Soils*, 7, 7–17

A Selection of references to classification systems in different countries

AUSTRALIA, *Agricultural Land Classification for New Guinea Land Resource Surveys*, HAANTJENS, H. A., Technical Memorandum CSIRO, Division of Land Research, Canberra 1965

CANADA, Soil Rating and Classification for Irrigation Lands in Western Canada. BOWSER, W. E. and H. C. MOSS *Canadian Journal of Agricultural Science*, 30, 165–171 1950

FEDERATION OF RHODESIA AND NYASALAND, Classification methods, criteria, terminology and scales used for Land Use Planning and Mapping. *African Soils* 7, 121–146 1962

GREAT BRITAIN, Agricultural Land Classification. *Technical Report* 11, *Agricultural Land Service*, Ministry of Agriculture, Fisheries and Food 1966

INDIA, *Soil Survey Manual*, RAYCHAUDHURI, S. P. India Agricultural Research Institute, New Delhi 1958

ISRAEL, *Soils of Israel and their Land Use Capabilities*, GIL, N. and ROSENSAFT, Z. Publication 54, Ministry of Agriculture 1955

MALAYSIA, *Land Capability Classification in West Malaysia—An Explanatory Handbook*. ECONOMIC PLANNING UNIT, Department of Prime Minister, Kuala Lumpur 1967

NEW ZEALAND, Soil Capability Classification based on the Genetic Soil Map. CUTLER, E. J. B. *Transactions of International Soil Conference, New Zealand*, 743 1962

PHILIPPINES, *Handbook of Soil Survey for the Philippines*, BARRERA, A. Bureau of Soils, Department of Agriculture and Natural Resources, Manila 1961

REPUBLIC OF SOUTH AFRICA, A Simplified Soil Survey Procedure for Farm Planning, LOXTON, R. F., *Science Bulletin* 383, *Department of Agriculture Technical Services* 1966

SARAWAK, *Soil and Land Potential in the Serian Development Area*, ANDRIESS, J. P. Soils Research Division, Department of Agriculture, Sarawak 1964

UNITED STATES OF AMERICA, Land Capability Classification, KLINGEBIEL, A. A. and P. H. MONTGOMERY, *Agricultural Handbook* 210, United States Department of Agriculture, Soil Conservation Service 1961

UNITED STATES OF AMERICA, *Land Classification Handbook.* Bureau of Reclamation Manual, Vol. V, United States Department of Interior 1953

Chapter 10 The universal soil-loss equation

10.1 THE EQUATION

Land management is the science of selecting the most appropriate agricultural use for land. Crop management is the more detailed management of the crops grown on land selected as arable. The two are complementary, but to be effective crop management must follow correct land management.

A methodical system of classification such as Land Capability Classification will indicate in general terms the kind of land use, but within the bracket 'arable farming' wide variations of detail are possible. Different ways of cropping can have very large effects on the amount of soil erosion, and a numerical assessment of the soil loss under particular management practices is a useful weapon in the armoury of the soil conservationist.

Attempts have been made for years to quantify the erosion effect of cropping practices in a numerical form which would allow erosion to be predicted for given circumstances. The accumulation of knowledge in the United States has made it possible for their Conservation Service to do this with the Universal Soil-Loss Equation (USDA, ARS *Agricultural Handbook* 282 1965).

Soil erosion is influenced by many different variables. The essence of the Universal Soil-Loss Equation is to isolate each variable and reduce its effect to a number so that when the numbers are multiplied together the answer is the amount of soil loss. This sounds simple enough, but the difficulty lies in progressing from a qualitative assessment of a variable (such as that soil x is more erodible than soil y) which is often observable, to a quantitative measure of the effect (such as that the soil loss from soil x is 1·43 times that from soil y), which can only be established after it has been measured.

The equation is presented in the form

$$A = R \times K \times L \times S \times C \times P$$

where A is soil loss in tons per acre

R is the rainfall erosivity index—a number which indicates the erosivity of the rain on a scale based on the EI_{30} index described in section 4.3.1.

K is the soil erodibility factor—a number which reflects the liability of a soil type to erosion. The units depend upon the amount of soil loss occurring per unit of erosivity R under specified standard conditions.

L is the length factor—a ratio which compares the soil loss with that from a field of specified length of 72·6 ft (22·6 metres).

S is the slope factor—a ratio which compares the soil loss with that from a field of specified slope (9 per cent).

C is the crop management factor—a ratio which compares the
soil loss with that from a field under a standard treatment
(cultivated bare fallow).

P is the conservation practice factor. A ratio which compares
the soil loss with that from a field with no conservation practice
(ie ploughing up and down the steepest slope).

10.2 APPLICATIONS OF THE EQUATION

Before considering the details of these variables it is worth looking at
the uses of this numerical equation. There are two main applications.

10.2.1 To predict soil erosion losses

In a given situation the value of each factor in the equation is fixed—
that is here is a field, of a certain soil, known length of slope and steepness, with a certain crop pattern. For each of these variables the
appropriate numerical value is selected, and when multiplied together
they give the amount of erosion which the equation predicts will occur
in this particular situation. That is, we know all the terms on the right
hand side so the equation can be solved for A. We can also predict
how much the soil loss will change if we alter the value of any of the
variables.

10.2.2 To choose agricultural practices

In this case the left hand side of the equation, the erosion A, is made
equal to the maximum soil loss which is considered acceptable. On the
right hand side of the equation some factors represent variables which
cannot be controlled, such as the erosivity R, the erodibility K, and the
land slope S, and so the value of these is already determined. The other
factors on this side represent the variables where there is a choice of
different cropping systems, of different methods of ploughing and so
on. The equation allows a choice to be made of various combinations
of these factors so that the equation is in balance, ie, so that the erosion
will not exceed the target figure. This application is useful to advisors
making recommendations to farmers on crop management.

The kind of solution produced by the equation might be—'Without
any conservation practice (ie, a high value of P) the rotation will have to
include a high proportion of forage crops (a low value of C is necessary
for the equation to balance) but if the land is terraced (thus reducing P)
the rotation could contain more cash crops (allowing a higher value of
C). There is no single absolute solution to the equation in the same
way that there is more than one answer on how to farm the land.

10.3 DEVELOPMENT OF THE EQUATION

The equation in its present form was not an instantaneous creation,
but rather evolved and developed as information became available

through research. The starting point for numerical expressions of erosion was probably ZINGG'S work (1940) when the effects of length of slope and degree of slope were evaluated. Soon after this SMITH (1941) defined the concept of a permissible soil loss, and made a first evaluation of a crop factor, and a factor allowing for different degrees of mechanical protection. BROWNING and co-workers in Iowa studied particularly the erodibility of soils, and the effect on erodibility of rotations and crop management (1947). About the same time a committee was appointed to integrate previous studies with information then coming forward about the importance of splash erosion. New values were used for several of the variables, and for the first time provision was made for variations in rainfall. The result was sometimes known as the *Musgrave Equation*, after the chairman of the committee, but more commonly as the *Slope-Practice Equation*, because the slope and the farming practice were two of the more important variables (MUSGRAVE 1947). The form of the equation was

E (erosion) $= T$ (soil type) $\times S$ (slope) $\times L$ (length) $\times P$ (agronomic practice) $\times M$ (mechanical protection) $\times R$ (rainfall).

After serving the SCS well for nearly 10 years it was replaced in the late fifties by the Universal Soil-Loss Equation which, like Wischmeier's EI_{30} index of erosivity, was a result of the Purdue study of all the available data from field experiment stations (WISCHMEIER *et al* 1958). Several refinements were added, particularly

1 the new erosivity index allowed much more accurately for variations in rainfall from one storm to another, or between seasons.
2 It also made it possible to identify local climates, and to allow for crop management techniques related to these.
3 The comparison of results from experiment stations on different soils extended the range of erodibility values, and these were redrawn on a new scale.
4 Allowance was made for inter-relations between some of the component parts of crop management such as the level of productivity, crop sequence in the rotation, and the management of residues.

10.4 THE BASIC EQUATION

Some of the factors used in the equation are measured in derived units, that is the units are specially made up for the purpose. They therefore need careful definition and explanation, but the equation is very simple once its structure and units are understood.

A is measured in tons per acre (short tons of 2000 lb) and is the annual soil loss which occur in the conditions defined by the terms of the equation. When the equation is used for the selection of suitable farming practices the value of A is the *soil-loss tolerance*, that is the greatest amount of erosion which can be tolerated without productivity declining. Values usually range from 1 to 5 tons per acre per year, and the grounds for choosing these figures were discussed in section 2.1.3.

The values of erosivity R are obtained (as explained in section 4.3.1) by computing the EI_{30} erosivity index from rainfall figures. To make the figures more manageable the annual values are divided by 100 and then plotted (figure 4.4) as *iso-erodents* on a map. Since the calculation is empirical the units of this scale of values is irrelevant and they can be considered as numbers. The range is from 62 to 220 in the North East of the United States, from 64 to 260 in the North Central region, and from 142 to 779 in the South East where the rain approaches tropical conditions.

The basic equation is $A = R \times K$

and since A and R have been defined, this establishes what is meant by K. The value of K for a given soil is such that when multiplied by the erosivity R, the product equals the annual soil loss from that soil under specified standard conditions. These standard conditions are a slope length of $72\frac{1}{2}$ ft on a slope of 9%, when the land use is a bare cultivated fallow with ploughing up and down the slope. These conditions may at first sight appear very arbitrary, ie why $72\frac{1}{2}$ ft instead of a round figure like 100? They arise because these were the conditions which most often occurred on the plots of the field experiment stations whose measured soil losses provide the basic data. A plot size of $\frac{1}{100}$ acre was convenient, and so was a plot width of 6 ft, and this gave a plot length of $72\frac{1}{2}$ ft. The standard conditions are thus historical accidents and have no special significance.

When the data from the experiment stations was studied it was found that plots with these standard conditions were installed on 7 different soil types, and knowing A and R, the values of K could be calculated for each of these soils. On another 16 soils there were plots of the right length and slope but with slightly different cropping patterns. With some adjustment for the different cropping, K values could be obtained for these soils also. The values for these 23 soils range from 0·03 for Albia gravelly loam in New Jersey, to 0·69 for Dunkirk silt loam in New York. Given an accurate assessment over a range of 23 soils it was possible to extrapolate this information and deduce by comparison the erodibility of other common soil types. Values are now tabulated for most common American soils.

10.5 SUBSIDIARY FACTORS

The other factors in the equation are subsidiary to the basic equation and they are all ratios which allow for conditions other than the standard conditions of the basic equation. To use slope as an example, the basic equation has built into it the assumption that the slope is 9%. If the actual slope is less than this (say 6%), the erosion will be less, and the slope factor in the equation will be a ratio to allow for this. Numerically it will be the fraction of the soil loss from a 6% slope divided by the soil loss from a 9% slope—all other conditions being held constant. Some idea of the magnitude of the subsidiary factors can be deduced by thinking whether the standard conditions represent average or extreme conditions. The conservation practices condition is ploughing up and down the slope. This is the worst erosion situation which can occur, so all values of the P factor can be expected to be less than unity. Similarly the crop condition of bare cultivated fallow is the most erodible situation imaginable and will cause erosion very much greater than normal crop rotations, so the values of C are very small fractions. The length of slope of $72\frac{1}{2}$ ft is perhaps shorter than the average horizontal interval between channel terraces but is fairly close to real situations. Similarly the standard slope of 9 per cent is a normal condition so the values of the factors for slope S and length L will be about unity but may be either above or below this value.

10.5.1 Slope S and length of slope L

Both of these two variables can be evaluated separately and so there could be separate numerical values for each. However when land has mechanical protection works the effective length of slope is the distance between channel terraces. This distance is designed as a function of the slope (section 8.3.1) and so the two variables are interconnected. It is therefore convenient to have a single factor LS to represent the effect of both in the equation, but to explain this combined factor it is easier to first consider each component separately.

Obviously the steeper the slope, the greater the erosion for a number of reasons. There is more splash downhill, there will be more run-off, and it will flow faster. Not surprisingly then the amount of erosion is not just proportional to the steepness of the slope, but rises rapidly as the slope increases as shown in figure 10.1. Mathematically the relation is

$$E \propto S^a$$

where E is the Erosion, S the Slope in per cent and a is an exponent.

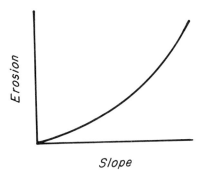

FIGURE 10.1   *The relationship between erosion and slope*

ZINGG (1940) analyzed the results of laboratory and field plot experiments and found a value for 'a' of 1·49. The Slope-Practice equation used $a = 1·35$ (MUSGRAVE 1947). WISCHMEIER (1958) found that the combined data from the USDA field experiments best fitted a slightly different form of equation,

$$E = 0·43 + 0·30S + 0·04S^2$$

where E is the soil loss in tons per acre, and S the slope in per cent, but this expression also gives a very similar shape of curve.

There is some evidence that in the more extreme erosion conditions of the tropics, the slope effect is more exaggerated than in America, and that a figure of about 2 is more appropriate for the exponent, ie,

$$E \propto S^2 \quad \text{(HUDSON and JACKSON 1959)}.$$

The length of slope has a similar effect on soil loss. On a long slope there is a bigger build up of the amount of surface run-off and its velocity and depth. This will lead to scour erosion which would not occur on a shorter length of slope, or where the effective down-hill slope is reduced to the distance between channel terraces. In this case when expressing the soil loss as a function of length of slope it is necessary to differentiate between *total* soil loss and the soil loss *per unit area*, for the longer slope will have a greater total soil loss just because it is bigger. Thus in Zingg's expression

$$X = CL^n$$

X is the total soil loss, C a constant, L is the length of slope, and n an exponent, Zingg's value for n was 1·6 but X is the total soil loss. In the more usual form

$$E \propto L^b$$

where E is the soil loss per unit area, then the value of b would be 0·6 for Zingg's data and the form would be as in figure 10.2. Again, the indications are that in tropical conditions the effect is more pronounced and a higher value of the exponent is appropriate (HUDSON 1957).

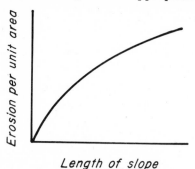

Length of slope

FIGURE 10.2   *The relationship between erosion and length of slope*

In the Universal Soil-Loss Equation a combined factor is used for slope length and steepness as in figure 10.3. The standard conditions are 9% slope and length of 72½ ft so at this point on the graph the ratio is unity. Entering the graph for any other values of slope and length gives the *LS* ratio which is to be applied in the equation.

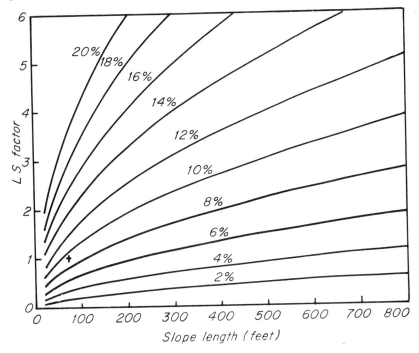

FIGURE 10.3   *The combined Slope-Length factor*

10.5.2   **Crop management *C***

This factor is at the same time the most complicated, because there is an almost infinite number of different ways of managing the growing of crops, and also the factor which is evaluated in most detail, because there is a wealth of experimental evidence available about the effects of crop management on soil loss. In the early systems, such as the Slope-Practice Equation, a single value for the crop factor was used to give the average effect over the whole season. All the common crops and rotations were tabulated against values for *C*, and tables were produced for local regions so that the cropping practices important in the region could be specified in detail.

However there are clearly major interactions between crop management and climate. For example a period in spring when the soil is newly ploughed and without any plant cover is going to be dangerous if the spring rains are highly erosive, but less important if the spring rains are gentle. Similarly the effect on erosion of the state of the ground after harvest in the autumn will depend on whether or not the autumn rains are severe.

In the Universal Soil-Loss Equation a procedure is adopted to allow for such effects. Ordinarily an annual value of the C factor is multiplied by an annual value of the rainfall factor R, that is each is averaged for the whole year before they are combined. However it is equally possible to divide the growing season into periods and multiply C and R values for each period, averaging the products to get the annual combined effect. Mathematically the effect is the same, ie

$$C \times R = c_1 r_1 + c_2 r_2 + c_3 r_3 \quad \text{etc.}$$

Five crop stage periods are used, and the length of some of them can be varied for different crops.

Period F Rough Fallow—from ploughing to seeding.
Period 1 Seedling—from seed-bed preparation to 1 month after planting.
Period 2 Establishment, from 1 to 2 months after spring or summer seeding.
Period 3 Growing and Maturing crop, from end of period 2 to crop harvest.
Period 4 Residue or Stubble. From crop harvest to ploughing.

An example using figures from *Agricultural Handbook* 282 will demonstrate the calculations. For a maize crop in North Carolina the dates for the 5 crop stage periods might be

Period F Fallow—from previous years autumn ploughing on 15 October to spring discing and harrowing on 10 March.
Period 1 Seedling. 10 March—10 April
Period 2 Establishment 10 April—10 May
Period 3 Growing 10 May to harvest on 15 August
Period 4 Residue from harvest to autumn ploughing on 15 October.

The cumulative distribution curve of erosivity during the year is plotted for 33 geographical regions, and the example shown in figure 10.4 is curve No. 28 for parts of South Carolina, North Carolina and Virginia. The percentage of erosivity for each period is found from the difference in the cumulative erosivity at the beginning and end of the period. For example at the beginning of Period 1 on 10 March the erosivity is 8 per cent and at the end of the period on 10 April it is 14 per cent. The difference of 6 per cent is the figure entered in Column 3 of the calculation shown in Table 10.1. The value for the fallow period is the sum of two parts—from 15 October to the end of the year (from 90 to 100) and from January to 10 March (from 0 to 8).

The proportional values of C, ie, the value to use for each period, are tabulated in *Agricultural Handbook* 282 which lists 128 possible cropping practices. For the crop in this example, maize, there are 60

TABLE 10.1 *Calculation of annual value of the crop practice factor* C

1	2	3	4	5
			Propor-tional C	*Total C* *Col 3 × Col. 4*
Period	*Dates*	*% Erosivity*[1]		
F Fallow	Oct. 15–Mar.10	90–100 18[2] 0–8	10	180
1 Seeding	Mar. 10–Apr. 10	8–14 = 6	28	168
2 Establishment	Apr. 10–May 10	14–20 = 6	19	114
3 Growing & Maturing	May 10–Aug. 15	20–67 = 47	12	564
4 Residue or Stubble	Aug. 15–Oct. 15	67–90 = 23	18	414
	Totals	100		1440

Annual C 0·144

[1] Erosivity values taken from figure 10.4.
[2] The fallow period erosivity is calculated as two parts; from 15 October to 31 December (from 90 to 100%) and from 1 January to 15 March (from 0 to 8%).

sets of values for different ways the crop might be grown. If it were 1st year maize after a grass and legume lay there are 12 alternatives, 6 for conventional tillage, (ie, clean cultivation) and 6 for minimum tillage. The 6 alternatives at this stage correspond with alternative levels of fertility which are defined by the crop yields of hay and maize. In our example, if the maize yield were over 75 bushels, and the hay yield 2½ tons, with conventional tillage, then the *C* values would be— Period *F* 10, Period 1 28, Period 2 19, Period 3 12 and Period 4 18, and these are the values entered in column 4 of table 10.1.

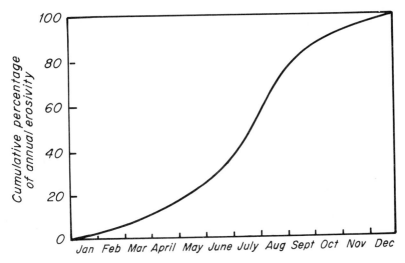

FIGURE 10.1 *The distribution of erosivity during the year*

All probable crop practices can be allowed for in this method. For example if the crop residues are removed at the time of harvest there will be less protection for the soil, and the C value for Period 4 (residue or stubble) would be increased from 18 to 40. If, after this corn crop, the land is going down to grass, and the grass can be seeded immediately after harvest, then the autumn cover will be better than the maize residues, and the C value would reduce from 18 to 11.

The tabulated list of common rotations and practices cannot cover all possibilities so a supplementary list is provided of suggestions as to how approximate values of C could be estimated by an experienced extension advisor to cover every conceivable crop situation.

Returning to the calculation in table 10.1 the products of proportional C and proportional R for each period are entered in column 5 and summed for the year. In both columns 3 and 4 the figures are entered as whole numbers although they are really percentages, and so the final total of 1 440 is divided by 10 000 to give the final annual value of 0·144. This is the factor to be used in the equation. In a rotation which spans several years a similar calculation would be carried out to give a C value averaged over the whole rotation.

10.5.3   Conservation practice P

The standard conditions assumed in the basic question are that bare fallow is cultivated straight up and down the steepest slope. This is of course the worst possible erosion situation and so the P factor consists of a ratio by which the erosion will be reduced from the theoretical loss in this worst case.

The Universal Soil-Loss Equation is designed for use in a sophisticated agriculture where proper conservation practices can be expected as the normal order of things. The practice of ploughing, planting, and tilling on the contour is widespread, but the effectiveness of this alone varies according to slope. Observation and experiment indicate that contouring is most effective on middle range slopes from 2 to 7 per cent, and less effective on flatter slopes, and on steeper slopes. The P values adopted for contour cultivation without other mechanical protection works are given in table 10.2.

TABLE 10.2   *Values of conservation practice factor* P

Slope %	P value
1 to 2	0·60
2 – 7	0·50
7 – 12	0·60
12 – 18	0·80
18 – 24	0·90

Contour listing, that is throwing up small ridges while cultivating on the contour, is even more effective, but the effect only lasts until the ridges are flattened by subsequent cultivation. If listing is practiced the P value may therefore be reduced by 50% but only for the crop stage periods when the ridges will be effective.

Terracing or contour ridging is the normal practice when erosion is serious and the land slope more than about 2% so this must be reflected in the P factor. However, the spacing of such works is, as we have already seen, dependent upon the steepness of the slope and so the effective length of slope is also reduced. The procedure is to use the same P value as for contour cultivation alone, and then use an LS factor appropriate to the spacing between the terraces.

10.6   EXAMPLES OF USING THE EQUATION

10.6.1   To predict erosion

This is the simplest application of the soil-loss equation, and consists of calculating the predicted erosion when all conditions are known. Sample values might be

Rainfall index $R = 300$
Soil erodibility $K = 0.33$
Field slope 4 per cent
Length of slope 600 ft LS factor $= 1.0$
Conservation practices   0.5
Cropping practice   0.2
Then $A = R \times K \times LS \times C \times P$
$ = 300 \times 0.33 \times 1.0 \times 0.2 \times 0.5$
$ = 10$ tons per acre per year.

10.6.2   To select crop management practices

An example will illustrate this application. A farmer has asked for advice on management for a particular field. The fixed factors are:

        The rainfall index for this district is 300
        The soil erodibility index is 0.33
        The field slope is 6 per cent
        The field length is 200 ft
        The soil-loss tolerance is 5 tons/acre/year.

The basic equation is $A = R \times K = 300 \times 0.33 = 100$

which means that for a standard plot ($72\frac{1}{2}$ ft long and 9% slope) under bare fallow and no conservation practices, the erosion would be 100 tons/acre/year. For this particular field $S = 6$, $L = 200$ and hence (from figure 10.3) the LS ratio is 0.95, so the erosion under the standard management is 95 tons/acre/year. Substituting the soil-loss tolerance for A the equation now becomes

$$5 = 95 \times C \times P$$

If the farmer is unwilling to put any conservation protection practices then P will remain 1, and $C = \frac{5}{95} = 0.053$. This means the erosion will be excessive under any crop practice whose C value is more than 0.053. To achieve such a low C value would require almost continuous forage crops with hardly any cash crops so that solution is not very practicable.

If the farmer agrees to contour cultivation, P would become 0.5, and

$$C = \frac{5}{95 \times 0.5} = 0.106.$$

Any rotation whose C value is less than this value is possible, and a large range of possible rotations could be used.

If the farmer agrees to contour cultivation and channel terraces the P value remains 0.5 but the value of LS is reduced. If the spacing between terraces were 100 feet, the LS value becomes 0.65, and so the equation becomes

$$5 = 300 \times 0.33 \times 0.65 \times 0.5 \times C$$

hence $C = 0.15$.

At this value an even wider choice of rotations is available to the farmer. In this example the conservation officer would encourage the farmer to adopt channel terraces and then check that the C value of the chosen rotations does not exceed 0.15.

Since the solution of the equation consists of a series of simple multiplications special-purpose slide-rules can be constructed for the purpose, and two examples are illustrated in plate 10.1.

10.6.3   To predict erosion from catchments

Several attempts have been made to use the Universal Soil-Loss Equation for estimating the amount of soil erosion lost from small catchments (BEER *et al* 1966) or the amount of sediment in streams. This is not likely to be successful for two reasons. First, the equation considers only the factors influencing the soil lost from arable land, and takes no account of the possibility of the soil being redeposited within the catchment. Secondly it only attempts to predict splash, sheet, and rill erosion from arable land with no consideration of gully erosion, streambank erosion, or erosion from non-arable land within the catchment.

10.7   MODIFICATIONS FOR OTHER COUNTRIES

10.7.1   The principles

It is clear that the Universal Soil-Loss Equation is a very sophisticated method of making effective use of the vast amount of information on

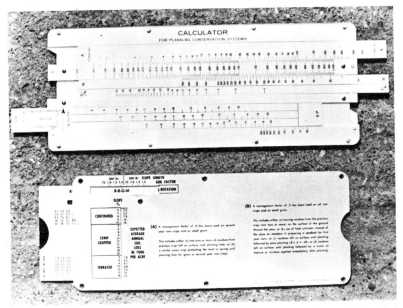

PLATE 10.1 *Examples of special purpose slide rules for the rapid solution of the Universal Soil-Loss Equation*

the erosion process which has been collected in the United States during the operation of a massive research programme over fifty years. Indeed this account has only described the main features of the application of the equation, and readers wishing to pursue the subject in depth should refer to the USDA publications quoted. What is perhaps more important to the rest of the world is how the basic principles of the equation can be applied in countries which do not have this vast accumulation of research data, but which desperately need some working guide lines to achieve the same objectives as the Universal Soil-Loss Equation—ie, to predict erosion in given conditions, and to select practices which will best reduce or minimize erosion. The important thing is to use whatever information is already available, while leaving room for the system to be improved or modified as new information comes from research.

Let us consider how the principles of the soil-loss equation could be applied by the conservation service of a developing country. For each of the terms in the equation $A = R \times K \times LS \times C \times P$ it is possible to use available knowledge to set up a scale of values, even if only a rudimentary scale with one or two steps. Consider the tolerable soil loss A. In the United States the range of values used is only from 1 to 5 tons per acre (2 to 11 tons/hectare) per year, so it is not difficult to guess a suitable value for use in another country; for a shallow erodible sandy soil where a little erosion will greatly reduce the productivity a low value of 2 or 3 would be suitable (about 4 to 6 tons/hectare). A very deep fertile loam, derived in situ from volcanic rock formations, is a situation which occurs in Kenya in Africa but is outside the range of American conditions, and so a value of 6 or 7 would be appropriate (about 13 to 15 tons/hectare). In Rhodesia a simple two-stage scale is used—4 tons per acre per year for the lighter sandy soils, and 5 tons per acre per year for the heavier clay soils.

Similarly for the rainfall erosivity factor R there is always some information which can be usefully applied. If sufficient rainfall records are available, it is straightforward to calculate R values for each station, and draw on a map the areas for which the station is representative. Even if rainfall data of the required kind is not available, there will be sufficient evidence to divide the territory up into a number of rainfall regions. If the relative erosivity of the rainfall in each region can be compared then this gives a simple scale of R values. Even if a numerical comparison is not possible we could use a different equation in each region and so make effective use of the knowledge that because the rainfall varies, so will the erosion and the required control measures.

In the basic equation the numerical value of erodibility K is chosen arbitrarily so that the equation balances. A few simple field experiments will easily give a first approximation to the actual soil loss for given soil and crop conditions. If there is no time or money for an experimental programme, a study of the published data from the experiments which have been carried out in every continent will give enough guidance for a good guess. This may not sound very scientific but it is no good waiting for 50 years research before tackling present problems. A sensible intelligent guess will serve until it can be replaced by a more accurate measurement. It should be remembered that although the USDA now lists K values for several hundred soil types, these stem from measurements on only 23 soils. The extension from these 23 is based more than anything else on the pooled judgment of panels of experienced field workers. This principle of getting a little factual evidence and stretching it to its limits (and beyond) by shared experience is one which must be used in the developing countries.

The factors for slope S, and length of slope L present no problems. The basic equations $E \propto S^{1 \cdot 5}$ and $E \propto L^{0 \cdot 5}$
are well tried and tested and will serve in most situations, until local experiments produce other results.

The effect of conservation practices is not likely to vary from one country to another. The practices themselves may be different, and the design and construction methods for mechanical protection works, but the American values of P for contouring, terracing etc., could certainly be adopted until local experience suggests improvements.

The effect which is going to be entirely local is the crop management factor C. The details of the cropping practices in the United States system relate to complicated rotations over 4 and 5 years, at very high levels of production, and using the most sophisticated tillage techniques and equipment. In most other countries where soil erosion is a major problem none of these conditions apply, and a completely different set of conditions have to be represented. A useful approach would be to first identify the main groups of practices which have different effects on erosion. Plantation crops which remain on the land for several years provide on the whole good cover and so suffer relatively little erosion. On the other hand annual cash crops are usually associated with high erosion risks. A third group might be irrigated crops on levelled terraces and padi rice where the erosion should be very low. In any country some broad divisions like this could easily be defined. Within each of these groups the more detailed crop management practices can be listed and their effects on erosion either estimated or measured. For plantation crops the worst erosion risk is during the years of establishment. Is the tea planted on bare soil (high C)—or in patches cleared in the existing vegetation? (reduced C) or with a grass mulch applied? (very low C). Measurements by field experiments are the ideal on which to base a table of C values, but an estimate by field advisory officers is better than nothing. The beauty of the Universal Soil-Loss Equation is that although it was designed for the special conditions of America, it happens, because of its logical structure, to establish a methodical approach which can be followed in any country or in any situation. And the great merit of the system is that it can make use of whatever local knowledge, experience, or research is available. It can be progressively refined as further knowledge is gained, but it can start being applied at a very simple level.

10.7.2 A case study

There is an interesting example of an application of the principles of the soil loss equation in which the end product is so different that it is not immediately obvious that it is in fact a modified soil-loss equation. A study of the rainfall pattern of the country showed that there was considerable variation in the mean annual rainfall but that the regions of lower rainfall had on the whole a poorer vegetation cover and a lot of heavy storms early in the season. There seemed to be a similar erosion risk whatever the annual rainfall so it was decided to not have any variations—in effect to have a single R value for the whole country.

It was also possible to eliminate the length of slope factor L and the conservation practices factor P. The official policy was to build channel terraces on all arable land with appreciable slopes, and this had been carried out on most arable land. The spacing between the terraces being a function of slope, the length L is not required as a separate variable.

The equation

$$A = R \times K \times L \times S \times C \times P$$

has therefore been reduced, by making $R = 1$, $L = 1$ and $P = 1$, to

$$A = K \times S \times C$$

This means that for the given conditions specified the erosion will be a function of soil type, slope and crop management.

The soils of the country could be divided into two main groups, and there was a strong correlation of soil and cropping practice, at least in the plantation farming sector of the agricultural industry. The group of light sandy soils was particularly suitable for growing tobacco, whereas the heavier red clay and clay loam soils were better for maize and other grain crops and cash crops. The effect of variability of soil on erosion can therefore be taken care of by having one equation for sandy soils, ie, where $K = K_1$ for sand, and another equation where $K = K_2$ for clay.

The two remaining variables, slope S and cropping practice C can now be connected with erosion by diagrams which give the variation in erosion for various degrees of slope under any particular crop management practice. The examples shown in figure 10.5 relate to maize where the effect of several management factors such as plant population and fertilizer application can be combined into the single assessment of crop yield. Other curves of similar form would be required for each crop or each management variation. Some hard facts from field experiments are necessary to provide a base (or in mathematical terms to determine the constants a and b in $E = aS^b$) but once one particular practice has been measured then estimates of many others can be made by comparison.

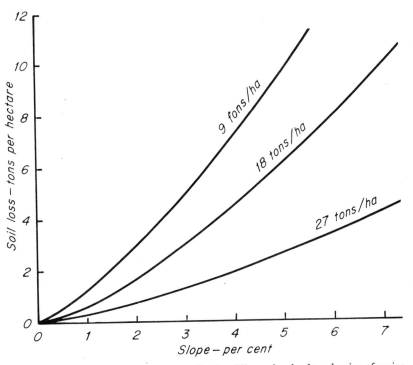

FIGURE 10.5   *The effect of slope on erosion for different levels of production of maize*

References

BEER, C. E., C. W. FARNHAM and H. G. HEINEMAN 1966 Evaluating Sediment Prediction Techniques in Western Iowa. *Transactions of the American Society of Agricultural Engineers*, 9, 6, 828–831, 833

BROWNING, G. M., C. L. PARISH and J. A. GLASS 1947 A method for determining the use and limitation of rotation and conservation practices in control of soil erosion in Iowa. *Journal of the American Society of Agronomy*, 39, 65–73

HUDSON, N. W. 1957 Erosion Control Research—Progress Report on Experiments at Henderson Research Station, 1953–56. *Rhodesia Agricultural Journal* 54, 4, 297–323

HUDSON, N. W. and D. C. JACKSON 1959 *Results achieved in the Measurement of Erosion and Run-off in Southern Rhodesia.* Paper presented to the Third Inter-African Soils Conference, Dalaba 1959

MUSGRAVE, G. W. 1947 Quantitative Evaluation of Factors in Water Erosion—A First Approximation. *Journal of Soil and Water Conservation* 2, 133–138

SMITH, D. D. 1941 Interpretation of Soil Conservation Data for Field Use. *Agricultural Engineering*, 22, 173–175

WISCHMEIER, W. H. and D. D. SMITH, 1965 Predicting Rainfall—Erosion losses from Cropland East of the Rocky Mountains. *Agricultural Handbook 282, Agricultural Research Service, United States Department of Agriculture*

WISCHMEIER, W. H., D. D. SMITH and R. E. UHLAND 1958 Evaluation of Factors in the Soil-Loss Equation. *Agricultural Engineering*, 39, 8, 458–462, 474

ZINGG, A. W. 1940 Degree and Length of Land Slope as it affects Soil Loss in Run-off. *Agricultural Engineering* 21, 59

Chapter 11   Control of erosion by crop management

11.1   The importance of the effect of crop management

The orderly arrangement of all the factors affecting erosion into the universal soil-loss equation provides an opportunity to compare the relative importance of each factor in the control of erosion. Some items affect the amount of erosion but are outside man's control. The regulation or alteration of rainfall (for example by the seeding of rainclouds) is a very inexact science still in its infancy so for practical purposes the erosivity value R is fixed. The value of K reflects the fundamental characteristics of a soil, not its management, and so this too is beyond our control. The slope of the land can be modified by major earth-moving practices, but apart from bench terracing and some very expensive land shaping techniques practised in America it is not generally practical to change the slope of arable lands, so S is usually also fixed.

This leaves as variables which can be altered the length of slope L, and the two management factors—the conservation practice P and the crop management C. The standard value for L is 1, and the range, for medium slopes, is from a little less than one to about 2 or $2\frac{1}{2}$. This means that if the length is reduced by terracing the soil loss will be roughly halved. Changes in conservation practice will cause reductions of the same order of magnitude. The worst practice corresponds with a P value of 1, and improved methods have values going down to 0·5—again a halving of the soil loss.

The effect of crop management is very different. The worst practice has a C value of 1, but good management techniques have C values down to 0·05. This means a reduction of erosion to one twentieth of the worst case. Clearly improved conservation practices like terracing are important, but good crop management can be up to ten times more effective in reducing the amount of erosion.

11.2   Erosion control by good farming

It is remarkable how often the management required for good erosion control coincides with intensive efficient profitable farming. There is no substance at all in the fear sometimes felt by farmers that conservation farming means restricted production or uneconomic practices.

This link between reduced erosion and improved farming can best be demonstrated by some examples. The first is the case of growing tobacco in the sub-tropics. The growing season for flue-cured tobacco is shorter than the rainy season, and the alternatives open to the grower are either to plant early and have the crop matured and harvested well before the end of the rains, or to delay planting so that the end of the harvesting coincides with the end of the rains. In either case there will be a period either at the beginning or at the end when there is poor vegetative cover and so high risk of erosion. Field experiments showed a soil loss of 2·1 tons per acre (4·7 metric tons per hectare) from the early planted crop compared with 3·9 tons per acre (8·7 metric tons per hectare) from the late planted crop (HUDSON 1957a). It was also found by the Tobacco Research Board that the yield and quality of the tobacco are better from the early planted crop, and so there was a direct link. The same practice was desirable both for erosion control and better crop management.

A similar situation exists in the case of the management of grazing land. This is discussed more fully in Chapter 13 but the main point is that in order to achieve maximum yield, whether of meat, wool, milk or any animal products, certain conditions are required: correct stocking rate, uniform distribution of grazing, optimum grass growth, and so on. Again these are precisely the things which are required for optimum soil conservation, and so good management equates with good erosion control.

Further evidence comes from experiments with maize production. Twenty years ago it was topical to classify crops as *soil-depleting* and *soil conserving* and to speak of *soil robbers* or *soil builders*. Fashions change slowly in agriculture and this concept is still alive today although it has little relevance in the modern agriculture of hybrid varieties, mechanization, and inorganic fertilizers. The fact is that it is not the crop which is or is not soil depleting but the crop management. Loss of fertility is not a question of *which* crop is grown but *how* it is grown. Certainly some crops will be particularly prone to erosion because of the way they are grown, like clean-tilled row crops. Other closely growing crops like grass will usually suffer less erosion. But these general trends can be quite overruled by the effect of management. Grass, if over-grazed and under-fertilized, can allow so much erosion that instead of being a soil builder the fertility actually declines. And maize can under suitable management both slow down erosion and raise the fertility as will be shown later in an example.

It is because the effect of the management has been confused with the effect of the crop, that erosion has quite unjustly been attributed to some crops, and this is the situation in the case of maize. When the virgin soils of Africa and America were first ploughed by immigrant farmers and cropped extensively to maize, the yields started high but soon fell away. The crop was always blamed but the real cause was that the plant nutrients were not properly replaced, the organic matter was run down, and in addition to the removal of these by the crop, there was uncontrolled erosion which washed away as much again.

In parts of central Africa a solution to the problem of declining yields was sought by introducing a rotation of maize alternating with a *green-manure* crop, that is a leguminous crop grown in order to be ploughed in to restore both the nitrogen and the organic matter. One crop commonly used was sunn-hemp (*Crotelaria juncea*) and usually sown fairly late during the season as earlier plantings suffered the disadvantages of being more subject to attack by pest and disease, and also to setting seed before the crop can be ploughed in. According to conventional agronomic theory the change from continuous maize to this rotation should be a major improvement. In fact it showed no real improvement in yield, and when detailed measurements were made of the erosion losses they were found to be even higher from the rotation than from the continuous maize (HUDSON 1957b). This resulted from the quite inadequate cover provided by the green-crop in mid-season at a time when the erosion hazard is high, and the attendant loss of fertility and organic matter quite offset the advantage of the green-manure crop.

This was a case of jumping out of the frying pan into the fire, and resulted from an incorrect diagnosis of the problem. To continue the medical simile the green crop was used as a tonic, not as a cure. When the real cause, poor crop management, was attacked a much more successful result was obtained. The soil and water losses were also measured from plots where maize was grown continuously both according to current practice, and also according to the practice recommended by the advisory services for maximum yield. The crop treatments and the soil and water losses are shown in table 11.1. Both the soil and water losses were reduced to something like one fifteenth by the improved crop management.

TABLE 11.1 *The effect of crop management on the soil and water losses from maize*

Plot A Maize at medium level of production		Plot B Maize at high level of production
25 000 plants/ha	Plant population	37 000 plants/ha
N 20 kg/ha	Fertilizer application	N 100 kg/ha
P_2O_5 50 kg/ha		P_2O_5 80 kg/ha
Removed	Crop residues	Ploughed in
5 ton/ha	Crop yield	10 ton/ha
250 mm	Run-off	20 mm
12·3 ton/ha	Soil Loss	0·7 ton/ha

Results for season 1954/55 (rainfall for the season 1130 mm)
From HUDSON 1957(b)

Again the management specification for good erosion control is exactly the same as for maximum production and maximum profits. The high applications of fertilizer mean a high investment cost, but are very well repaid by the higher yield, and the reduced costs of cultivating a smaller area for each ton of grain produced. The water balance is also much better in the case of the high-yielding crop. There is sometimes a reluctance on the part of farmers to aim for high yields on the theory that this might exhaust the available moisture and give a complete crop failure whereas a less ambitious crop might just get by and give some yield. This has been clearly disproved. The water consumption of a crop is determined more by climatic factors like incoming radiation than by the density of the crop, and a high yielding crop is the result of using water more efficiently rather than in greater quantity. Several examples of this are given by RUSSELL (1950). In the experiment of table 11.1, any increased use by the higher yielding crop will certainly be less than the 230 mm which become available when the run-off is reduced, and in fact the soil moisture status of this plot improved over the years (JACKSON 1958). As a result of returning to the soil the large quantity of crop residues from such a vigorous crop the organic matter was maintained. It did not increase because the rapid breakdown of organic matter in tropic soils makes it most unusual for this to happen, and to maintain it at a level comparable with a virgin soil is very satisfactory. In fact the effect of applying the maximum-yield crop management treatment for many years completely disproved the fallacy that continuous maize is necessarily a bad practice. In this case after 10 years the soil was in better condition physically than at the start of the experiment, the moisture status better, the yields maintained, and the soil loss during the whole period was of negligible proportions.

The beneficial result of producing grain at high rates of yield can be shown by a simple numerical example. Imagine that a village or district needs to produce each year for its own consumption and for sale 100 tons of grain. It can produce this at a low level of production, requiring a large area, and with resultant high soil loss, or the same total quantity of grain can be produced at a high yield, on a smaller area, and a total soil loss only a small fraction of the loss from the low yielding crop. Table 11.2 shows that the total soil loss could be reduced to something like one twenty fifth. It has been said that if all the maize grown in Africa were produced at an average yield of 5 tons per hectare instead of the present average of something like 1 ton per hectare, then half the erosion

TABLE 11.2   *The effect of the level of production on soil loss*

The soil lost during the production of 100 tons of grain might be		
at low level of yield		*at high level*
1	Yield of crop (ton/ha)	5
100	Area required (hectares)	20
50	Probable soil loss (ton/ha)	10
5 000	Total soil loss (tons)	200

In imperial units, 1 000 bushels at 20 bushels/acre would need 50 acres, losing perhaps 20 ton/acre—a total of 1 000 tons. At 100 bushels/acre it needs 10 acres losing 4 ton/acre—a total of 40 tons. The difference is 25 times.

problems of the continent would disappear. There may be a touch of poetic imagination in this view, but it is certainly true that the present erosion damage could be tremendously reduced by the general adoption of the basic rules of good agronomy.

11.3 THE PLACE OF ROTATIONS

The fact that in the example quoted the erosion from the alternative rotation of maize and green-manure crop was worse than that from continuous maize does not mean that rotations are undesirable or unnecessary. To maintain fertility by continuous monoculture at yields like 5 metric tons per hectare (80 bushels per acre) requires a high level of management, and incurs high capital and recurrent costs. It may be cheaper on a big commercial farm to apply nitrogen out of the bag than to grow a legume, but the peasant farmer often has no choice—he can only afford to ease the demand on his soil by manure from his animals and by rest crops and rotations. Apart from fertility there are other reasons why rotations may be desirable; a change of crop to break the build up of pest or disease, a change in rooting depth to vary the uptake of moisture or nutrients, a nurse crop to prepare the way for a subsequent crop, and many other reasons. Often the primary purpose of a rotation is to interrupt the progressive development of unfavourable features, for example the introduction of grass to restore structure.

It was found after over 30 years of field experiments in Iowa that although erosion losses were greatly reduced when maize was grown with high nitrogen applications, the losses were reduced still more by growing the maize in rotation with meadow (MOLDENHAUER *et al* 1967).

When considering the characteristics of rotations which are intended to help in the reduction of erosion, one of the main features appears to be that short rotations with quick changes are preferable to long-cycle rotations. In temperate climates the beneficial effects of grass on soil structure appear to result from the development of a crumb structure which builds up slowly but is very stable. When land has been down to a long grass ley which is ploughed out, and the land then put to arable crops, the structure will persist through several years of cropping. By contrast the beneficial effect on erosion which arises from grass or forage crops in tropical conditions appears to stem from a fairly loose aggregation rather than a tightly cemented crumb structure, and to hinge on coarse organic matter rather than humus, and to build up and break down quickly. Rotation experiments were carried out with some of the grasses commonly used in Africa, such as *Cynodon Plectostachyum* (Star grass in Africa, Bermuda grass in America) and *Pennisetum Purpureum* (Elephant grass or Napier Fodder) and *Eragrostis Curvula* (Weeping Lovegrass). These were tested in rotation with maize, tobacco, and forage crops, and one experiment was specially designed to test the effect on erosion of leaving the grass down for various lengths of time, and of cropping for various times after the grass was ploughed (HUDSON 1957b). Some of the results were as might be expected—the erosion fell off rapidly as soon as the grass was established and continued at a low level as long as the grass was continued. When the grass was replaced by maize there was a strong residual effect and erosion remained low. However, this effect was surprisingly short-lived. The erosion was low for one year only, with a lesser effect the second year, and none after that. This pattern was the same irrespective of how long the grass was maintained. The grass evidently built up a strong erosion resistance in the soil, but unlike the structure-building of temperate climates, this effect is built up quickly in a year or two, and it disappears equally rapidly. This leads to the conclusion that rotations planned to help in controlling erosion should be short, with quick changes from cash crop to forage crop and back again. The reduction in soil loss and run-off results from the free-draining open structure caused by the bulk organic matter, that is the decaying roots and leaves—the organic matter which can be *seen* in the soil and this builds up very rapidly. In the first year of grass 80% of the erosion resistance is acquired, and another 15% in the second year. From the erosion control point of view there is little advantage gained by continuing beyond two years. The breakdown of this coarse vegetal matter is equally rapid and so the cropping periods should also be of short duration.

An illustration of how this information can be applied in the planning of rotations is the combination of tobacco and grass. Tobacco lands are very subject to erosion. The quality of the crop deteriorates if it is grown in lush fertile conditions and it does best on poor sandy soils. It cannot stand wet conditions so is grown on graded ridges, and it is clean cultivated. It is also subject to infestation of the roots by eelworm (*nematode*) which builds up if the crop is grown too long on the same ground. Resistance to both erosion and nematode is gained by introducing pastures of lovegrass (*Eragrostis Curvula*) into the rotation. The two best alternative rotations are one year tobacco followed by two years of grass, or two years tobacco followed by four years of grass. Both have the same ratio of crop to grass and both are acceptable to the farmer, but they have a different resistance to erosion. Figure 11.1 shows the erosion losses for tobacco and grass, and using these figures table 11.3 shows that the loss from the short rotation is significantly better.

An interesting way of comparing the effectiveness of rotations is by considering at the same time the level of production and the amount of soil erosion. Several maize growing regimes were compared in this way (HUDSON and JACKSON 1959), using as the index of performance the grain yield (per year per unit area) divided by the weight of soil loss (per year per unit area). The differences between alternative practices are highlighted because the better practice has both a high yield in the top line and a low soil loss in the bottom line. Table 11.4 shows the results averaged over six years for three regimes on three slopes. It is strikingly apparent that the maize/green-manure rotation tested here

TABLE 11.3 *Erosion losses from alternative tobacco-grass rotations*

Losses (in tons/ha/year) for a 6% slope (from figure 11.1)

Rotation A	Soil loss		Rotation B	Soil loss
1st crop of tobacco	18		1st crop of tobacco	18
1st crop of grass	15		2nd crop of tobacco	45
2nd crop of grass	3		1st crop of grass	15
	—		2nd crop of grass	3
Total (3 years)	36		3rd crop of grass	3
	—		4th crop of grass	3
Annual Average	12			—
	—		Total (6 years)	87
			Annual average	14·75

The explanation is that the erosion increases more rapidly under successive tobacco crops than it decreases under successive grass crops (figure 11.1).

TABLE 11.4 *Comparison of maize growing regimes*

	6½% Slope			4½% Slope		
	Yield (kg/ha)	Soil loss (kg/ha)	Index	Yield (kg/ha)	Soil loss (kg/ha)	Index
ntinuous maize (high fertility) (1)	8 250	2 680	3·06	8 380	2 560	3·25
ntinuous maize (medium fertility) (2)	5 000	7 600	0·66	4 610	4 900	0·94
ernate maize and een-manure crop (3)	2 140	17 800	0·12	2 140	7 160	0·30

	3% Slope		
	Yield (kg/ha)	Soil loss (kg/ha)	Index
	8 430	2 240	3·75
	4 080	3 560	1·14
	1 780	4 930	0·36

1 37 000 plants per hectare. Maximum economic applications of fertilizer. Crop residues returned.
2 25 000 plants per hectare. Medium fertilizer application. Crop residues removed.
3 Maize as (2). Green-manure crop crotelaria. Planted mid-season. Whole crop ploughed under.

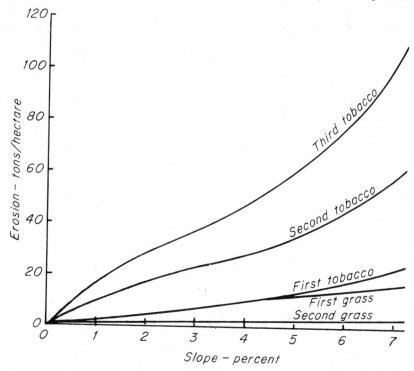

FIGURE 11.1   *The effect of slope on erosion for successive crops of tobacco and of grass*

is much inferior to the medium fertility continuous maize. However this particular rotation using a late-planted sunnhemp is by no means the best of the alternatives, and a different result would obtain if a green-manure crop were used which gave good protective cover early in the season. Also this limited comparison should not be taken as a justification for any kind of continuous growing of maize. A poor crop with low yield and high soil loss would be worse than any of these systems.

11.4   THE IMPORTANCE OF COVER

11.4.1   The experimental result

The dramatic reduction in erosion from a well-covered soil compared with a bare soil is clearly demonstrated in the experiment which was briefly mentioned in Chapter 4. Two small experimental plots, shown in plate 11.1 were 0·004 hectares ($\frac{1}{100}$ acre) in area, and 1·5 metres wide by 27·5 metres long (5 ft by 90 ft). Both were kept free of vegetation by hand weeding, and over one plot was suspended a double layer of fine-

PLATE 11.1   *Experimental plots showing the vital effect of cover. The covered plot on the right has lost no soil, the bare plot has lost a great deal*

mesh wire gauze. This allowed all the rain to pass through (this was measured by raingauges in each plot) but broke up the falling raindrops so that they reached the soil surface as small droplets. The two plots thus compare the effect of no protective cover with a 100% cover, and the resulting soil loss is shown in table 11.5. The soil loss from the bare plot is more than one hundred times that from the protected plot.

TABLE 11.5   *Soil losses from bare and covered soil*

	Plot covered by gauze	Bare plot
1953/54	Nil	146·2 ton/hectare
1954/55	2·0 ton/hectare	204·5 ton/hectare
1955/56	4·5 ton/hectare	135·6 ton/hectare
1956/57	0·2 ton/hectare	132·4 ton/hectare
1957/58	0·2 ton/hectare	49·5 ton/hectare
1958/59	2·5 ton/hectare	202·0 ton/hectare
1959/60	Nil	7·4 ton/hectare
1960/61	Nil	121·4 ton/hectare
1961/62	Nil	138·5 ton/hectare
1962/63	Nil	128·2 ton/hectare
10 year totals	9·4 ton/hectare	1265·7 ton/hectare

A vegetative cover as complete as the artificial cover of the wire gauze is only obtained from grass and forage crops. In the case of row crops only part of the soil is covered, and in the case of broadcast crops such as small grains the cover may be uniform but it is not dense, and so in both cases the effect of variations in the amount of cover is important. It is evident that small differences in cover can cause big differences in soil loss. Table 11.1 gave the results of a comparison of maize grown at two levels of production and the erosion differed 15 times. If differences of this size can occur with different densities of the same crop, then it is not surprising that there can be even bigger variations between different kinds of crop.

The reason why small changes of cover cause big changes in erosion becomes clear when the erosion process is analyzed. Erosion takes place from the soil which is damaged by the rain, and so the amount of erosion depends on how much of the soil is exposed, not on how much is covered. The point is best illustrated by example. Photographs were taken vertically downwards on various densities of crops at various stages of

growth and the percentage of the ground covered by the crop was measured on the photographs. Plate 11.2 shows the maize on the two plots of table 11.1, one with 24 000 plants per hectare, the other with 36 000 plants per hectare, both being planted at the same time and photographed at the same time after 6 weeks growth. Calculations on similar photographs showed that at 10 weeks the lower population covered 60% of the ground leaving 40% exposed. The higher population covers 90% of the ground, leaving 10% exposed. The cover is only increased by 50%, but the erosion is proportional to the bare ground and is reduced to one quarter. This was in fact precisely the long-term result of the experiment referred to in section 11.2, table 11.1 when erosion was measured from maize grown at these two populations. In individual years the difference was as much as 15 times as quoted in table 11.1 but the average over ten years was that the high population plot lost exactly one quarter of the soil lost from the lower population— corresponding precisely with the relative amounts of exposed soil.

A large reduction in erosion can thus result from quite small changes

PLATE 11.2 *Photographs taken vertically downwards show the difference in the amount of soil covered by maize at 24 000 plants per hectare (left), and 36 000 plants per hectare (right)*

in management practice. This argument should not be carried to extremes—it does not follow that a grass crop with 98% cover and 2% exposure will have twice the erosion of a crop with 99% cover and 1% exposure, for erosion would be insignificant in both cases with cover so dense. But in the range of cover which is most usual for arable crops, variations in the density of cover will influence erosion more than any other management factor.

11.4.2 Crop management for cover

Several principles of crop management emerge from this result, and a number of agronomic techniques have been developed to reduce erosion by ensuring adequate cover.

The example of increased density of cover from higher plant population referred to maize, but exactly the same argument applies, and similar experimental evidence is available for tobacco, cotton, sorghums, rice, groundnuts or any other cash crop. The combination of improved varieties, with enough fertilizer to get the best out of the variety, and dense stands lead at the same time to better crop, higher profits and reduced erosion.

However, annual crops cannot provide cover in the early season, in the young stages of growth. Protection at this time must be provided in other ways. Grass and forage crops grown in rotation will greatly lower the erodibility of the soil, and the same effect of increasing the bulky organic matter can also be achieved by returning to the land the crop residues from the previous years crop. Experiments were carried out by the author to measure whether there was any difference between the effect of spreading the crop residues on the surface compared with incorporating them into the soil by tillage. The technique of chopping the crop residues and spreading them on the surface soil is known as *stubble mulching* and was developed in North America originally as a defence against wind erosion in the grain-growing prairies. It was also later used against rain erosion, when it is equally effective as the surface mulch provides excellent protective cover. However there are disadvantages when the method is applied to row crops. It is difficult to arrive at the required state of a properly prepared seed bed with a layer of mulch on top. With some crops, like maize, it is possible to stockpile the crop, plough and prepare the soil, then spread the chopped crop residues on top after threshing, but this is very laborious. The alternative is to harvest the standing crop, leaving the stubble on the surface and then till the soil without inverting it, for example by chisel ploughs and tine cultivators so that the surface mulch is disturbed as little as possible. There are also the problems of planting through this surface mulch, and of controlling the weeds which grow through it. All of these problems can be overcome, and solutions and implements have been developed for the case of wind erosion control under small grains, but it is adding a number of unwelcome complications to the conventional manner of managing row crops. The alternative system tested was *trash farming*, that is harvesting the standing crop, then cutting and spreading the crop residues on the surface as in stubble mulching, and then plough- ing and cultivating in the normal manner. This means that the mulch is incorporated into the plough layer, with some buried and some show- ing at the surface. Field-scale tests on plots of 2 hectares showed that this method was much simpler, and cheaper to operate, but was just as effective as the surface mulch in reducing erosion to very low and quite acceptable levels. Evidently the combination of some trash on the surface giving top cover and some close to the surface giving an open texture and good drainage is as effective as having the mulch entirely on the surface. The problem of providing protection is most satis- factorily solved by a combination of trash farming and high-yield cropping. At the beginning of the season the trash is most effective, but the effectiveness declines as the trash decays, is buried during cultiva- tion and consumed by termites. At the same time the growing crop progressively takes over the job of providing the cover. The trash farming technique has proved to be extremely efficient and effective in many parts of Africa and is undoubtedly a most powerful measure for erosion control.

Many other variations have been developed, particularly in America. *Minimum tillage* is a general term covering several methods. One approach is to reduce the number of operations by planting directly after ploughing without any of the intervening cultivations which are usually carried out to give a fine seed bed. This is called *plow-plant* when the planters are attached to the back of the ploughs and the opera- tion is completed in one pass, or *plow* and *plant* when two passes are made, as when the ploughing is in autumn, and the planting in spring.

Sometimes planting directly onto roughly ploughed land full of crop residues causes problems. One solution, to provide smoother conditions for the planter to work in, is *wheel-track* planting. The spacing of the two front wheels of the tractor is set to the required row width, and the two rear wheels are mounted on extra-wide extensions of the half shafts so that a 4-row planter can be set to plant one row in each of the four wheel tracks. In this method the ploughing and planting are two separate operations.

An alternative way of reducing both the amount of tillage and the area of vulnerable soil is *strip planting*. Strips of soil are tilled, and the seed planted in the strips, leaving the space between rows untouched. The tilling and planting is usually done in a single pass and this method lends itself well to the use of rotary cultivators designed for the purpose. Other variations of minimum tillage include *listing* or planting in the bottom of furrows opened by a lister or ridger, and *mulch tillage* in which the crop residues are swept into bands and buried before the seed is planted.

The advantages claimed for these advanced tillage practices are that the number of operations can be reduced, and hence the cost. In some cases the number of implements required is less, although those which are used may be more complicated. Certainly the ability to select the best practice for given crop and soil should lead to more efficient production (LARSEN 1962). However, these factors are less significant outside of the very specialized agriculture of North America, and the other aspect, the effect on soil and water loss, is more important. The various methods have been tested on field plots with natural and artificial rain (MEYER and MANNERING 1961) and the answer is that the differences between the various methods is not significant, but that all of them greatly reduce soil loss compared with conventional crop management.

The detailed operation of these very advanced techniques will usually be quite inappropriate in the rest of the world, but the principles are just as applicable. The object of any crop management should be to ensure maximum incorporation of bulk organic matter, maximum protective cover, and avoiding at all costs the bare fine smooth tilth which is usually the desired objective in temperate climates.

References

HUDSON, N. W. 1957a Soil Erosion and Tobacco Growing. *Rhodesia Agricultural Journal* 54, 6, 547–555

HUDSON, N. W. 1957b Erosion Control Research. *Rhodesia Agricultural Journal* 54, 4, 297–323

HUDSON, N. W. and D. C. JACKSON 1959 *Results achieved in the measurement of Erosion and Run-off in Southern Rhodesia.* Paper presented to the Third Inter-African Soils Conference, Dalaba

JACKSON, D. C. 1958 Some preliminary indications of Soil Moisture Changes under Arable Crops. *Rhodesia Agricultural Journal* 55, 4, 426–438

LARSON, W. E. 1962 Tillage Requirements for Corn. *Journal of Soil and Water Conservation*, 17, 1, 3–7

MEYER, L. D. and J. W. MANNERING 1961 Minimum Tillage for Cover: Its Effect on Infiltration and Erosion. *Agricultural Engineering* 42, 2, 72–75, 86

MOLDENHAUER, W. C., W. H. WISCHMEIER and D. T. PARKER 1967 The Influence of Crop Management on Run-off, Erosion and Soil Properties of a Marshall Silty Clay Loam. *Proceedings of the Soil Science Society of America*, 31, 4, 541–546

RUSSELL, E. W. 1950 *Soil Conditions and Plant Growth*, 8th Edition. Longmans, Green, London

Chapter 12 Gully erosion

12.1 THE NATURE OF GULLY EROSION

Gully erosion is spectacular and widespread, and so it is often used by conservationists as a characteristic symptom of erosion. As a result there is a danger of its importance being over-emphasized. Certainly it is most important as a source of sediment in streams, but in terms of damage to agricultural land or reduction of agricultural production, it is usually not very important for the simple reason that most land subject to severe gully erosion is of little agricultural significance. The really spectacular erosion so popular in non-technical reports shows large areas cut up by deep interconnecting gullies, but this situation is usually found in semi-arid climates unsuitable for any serious agriculture, or on soils which have such adverse chemical or physical properties that their potential production is very low. Added to this is the fact that gully control is always difficult and expensive, so the cost of reclamation usually exceeds the value of the land. Certainly in the sense of reducing the amount of eroded soil choking the dams and rivers it may be highly desirable to do something about gully erosion, but it is very much a case of prevention being better than cure. Limited resources in man-power, money and materials can usually be better employed in preventing future gullies than in curing existing ones.

The worldwide occurrence and recognition is well demonstrated in the variety of names: in English and American—*gully*, in Egypt—*wadi*, in South Africa—*donga*, in French-speaking lands—*ravine*, in India—*nulla*, in South America—*carcava*, or *arroyo* and many others. The definition is the same in each case—a steep-sided eroding watercourse which is subject to intermittent flash floods. They are more common in semi-arid climates with infertile soils and sparse vegetation, but some spectacular examples are found in tropical forests in deep soils with dense vegetation.

12.2 THE CAUSES OF GULLY EROSION

The common factor in all cases of gully erosion is that the basic cause is the same, and the whole cycle of gully formation and growth is clear and understandable once the cause is defined. In engineering terms the cause is the breakdown of a state of *metastable equilibrium* in the stream or watercourse. In physics a body is said to be in equilibrium if it will return to the same position after being displaced slightly; for example if a pendulum is pushed to one side it will return under the force of gravity to its position of equilibrium. Metastable equilibrium is when the body will only come back to its equilibrium position if it is not displaced too much. A match box standing on one end can be tilted slightly and it will return to its original position, but if it is displaced too far it falls over and the equilibrium is lost. The second feature of metastable equilibrium is that in order to restore the original position it is necessary to apply a force which is greater than the force which toppled the body over in the first place.

Gully erosion occurs when a natural watercourse is displaced from its state of metastable equilibrium. A watercourse is ordinarily in balance, that is the size of the channel and its shape and gradient are on the whole suitable for the flows it has to carry—it is in fact in equilibrium. If the balance is slightly changed by an external force the stream will tend to come back to its equilibrium position. Thus, if the maximum flow increases the channel may enlarge itself, or the gradient might increase, until the new balance is found. But the stream, like the match box standing on one end, can only come back to its original position after small disturbances. If given a hard push the matchbox falls over, and if given too big a change the stream starts gullying, and once the starting position has been lost, then it requires a greater effort to get back to it.

The disturbing influence which upsets the balance of a watercourse may result from either of two sources. Either there is an increase in the amount of flood run-off which the channel has to carry, or the flood water remains the same but there is a decrease in the ability of the channel to carry that flood.

12.2.1 Examples of increased floods

The most common causes of an increase in flood run-off are changes in land use. If in a heavily timbered catchment there is much cutting of the trees, then the maximum flood flow will usually increase. Increases in the proportion of arable land in a catchment could have the same effect, and so could excessive burning of the vegetation or overgrazing. All of these have caused innumerable gullies by increasing the flood run-off so much that the watercourse could not adjust and lost its metastable equilibrium.

The maximum flood flow will also be increased if the catchment area is increased, and two examples of this can be illustrated. When major roads are constructed this often changes the natural drainage patterns and the natural catchments. Figure 12.1 shows a commonly occurring situation. Several small catchments each have their own watercourse carrying flood flows, but when the road is built it would be expensive to carry each minor stream under the road by means of a bridge or culvert. A common method is to close one watercourse (A in figure 12.1) where it crosses the line of the road, and to divert the run-off along the road drain and add it to that of the next watercourse (B in figure 12.1), passing the combined flow through a culvert. Where the culvert discharges, the watercourse is capable of handling the flow from catchment B, but is quite unable to cope also with the added flow from A, and gully erosion starts at point C.

Another example of artificially increasing the catchment area is when flood run-off is by-passed into an adjoining catchment as the result of the construction of a dam. In figure 12.2, catchment A is made into a reservoir and a convenient way of passing the flood flows when the dam is full is to spill the water over the ridge on the left bank and into the adjoining catchment. The stretch of stream from point B, where the flood flows now enter this stream, down to point C, the original confluence, is now being asked to carry a greater flow than previously. If the increase in the catchment is large there is a strong probability that the equilibrium will be upset leading to gully erosion.

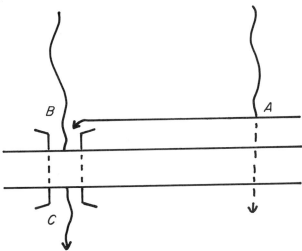

FIGURE 12.1   *Gully erosion can be started by changes in road drains*

12.2.2   Examples of decreased channel capacity

In Chapter 8 the capacity of a channel was shown to depend on the physical characteristics of the channel, like cross-sectional area, shape, gradient and roughness. Changes in these channel factors can easily upset the equilibrium. For example, the nature of the vegetation in the channel has a big influence on the velocity of flow. An increase in the density of vegetation could result from natural or man-made causes. Perhaps the stream banks have been planted with trees or shrubs and these are now growing well, or perhaps the natural grass has been replaced with a more vigorous type, or the grass is increasing as a result of fencing which now keeps out livestock. Any of a dozen such reasons could result in a denser or taller vegetation, with more resistance (ie, higher values of roughness coefficient n). If flood waters cannot flow away quickly enough down the channel, they may spill over the banks and start new erosion patterns.

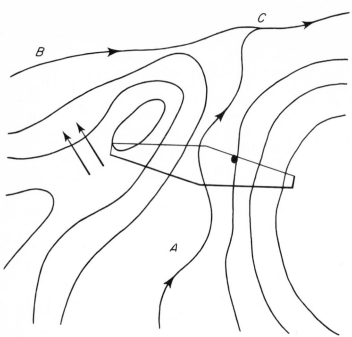

FIGURE 12.2   *An example of a change in the catchment area*

On the other hand a reduction in the density of vegetation may also be the trigger which sets off gullying. Overgrazing or fire are probable causes, and the effect is a lowering of the hydraulic friction, and an increase in velocity, with the risk of scour erosion starting.

The capacity of a channel is also affected by its shape, which can be defined numerically by the term hydraulic radius (section 8.1.1). Any changes in the shape may affect the capacity, and again these may be natural or man-made or a combination of both. The deposition of sand bars or the collapse of streambanks will result in lower values of hydraulic radius, and lower velocity, and hence reduced channel capacity. On the other hand scouring of the bed will give increased capacity, but the velocity will also increase and so the scouring action may continue. Small localized problem areas in a watercourse can have a significance out of proportion to their size by starting a cycle of events which expand and multiply. There are countless examples of large gullies which have resulted from insignificant beginnings like a small cattle track.

The concentration of flood waters into restricted channels is another potential cause of gullies. An example is a road which crosses a natural stream. Before the road is built, any flood waters can spread out over the whole of the valley, in fact if the stream is prone to floods there will probably be a flood plain which is part of the balanced equilibrium which the stream has achieved over the years. When the road is built there will be a bridge, or causeway, or culvert, to pass the floods but whichever of these is used there will be some restriction of the cross-sectional area available. The flow will be concentrated into a smaller area so the velocity will increase, and there is a good chance of gully erosion developing immediately downstream of the crossing. Large streams and rivers are likely to have cut a fairly stable channel down to rock or hard earth, and so the danger of this type of erosion is less serious in the case of main roads or railways crossing major rivers. But when a lightly trafficked farm road is put through a small watercourse which carries only intermittent floods, then the danger is much greater.

Another case of concentration which can lead to scouring is the design of earth spillways from small conservation dams. A common practice is to pass the overflow back to the stream by a cut channel round the end of the dam wall. This part is usually properly designed to cater for the maximum estimated flood, but the water then leaves the cut spillway and runs down the bank to the stream bed. Here there is a concentration of flow over ground quite unused to it, and a gully which starts at this point can quickly cut back until it empties the dam and makes it useless.

The progressive action of gullies, where once the balance is upset the problem gets increasingly worse, is also seen in the longitudinal profile of the floor of gullied streams. For a stream in balance (sometimes referred to as *in regime*) the stream gradient and the roughness are two of the interrelated factors. Manning's formula links them with velocity in the form

$$V \propto \frac{R^{\frac{2}{3}} S^{\frac{1}{2}}}{n}$$

Once gullying starts the gullied channel has a more angular and deep shape than the original bed, ie, R increases. The gullied channel is bare of vegetation so the roughness coefficient, n, probably decreases. For the velocity to remain constant the gradient must therefore decrease, and this is what almost invariably happens; the gradient of the floor of the gully is flatter than the original stream. The result, as shown in figure 12.3 is that as the head of the gully works back upstream the

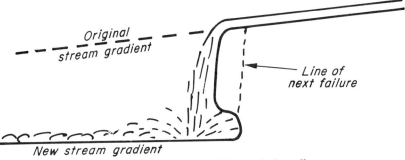

FIGURE 12.3 *The progressive development of the head of a gully*

height of the overfall increases. This overfall is usually the most actively eroding part of the gully. The waterfall action both scours the soil where it lands and also it splashes and swirls against the face of the waterfall. The bottom of the face is eroded away leaving the top overhanging. The overhang breaks away to give a vertical face, then the cycle starts again.

Reverting to Manning's formula, the changes, once gullying starts, are that hydraulic radius, R, will increase, roughness coefficient, n, will decrease, and the gradient, S, will probably decrease. On balance the overall effect is most likely to be an increase in velocity, and this is yet another reason why gully erosion is nearly always self-perpetuating and not self-correcting.

12.3   CONTROL MEASURES

12.3.1   The economics of gully reclamation

The control of gully erosion is difficult and expensive. The definition of metastable equilibrium is relevant—once the balance is disturbed by an upsetting force something is irretrievably lost and it requires a greater force to restore the original state. 'Prevention is better than cure' is a trite saying but very appropriate to gully erosion. The restoring force usually requires a great deal of time, effort, and money, so much so that often the same effort would be better employed in preventing new gullies from starting, rather than trying to cure or restore existing gullies. In terms of simple economics, the repair of gullies is seldom justified since the cost of repair is likely to be higher than the value of the land after it has been reclaimed, particularly as gullies are most common in semi-arid conditions with poor soils of low agricultural value. However, other factors have to be considered before deciding whether control work is justified. Quite apart from the on-site damage it may be necessary to do something about the erosion because of downstream effects such as a storage dam being silted up or irrigation works threatened. Or there may be on-site damage other than the obvious loss of land. Examples are the lowering of the water table, the interference with fences or roads, or perhaps the possibility that if allowed to continue unchecked the gully may work back in time to a road, a bridge, or a building. All these factors must be considered but they can seldom be evaluated in terms of actual cash, and so cost-benefit analysis techniques do not help. In fact they seldom make sense in any aspect of conservation work because there is no scale of values with which to measure the cash value to the community of benefits like not lowering the water table. In practice what happens is that the economic overlords rule that schemes may only be undertaken if the ratio of benefits to costs exceeds a certain value, say one and a half. The conservationist then decides on the basis of his knowledge and experience which works should be done, and works out the cost. He then multiplies the cost by the required ratio and uses this figure to make up his estimate of the benefits. When the scheme is submitted it meets the cost/benefit requirement and so is approved. In this way the right works are built, the administrators are kept happy, and the correct use of public funds can be demonstrated, but one cannot help feeling that there ought to be a better way.

One form of gully control which is usually economically sound is partial control, that is where the object is not to reclaim or restore the gully, but merely to prevent it getting any worse. Again this may be required because of on-site problems, for example the gully head is working back each year, and unless it is halted a road bridge will be in danger. Alternatively it may be necessary to prevent further sediment load in a stream, but the land already gullied is not worth reclaiming. Theoretically the solution would be a cheap simple structure at the gully head and nothing more. Unfortunately partial control is like trying to find an intermediate position of equilibrium half way back to the original state of metastable equilibrium. In the example of the match box, when it is standing on end it is in metastable equilibrium. The collapsed state, corresponding to the gully, is when the box is lying flat. What is quite impossible is to balance it on one corner in a half-way position. It is almost as difficult to achieve a half-way balance in gully control, and partial control measures seldom work except temporarily.

12.3.2 Principles of gully control

The reason why partial control is unsuccessful is that it does not conform to the first principle of gully control which is to determine the cause of the gully and to take counter measures. A doctor does not start trying to cure an illness until he knows the nature of the disease and its cause. If the stability has been lost and the gully started because the volume of flood water has doubled then minor patching up of the damage will not solve the problem. The second principle is to either restore the original hydraulic balance or to create new conditions. Either the flood has to be reduced to its original volume or a new channel has to be provided which can accommodate the increased flood. Some interesting experiments on vegetated channels for this purpose have been carried out in America (HEEDE 1968).

In most cases it will be found desirable to fence-off any area where control measures are being applied. Whether the controls are structures or plantings they are vulnerable while being established, and interference by grazing animals, or children playing, or from any other source must be minimized.

12.4 CONTROL BY VEGETATION

12.4.1 Why use vegetation?

A conservation engineer of many years experience is reported as having once said 'In gully control a bag of fertilizer is more effective than a bag of cement'. He would no doubt have amplified this by explaining that although structural works are sometimes necessary, it is on the whole preferable to restore gullies by the use of vegetation. Structures, whether of concrete, masonry, wood or any other building material, are subject to decay, and liable to be undermined or bypassed. They can only become less effective with the passing of time. Vegetation, on the other hand, can multiply and thrive and improve over the years. Structures also need various skills for their design and construction, and they are usually expensive.

The purpose of vegetation is twofold. First it provides the soil with physical protection against scour. It also slows down the velocity of flow by increasing the hydraulic resistance of the channel and thereby greatly reduces the scouring and abrading ability of the flood. If the velocity is sufficiently reduced then some of the sediment load may be deposited. This can lead to the desirable situation where the vegetation, growing vigorously in the deposited soil, gets denser and so traps more and more silt until the whole gully is filled. Of course this can only happen while the source of the sediment is erosion higher up the catchment.

However, there are considerable obstacles to the establishment of vegetation in gullies. The environment is usually just about as inhospitable as it could be. The bed of the gully is probably almost sterile sand with no structure, no organic matter, no available plant nutrients, and low moisture holding capacity. If there is any moisture it is most likely to be deep down, well below the rooting range of any newly established plants. Yet this is precisely where grasses, reeds, and sedges would be most useful. The banks of the stream and sides of the gully are probably not much better. The water regime is alternations between flood and drought, and problems of chemical imbalance like salinity and alkalinity are common in soils subject to gullying (HUDSON 1963).

12.4.2   Plants and planting techniques

The two ways of overcoming these problems are the selection of suitable plants and the use of special planting techniques. Using plants which have proved successful in other countries is always worth trying but may be disappointing. A good example of this is Kudzu Vine, *Pueraria Thunbergiana,* which has been successfully used in many parts of the United States. Given the right conditions it puts out vigorous creeping runners which can completely cover the floor, sides, and flanks of a gully with a dense blanket of vegetation. However, its performance has been most disappointing in several countries in Africa, though the explanation for this is not known. It is seldom possible to predict which plants will do well, and a useful practice is to make small trial plantings of a wide range of plants to see which flourish. Appendix 2 lists some plants which have been found useful in various parts of the world, and a useful review of plants used in America is given by BENNETT (1939).

In the search for suitable varieties, local material should not be overlooked. Any plants which are growing reasonably well in or near the gully must be accustomed to the local conditions. Sometimes a little help in the way of fertilizer will enable them to outgrow all the exotic varieties imported from other countries. The requirements for plants to be suitable for gully control are that they should grow vigorously in poor conditions and give good ground cover. A spreading, creeping habit is much better than an upright habit.

Plants are usually best established by planting out seedlings which have been germinated and started in a more favourable medium. One popular method is to use cylinders of thin black polythene to form bottomless plant pots. These are filled with good soil and the seedling makes good growth. When planting out, a cylindrical hole is made with a soil auger and the plant and soil placed in the hole. The plastic film can be left on to hold the soil in place. By the time the plant has outgrown its reservoir of fertile soil it is strong enough to survive in the tougher conditions outside. This method might be used to establish a clump of Phragmytes reed, planting out at about half-metre intervals. A variation on this idea, useful for establishing colonies of grass, is to plant into sacks of good soil (DURBACH 1964). The sacks are laid in shallow trenches in the bed of the gully so they are about level with the bed. A small cut is made in the bag and a seedling planted through the cut. The bag prevents the soil and plant being swept away by the first flood, and by the time the bag rots away the plants have made sufficient root growth and no longer need the protection of the bag. Old jute or hessian sacks are best because the grass can grow through them, but discarded plastic fertilizer bags, or strong paper sacks, can also be used.

Planting the sides of gullies is difficult, because they are steep, unstable, and eroding. When the cost is justified the banks can be levelled to a gentle uniform slope by heavy earthmoving machinery, and then seeded or planted. Sometimes sufficient soil is bulldozed in from the sides to convert the gully into a shallow grassed waterway (HARRIS and HAY 1963). Since the banks are almost sure to be infertile subsoil, some extra fertility must be added. One method is to insert pockets of better soil as was described for planting the floor of the gully. Alternatively it is sometimes possible to bulldoze a pile of top soil to the edge of the gully and then spread it as a blanket over the sloping sides of the gully. This can then be seeded or planted, but there is the problem that soil or seed or planting material all tend to get washed off the slopes before the vegetation can become established. Surface mulches of straw or other crop residues or long grass cut for the purpose are valuable in accelerating the establishment of vegetation, but the mulches too are prone to surface wash. In the United States several man-made materials are produced especially for anchoring mulches and planting material. One form is a coarse open-mesh woven net and this is made both from jute fibre and also from kraft paper. Another form is made from fine wood shavings and known under the trade name of *Excelsior*. Examples are shown in plates 13.2 and 13.3. The netting is unrolled over the top of the mulch and then fastened down with wire spikes pushed into the soil. The method is undoubtedly very effective and although the cost of importing these materials from America is prohibitive, there seems to be no reason why cheap substitutes could not be manufactured locally, especially in countries producing large quantities of cloth fibres. Some other methods of stabilizing sloping banks are discussed in section 13.3.3 in connexion with road embankments.

12.5 STRUCTURES FOR GULLY CONTROL

12.5.1 Temporary structures

It frequently happens that the establishment of vegetation is difficult because the newly planted material gets swept away, or because there is no soil for the vegetation to grow in. In either of these cases there may be a place for temporary structures whose purpose is to provide protection for just long enough to give vegetation a start. If the object is to slow down the water and so cause deposition of silt there is no need for the structures to be watertight, and the name *porous checks* describes this type.

Wire bolsters

A simple but effective method if there is plenty of loose rock available nearby is to build a loose rock-fill dam with the stones anchored in place by wire netting. Galvanized wire netting of a fairly stout gauge and two metres or more in width is laid out flat across the gully bed. Loose rock is packed on one half of the width of the netting and the other half is wrapped over the stones and laced to the other edge, forming a sausage or bolster of rock contained in a skin of wire netting. More substantial structures can be built using several layers of rock bolsters (HEEDE 1960). A more sophisticated commercial product is described under permanent structures in section 12.5.2.

Netting dams

Another use of wire netting is to form small check dams, usually near the top end of gullies. Wooden posts are driven into the bed of the gully, and used to support a strip of wire netting which forms a low wall across the gully. The height should be only a half metre or so and the lower edge of the netting is buried. Light brush or straw is piled loosely against the upstream side of the netting wall and is packed by the flow of water against the netting to form a barrier, which is porous but slows down the flow and causes a build up of sediment on the upstream side.

Brushwood dams

The main requirement of temporary control structures is that they must be quick and easy to construct, and use cheap readily available materials.

In wooded areas two types of silt retaining dam are used. The brush-wood dam, shown in figure 12.4 uses small branches, up to two or three cm in diameter, packed as tightly as possible across the direction of flow. They can be anchored by packing them between rows of vertical stakes, or by tying down with wire, or by sticks laid across the top and fastened down. The main points in building these dams are to pack the brushwood as tightly as possible and to secure it firmly. With attention given to both these points it is not uncommon for brushwood check dams to last for several years.

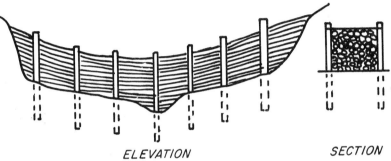

ELEVATION   SECTION

FIGURE 12.4   *A brushwood dam for gully control*

Log dams

When heavier timber is available it can be used for log-piling dams (HEEDE 1960). One method is to use logs in the same way as the brush-wood dam but to make a much more substantial structure. Two rows of vertical posts are driven into the bed of the gully and extending up the sides to above flood level, and then logs are packed in between. The vertical posts should be at least 10 cm diameter, 2 m long, and spaced about a metre apart in each row, with the two rows of posts half a metre apart. In a wide shallow stream it is best to drive in all the vertical posts to the same height above ground, about half a metre, so that the top of the dam follows the section of the stream bed (figure 12.4). If the gully

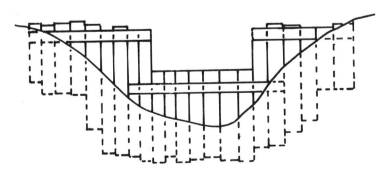

FIGURE 12.5   *Timber piling used to make a log dam for gully control*

has steep sides it is better to have a rectangular notch in the centre (figure 12·5) but the notch must be big enough to pass the whole of the flood. A common error in the construction of this kind of dam is to make the notch too small so that floods go over the top. This is very likely to start scouring at the ends of the wall. The vertical posts on either side of the notch will carry the brunt of the force of the flood waters and any logs or boulders swept down by the flood, so they should be particularly stout posts and driven in deeper than the others.

When the logs are packed between the rows of posts the bottom layer should be sunk below ground surface to avoid seepage and scour underneath. After the top logs have been placed they are held in position by strong wire ties between the vertical posts.

A simpler structure can be made, consisting only of a single row of vertical posts driven in side by side to form a wall of logs. Again they can follow the profile of the gully section or have a central notch. This structure depends on the firmness with which the posts are held in the bed, and so is most suitable where long posts can be driven deep into a firm soil. Some extra rigidity is obtained by lashing or bolting a few cross-members to the vertical posts.

Brick weirs

The dividing line between temporary and permanent structures is obviously quite arbitrary; many structures could have a very variable life depending on how they were constructed and maintained, and what pressure of use they had to withstand. Sometimes long-lasting materials are used in structures with a short design life, for example brick weirs designed to hold sediment or water long enough to establish vegetation. Some examples are shown in plates 12.1 and 12.2, from HUDSON (1963).

Since the object is cheapness and simplicity the materials and the design must be chosen to suit the site conditions. If the gully bed contains clean washed sand this can be used to make sand/cement bricks very cheaply. For quick production it is worth using metal moulds which allow each brick or block to be turned out as it is made. Hollow blocks reduce the volume of material and keep the weight down. The mix can be lean as 15 sand to 1 cement if care is taken over the other points which are to use as little water as possible, to ram the mix firmly into the moulds, and to cure the bricks slowly. If allowed to dry out quickly in the hot sun they will tend to crack and have little strength. They should be covered with old sacks or paper or grass and kept moist by sprinkling with water.

Where clay bricks are the traditional local building material they are probably cheap enough for use in gully control structures. Bricks burned in a kiln are normally resistant to the effect of water but sun-dried bricks will stand occasional wetting and may be used if the gully only experiences infrequent floods. Second-grade bricks or rejects not good enough for building but quite adequate for gully control can often be obtained very cheaply from commercial brickfields.

PLATE 12.1 *A simple brick weir, built up in several stages as the silt accumulated on the upstream side. The notch is much too small*

PLATE 12.2 *A simple arch weir built from sand-cement bricks. There are no foundations and the stresses are carried by the rock outcrop on each flank*

Some simple designs are shown in figure 12.6. The shape which gives the best strength/weight ratio is the arch weir, illustrated in plate 12.2 and a single thickness of brickwork can be built to a height of one or one and a half metres over a circular span of about two metres. A straight wall of similar size would need three or four times as much brickwork to achieve comparable strength. The arch wall works by transmitting the load round the arch to the buttresses at each end, and so it needs good solid support in the gully walls, preferably in the form of a rock outcrop. However the light wall does not need much in the way of foundations, and in fact the weir shown in plate 12.2 is resting only on a bed of sand between the rocks on either side.

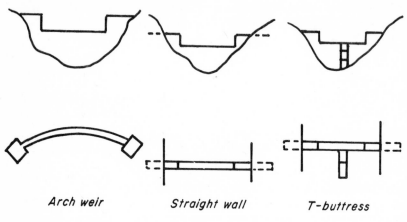

| Arch weir | Straight wall | T-buttress |

FIGURE 12.6   *Types of small brick weirs for gully control*

In the more usual situation of a rock bar which runs across the bed of the gully a straight gravity section wall is indicated. The width at the base should be approximately equal to the maximum height, and successive courses of brickwork are narrower so that the section is roughly triangular. It is common to find the upstream face of dams vertical, with all the slope on the downstream face, but while there is a sound engineering reason for this in the case of large water storage dams, it is not of any consequence in small gully control dams.

Since brickwork has little tensile strength the weakest feature of straight-wall brick dams is their resistance to the bending moment which results from the water pressure. The bending moment M is related to the length of wall l, and the load per unit length w, by the formula $M = wl^2/8$. In other words the risk of failure is proportional not to the length of the wall, but the square of the length. A buttress at the mid-point of a straight wall reduces the effective length by a half but cuts the bending moment to a quarter and so is usually worthwhile whenever the site conditions allow. Some other construction points are discussed in the following sections on permanent structures.

12.5.2 Permanent structures

Wherever possible gully control should be achieved by vegetative methods or a combination of vegetation and cheap simple structures whose life is not important. However there are cases where the problem can only be solved by the construction of permanent structures and the main point is that for such works to be successful they must be done thoroughly and carefully. Everything is against their being successful. They will be built in adverse conditions, in poor unstable soils, in remote inaccessible areas where maintenance will be poor, and then expected to withstand the onslaught of torrential floods and to last for ever. The gullies of the world are littered with the remains of ruined structures which demonstrate that half-measures or jobs done on the cheap are a waste of time and effort in gully control.

Silt-trap dams

One example where the problem can best be solved by a permanent structure is the case of an excessive sediment load which threatens down-stream water supplies. Trapping the silt in sufficient quantity by vegetative means may be slow and uncertain. A quick positive reduction in sediment movement can be achieved by building permanent silt trapping dams. A programme of this nature was carried out in the Republic of South Africa when serious gully erosion in the Tarka Conservation Area threatened Lake Arthur. Permanent silt trap dams of many shapes and sizes were built wherever suitable sites occurred, and plate 12.3 shows an ingenious and original design of multiple-arch dam on one of the larger rivers.

PLATE 12.3 *A multiple-arch silt-trapping dam in the Republic of South Africa*

Regulating dams

Another useful application of permanent dams is to regulate flash floods by what is sometimes called the leaky bath-tub principle. A permanent dam is built at the top of the valley with sufficient storage for the run-off from a single storm.

The outlet consists of a permanently open pipe of about 15 to 20 cm diameter which allows the flood water to drain away in a day or two, leaving the storage reservoir empty for the next storm. The flow down the gully now being reduced to the flow through the outlet pipe, it is fairly easy to create stable conditions which can cope with this flow. Practical construction points are to have the inlet to the pipe raised above the bottom of the dam so that it is not in danger of being silted up, and to discharge the pipe outlet into an energy-dissipating chamber, not directly into the bed of the gully.

Gully-head dams

A third example of a case for permanent structures is when an active gully head is eating its way steadily upstream and must be stopped before it threatens a road or bridge or similar asset. An effective way of controlling the erosive force of the run-off over the gully head is to submerge the head of the gully in the pond of a permanently impounding dam as shown in figure 12.7. The energy of the inrushing water is then dissipated as it flows into the pond. There is one danger to be guarded against, and that is that although there is no danger of the head cutting back when the dam is full, it may do so when the dam is empty and the run-off then runs over the edge of the gully head. In a climate with marked wet and dry seasons it is possible for the head to move back a little each year before the dam fills until eventually the head is at the full supply level of the dam and so is no longer submerged and continues to eat back unchecked. This is called 'the gully climbing back out of the dam' and avoiding action is to allow plenty of freeboard between the gully head and full supply level, and to adopt slowing down measures if the gully head continues to move back.

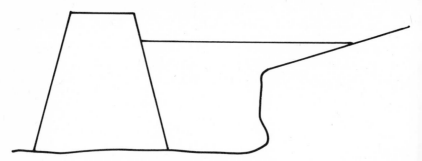

FIGURE 12.7   *Submerging the head of the gully by a dam*

Drop structures

The other approach to this problem is to stabilize the head of the gully with some masonry, brick, or concrete structure which allows the flood run-off to pass over harmlessly. A typical concrete drop structure is shown diagramatically in figure 12.8. The capacity of drop structures of this type is controlled by the size of the inlet, which acts as a rectangular weir with the flow proportional to the length of the weir.

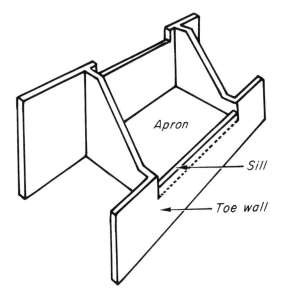

FIGURE 12.8 *A typical concrete drop structure for gully control*

Mathematically,

$$Q = C\,L\,H^{\frac{3}{2}}$$

where Q is the flow
     L is the length of the weir
     H is the head of water flowing over the weir and
     C is a constant depending on the entrance conditions.
The length of the weir (L) can be increased by the addition of a box inlet as shown in figure 12.9, thus greatly increasing the capacity at little extra cost and without increasing the overall width of the structure.

   Physical failure of this kind of structure, such as the wall collapsing, is much less likely than failure through the structure being undermined or bypassed. Particular care must therefore be given to the following points in the design and installation.

1   The notch must be big enough to take the biggest probable flood. If it is too small the flood water will pass over the whole width of the structure and erode the vulnerable banks on either side of the structure.

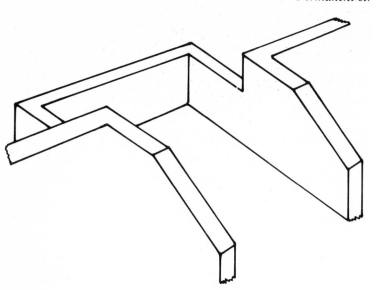

FIGURE 12.9   *The box-drop inlet increases the capacity of a structure*

2   To prevent lateral seepage round the end of the wall it must be carefully keyed in to the banks. The key should extend into the bank on either side for a distance of the height of the wall, and after the wall has been built the surrounding space must be carefully refilled with tightly rammed impervious material.

3   The flood water falling over the structure strikes the ground with much force, and an adequate protection must be provided to prevent scour at the foot of the wall. Loose rocks are only suitable if they are so large there is no danger of them being swept away. Smaller stones can be packed together and anchored with wire netting. With concrete structures a good method is to provide a flat apron, and a low sill built on the downstream edge will form a stilling basin which effectively absorbs the energy. In erodible soils a toe wall is also required at the downstream edge of the apron to prevent undercutting (figure 12.8).

4   The flood water leaves the structure with considerable velocity and turbulence, so the gully sides immediately downstream may be subjected to more severe attack than before the structure was built. Some mechanical or vegetative protection of the banks is usually required, and should be continued downstream to the point where the channel flow is normal again.

Many simpler or cheaper devices have been tried as alternatives to the drop inlet structure. Sometimes the same design has been followed but built more cheaply using timber or brickwork. Sometimes other designs have been used such as a sloping chute to carry the water down an inclined channel, and every conceivable lining material has been used—grass, asphalt, concrete, pre-cast sections, glass-fibre and so on. No doubt some of these have been successful or partly successful, but if it were possible to determine the number of cheap or unorthodox structures which were operating successfully after a life of say 10 years, this would be a disappointing figure. A well-designed and carefully constructed concrete drop structure will be expensive, but it will be effective, and it will last, so it will be a better choice than one which is cheap but fails after a few years.

Constructional details of some of the designs proven after long service in the United States are given in the standard textbooks (AYRES 1936, SCHWAB *et al* 1966), and also in the *Engineering Handbook* of the USDA Soil Conservation Service 1958.

Gabions

The main difficulty with rigid structures is that they cannot adapt when changes occur in the soil surrounding them or supporting them. Even slight movements, such as swelling and shrinking of the soil or a small settlement of the structure, can introduce stresses which the structure is ill-equipped to withstand. Concrete, masonry, and brickwork all have good resistance to compression but fail easily under tensile loads resulting from settlement. A construction method which overcomes this problem is a more sophisticated version of the wire netting bolsters described among the temporary measures. The method was developed in Italy and uses pre-fabricated rectangular baskets called *Gabions* made of heavy duty wire netting (plate 12.4). The basket is placed in position and filled with stones, then the lid is wired down. The baskets, up to 4 m long by 1 m by 1 m, are built up on top of each other like courses of brickwork, and can form large or small structures. The use of galvanized wire ensures a long lasting resistance to corrosion. The main advantage of these structures is that there is sufficient flexibility for the structure to adjust to settlement resulting from scouring of the foundations without any loss of strength.

PLATE 12.4 *A gully control structure built with gabions in Barbados*

References

AYRES, Q. C. 1936 *Soil Erosion and its Control*. McGraw-Hill, New York and London

BENNETT, H. H. 1939 *Soil Conservation*. McGraw-Hill, New York and London

DURBACH, S. 1964 Some Simple Methods of Gully Control. *Rhodesian Agricultural Journal* 61, 2, 31–37

HARRIS, W. S. and R. C. HAY 1963 Gully Control without Structures Part I. *Transaction of the American Society of Agricultural Engineers*, 6, 37–39. (Part II by B. A. JONES ibid. 39–40, 47)

HEEDE, B. H. 1960 A Study of Early Gully Control Structures in the Colorado Front Range. *Station Paper 55, Rocky Mountain Forest and Range Experiment Station, United States Department of Agriculture*

HEEDE, B. H. 1968 Conversion of Gullies to Vegetation-lined waterways on Mountain slopes. *Research Paper R.M. 40, United States Department of Agriculture Forest Service*

HUDSON, N. W. 1963 Gully control in Mopani Soils. *Rhodesia Agricultural Journal* 60, 1, 22–31

SCHWAB, G. O., R. K. FREVERT, T. W. EDMINSTER and K. K. BARNES 1966 *Soil and Water Conservation Engineering* (2nd Edition) Wiley, New York

Chapter 13 Erosion control on non-arable land

13.1 EROSION AND FORESTS

The problem of soil erosion from land covered by woods and forests is usually less severe than the erosion from arable land. The protective canopy of vegetation is usually good, often giving complete protection, because there is likely to be an accumulation of forest litter on the soil surface. The result is usually a lower rate of erosion, and reduced peak floods compared with similar land under other uses. However it does not follow that any forestry will automatically bring these results. In a study which compared the kinetic energy of falling rain with that of the through-fall under a forest canopy, the rather surprising result was that the energy was actually greater under the trees (CHAPMAN 1948). The explanation is that the rainfall was of fairly low intensity, and so would be composed of drops of many sizes, all falling at terminal velocity. Rain is intercepted by a tree canopy, and eventually drips through, but the size of the drops which drip slowly from the leaves is greater than the natural raindrops. The canopy was in this case about 10 metres from the ground, sufficient for the water drops to reach terminal velocity, so the net effect was that even though some of the rain was lost by evaporation and interception, and some would become stem-flow down the trunks of the trees, yet the total energy of the drips under the trees was greater than that of the rain reaching the ground direct.

This result should not be over-emphasised, for it might be different with a different kind of tree canopy, or more intense rainfall. Nor does it follow that erosion would be high because it is usual to find either an understorey of lower vegetation or an accumulation of leaf litter, and either would effectively protect the soil. What the result does show is that tree cover does not automatically provide protection against floods and erosion. This is particularly true in the tropics and sub-tropics. In temperate climates with slow rates of oxidation and decomposition there usually is a build up of surface litter under any permanent trees or shrubs, but in tropical and subtropical climates it can be quite different. The rate of chemical and biological breakdown is much faster, and the chance of physical removal probably higher, whether by erosion, consumption by browsing animals, or by harvester termites. Plate 13.1 shows the ground under trees stripped completely bare by a combination of these circumstances.

13.1.1 Mechanical protection of forest soils

Mechanical protection is usually not required for natural forests, but commercial plantings may well need some protection during establishment, and after harvesting. Two forms are most common, contour

PLATE 13.1   *The ground litter associated with trees in temperate climates may be completely absent in the tropics where it is consumed by termites and grazing animals*

trenches and contour furrows, and both are similar to the works used to protect arable land.

Contour trenches are commonly used in America on steep lands from 30 to 75 per cent (CUSKELLY 1969). Large areas of the United States National Forests were protected in the 1930s by trenches dug by hand, but nowadays larger trenches are constructed using heavy earth-moving equipment. The trenches are usually built without any gradient in the channel since the object is not to lead off surface run-off but to hold it until it infiltrates. Cross-ties are added every 10 or 15 metres to further restrict water movement, but the height of the cross ties is made lower than the main bank so that overtopping would first take place along the trench. This safety device is the same as used in tie-ridging (section 6.1.8), and like tie-ridging, this protection method should only be used when it will be able to absorb all the rain and so eliminate surface run-off.

Contour furrows are similar in form, but smaller, and used on gentler slopes up to about 35 per cent. They have a smaller water-holding capacity but are quicker and cheaper to construct. Several implements for their construction have been developed (CUSKELLY 1969), some on the principle of modified large-disc ploughs, some using angle-dozers—in either case mounted on a large crawler tractor.

13.1.2   Forest roads

The roads on forest lands present a considerable erosion problem for several reasons. The land is usually steep and the rainfall heavy. The roads are not used much and so expensive roads with careful construction are not justified. But the road use during harvesting operations is very damaging and bound to be associated with a high risk of erosion.

One question to be decided is at what stage in the forest development the road system should be constructed. Economics and the erosion hazard must both be considered. If the roads are put in at planting, there is a lot of unproductive capital lying idle, and a long time for erosion to occur on the roads and banks. On the other hand to delay the construction until extraction starts, means struggling with inadequate access for fire protection and for pruning during the main life of the plantation. It also means the probability of severe erosion during extraction over new roads which have not developed any cover at all on the raw scars inevitably associated with road construction. The most economical time to construct the roads is thought to be just before the first thinning (HUGGARD 1958) and this is also a good solution from the point of view of minimizing the risk of erosion.

An important point is that disused roads will be a constant erosion problem if they are just abandoned, with the near certainty of continuing deterioration until they become gullies. Simple and inexpensive control measures can prevent this. Some form of drain or ditch should be cut across the road at intervals to prevent the build-up of run-off down sloping stretches of road. Vegetation should be encouraged, and the two basic steps (discussed in more detail in section 13.4) are scarifying the surface and seeding.

13.1.3 Forest management and erosion

During the planting, establishment, and growth of a plantation the management practices required to minimize erosion are straightforward—a foundation of mechanical protection works followed by management aimed at maintaining a complete protective vegetative cover. The problems really arise during harvesting when the cover must be disturbed and the timber must be extracted, both of these tending to cause erosion. The choice of clear felling or selective extraction usually has to be decided on economic grounds, but from the conservation point of view selective felling is much less damaging and so preferable where possible. There is less drastic disturbance of the tree canopy, and also a good chance of some of the ground level vegetation surviving.

Clear felling is necessary with some species, or may be the most economic method. The tree cover will be entirely removed and the extraction usually leaves the surface cover largely destroyed. It is often debated whether the hauling of logs is better concentrated on a few routes which will be badly damaged, or whether to disperse the routes and spread a lower rate of soil disturbance over the whole area. In fact a more important issue is not the extent of the damage, but the restoration afterwards. A steep hillside badly scarred by clear felling is liable to continue to erode for years afterwards, with the log hauls and roads turning to gullies, and irreparable damage being done before a protective mantle of vegetation is re-established. Like a hospital patient after major surgery, the recovery can be greatly assisted by suitable after-care—in this case by digging cross-drains across the roads and log hauls, by not burning off the brushwood and trimmings, and by getting the next cycle of vegetation under way as quickly as possible, whether it is replanting another tree crop or establishing grass or natural vegetation. The use of nurse crops is highly commended to provide a quick cover during the first years after the new tree crop is planted.

In other aspects of management we find again the principle that good husbandry practices coincide with good erosion control practice. The forester concerned with yield and quality is anxious to keep out fire—and so is the conservationist for even if the trees are not damaged the forest floor litter will be. Invasion by bush and other vegetation is another problem. The forester does not want his stand of commercial timber debased with other tree species, but does want a tidy understorey. The forester and conservationist would both agree that the ideal combination is a clean regular stand of trees with a close ground cover of grass or similar vegetation.

13.2   Erosion and grazing land

On well-managed high-yielding grassland it is unlikely that there will be any erosion, for the ground will have a good uniform cover. But land which is not arable because it is too poor, too infertile, too stony, or too arid, and is only described as *grazing land* because it is unfit for more intensive use, is a very different matter. Again erosion control can be directly and precisely equated to improved management—anything leading to a better water-balance and a better ground cover will lead to reduced erosion.

13.2.1   Mechanical controls on grazing land

Good grazing land does not need mechanical controls, and poor grazing land has so low a production that only very simple inexpensive measures are economically justified. Those measures which are used do not attempt to control soil movement directly, but rather at improving the vegetation by reducing run-off and increasing infiltration.

The problem is to hold the run-off so it can infiltrate into the soil, and two types of structure are used for this. Pasture furrows are small open drains on level grade following the true contour and fairly close together. Like the larger channel terraces used on arable land they intercept the flow of surface run-off down the slope, but instead of leading the water away they try to hold it on the land. The individual furrows are small, often made with one pass of a single-furrow plough and closely spaced only a few metres apart. Sometimes the soil from the furrow is spread entirely on the uphill side so that there is no bank. In this case a furrow which is catching more water than it can hold helps to distribute the water by spilling it over the whole length of the level downhill edge of the furrow.

The other approach is to make many small surface depressions which hold and store run-off. Among the mechanical protection works for arable land was the tied-ridge method (section 6.1.8), which leaves the whole surface of the ground covered with rectangular boxes which hold the run-off. Another variation is basin listing, widely used in the United States for many years, and which produces a similar effect. These methods are effective, and can provide surface storage for up to 50 mm of rain on level ground, but they require soil preparation by ploughing and discing as well as the ridging, and so are too ambitious and expensive for poor range land.

A simpler and cheaper version is called *range pitting*, developed as a simple one-pass operation to give the same sort of effect on a reduced scale. The implement used is a modified large disc plough, such as a 5-disc model with alternate discs removed so that it draws three separate furrows. A piece is cut out of the rim of each of the remaining discs, so that when drawn forward, as the discs revolve, the furrow is broken each time the missing piece comes round. The plough is drawn by a large crawler and produces three shallow furrows in disconnected lengths of about one and a half to two metres (figure 13.1). The storage capacity of the depressions is only small, equivalent to about 5 mm of rain, but in addition to this slight increase in infiltration the method also provides a place where seeds can lodge and find a better chance of germinating in the damper soil.

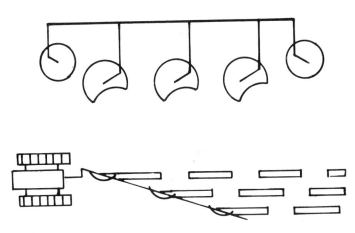

FIGURE 13.1   *Modified disc plough for range pitting*

Another technique for improving the water balance is *water spreading* in which flood waters are diverted from a stream or gully and used for a simple type of flood irrigation. If a small proportion of the land can be flooded occasionally, and as a result produces a small amount of green feed at times when the rain-grown vegetation is inadequate, this may extend the grazing season, and so increase the overall carrying capacity. At low levels of production of grazing animals the timing of the availability of feed and water is often more significant than the total amount. The efficiency of water use in water spreading is low, but if the flood water would otherwise be wasted, and providing the diversion dam and the spreading channels are cheap and simple, then such a scheme may be economic.

13.2.2 Management of grazing lands

Classification systems have been developed for grazing land along the same lines as the Capability Classification system for arable lands (described in section 9.2), that is the physical properties of the land are measured, and this information is used to plan the best use without the risk of erosion. Examples are the methods developed for the western States in America (RENNER and ALLRED 1962), and for Rhodesia (VINCENT 1962). However, whereas the Capability Classification system has proved remarkably versatile and capable of adaption for many countries, the classification of grazing land depends so much on the local flora that it is difficult to transpose one system to another area.

On the other hand the principles of management for control of erosion are simple and universal. The task is to reverse the downward spiral of poor vegetation leading to high rates of soil loss and water run-off, so that the vegetation can only become worse, and to substitute instead a favourable water balance with all the rain being available for plant growth which can then become more vigorous.

Correct stocking rate is fundamental to good management. Overstocking leads to a degeneration of the vegetation, with the annual grasses increasing at the expense of the perennials, and coarse tough weeds replacing the grasses. On overstocked land there is no opportunity for rest periods, or rotational grazing—both essential for continued high production. The form of land tenure so common in undeveloped countries whereby the grazing lands are communal property cannot possibly work unless there is a reasonable balance between the carrying capacity and the number of stock actually present. Like so many traditional patterns of primitive agriculture the system was perfectly satisfactory in the context of a small constantly moving population, but is disastrous when continued today with much larger populations living permanently in the same area and exerting a constant heavy pressure on the land.

Production at maximum efficiency also requires a considerable capital outlay. Fencing is necessary for rotational grazing, and there must be sufficient watering points, or the grazing pressure will be unevenly distributed. If cattle dip-tanks are required for the control of tick-born diseases they must be provided in sufficient number. In the Tribal Trust Lands of Rhodesia cattle dips are built by the Government and by law all cattle must be dipped regularly. But the dips are so few that each has to serve a large area and large numbers of cattle are herded to each one. The result is that from the air each dip can be seen as the centre of a raw eroding area where the vegetation has been almost completely removed, with the erosion decreasing outward in concentric circles, and rays of erosion along the radial paths leading to the dip. The necessary expenditure for the dips, water supplies, and fences is easy to find from high-producing land, but on the poor low-yield land which most needs help, some injection of capital from outside sources is necessary.

Control of fire is necessary for maximum yield, but control does not necessarily mean total exclusion. In Africa the best way of preventing invasion of grassland by undesirable bush species is to burn the dead grass in the dry season, killing off the bush seedlings. Too frequent fires damage the grass also, and the aim is usually to burn every few years in a controlled rotation of grazing and rest periods.

Rest periods can only encourage re-seeding of existing species, and it may be that the substitution or addition of other species is desirable. Again the value of the land usually precludes expensive operations like ploughing out the existing vegetation and replanting, but operations applicable on a large scale like seeding from aircraft may be economic. When cultivations are carried out, like contour furrowing, seeding devices operated by the tractor exhaust may be practical. The application of fertilizer is another example of the most needy cases being least able to afford the remedy. The high-yielding grass-clover pastures of New Zealand can support the cost of aerial applications of fertilizer, and also make economically efficient use of the extra plant nutrients. But for much of the world's grazing lands the problem is how to lift the level of production up to a point where it can be held constant without being dragged down by erosion.

13.3 EROSION CONTROL ON ROADS

13.3.1 Siting and alignment

The surprising thing about the problems connected with farm roads is how few of them really need to be problems, or putting it the other way round how many of the existing problems could have been avoided. In developed countries the siting of roads is usually determined by existing features like boundaries, but when putting in roads for the first time in a new agricultural development scheme, getting the roads right is one of the key steps in planning the scheme. The siting of new roads is one of the many tasks which nowadays can be done so much more efficiently by the use of aerial photography (SEESTROM 1966). Using a stereoscope to study pairs of photographs the planner sees a 3-dimensional model of the ground on which crests, valleys and other topographic features can be quickly and accurately picked out. Even without using the stereoscopic principle to get a 3-D image, the aerial photograph greatly simplifies the siting of new roads. The most striking example is planning the line of a new road through rugged country with indifferent maps and heavy vegetation. A ground party laboriously hacking its way through on foot or by Land Rover, frequently wasting time by back tracking from false starts and detouring round obstacles, can take months to do what could be done in a day using aerial photographs and the simplest interpretation equipment.

The first rule of road siting is to put roads on crests wherever possible, thus disposing of one of the most troublesome problems—drainage. A road along a crest has no catchment to shed water onto the road, and the run-off from the road surface can be easily discharged on both sides. There is no need for any bridges, culverts or crossings on a crest road, and maintenance is simpler and required less frequently. This applies equally to all kinds of roads, from main roads to the farm track through arable fields.

When it is not possible to put the road on a crest the next best alignment is on a gentle grade fairly close to the true contour. Gradients of the order of 1 in 100 to 1 in 500 will present no difficulty to traffic and are best for the open-channel drains which will be required alongside the road (section 8.2). Grades from 1 in 100 to 1 in 20 are not difficult for traffic, but controlling the erosion in the side drains may be more of a problem.

The road which goes diagonally down the side of a hill on a grade steeper than 1 in 20 is the worst choice, and it is usually better to use a zigzag layout or the combination of some lengths on gentle grades and some parts straight down the slope as in figure 13.2.

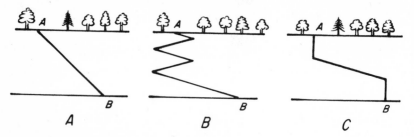

FIGURE 13.2   *Road alignment down steep hills*
A is undesirable because drains on so steep a grade must be lined and expensive
B or C, using grades suitable for grass-lined drain channels are preferable

13.3.2   Road drainage

In all soils the strength or resistance to deformation reduces greatly when the soil is wet, so a road cannot work efficiently unless it is properly drained. When siting roads, swamps and permanently wet areas should always be avoided for this reason. Getting the water off the surface of the road is fairly easy, and on a new road surface all that is required is a gentle camber. On earth or gravel roads, wheel ruts may prevent the water getting to the side of the road, and on a gradient there is the danger of each rut becoming a scouring watercourse. The solution is to divert the water sideways by very gentle depressions in the road surface. If made sufficiently wide these cross-ditches can be negotiated without any difficulty by traffic and by maintenance equipment such as graders. The size of the drain depends on the gradient and the speed of the traffic. On a farm road carrying only tractors the cross-drain need only be the depth of the wheel ruts and perhaps a metre across, whereas on a gravel road carrying fast-moving cars a gently dished section is required, with a top width of up to 20 metres.

Drainage along the side of the road is usually the more difficult problem, not so much because of the run-off from the road itself, but because the road is cutting across natural drainage lines and so picking up run-off from any nearby higher land. Only crest roads are entirely free from this problem and can manage without any side drains.

Roads straight up and down the steepest slope need side drains only to deal with the run-off from the road surface, and this water can be easily disposed of by *mitre drains*. These are extensions of the road drains leading away from the road at an angle of about 45° so that the storm run-off is dispersed before it can build up to unmanageable quantities and velocities. The spacing of mitre drains will depend on the intensity of rain expected, but would usually be from 20 metres to 100 metres. The cross-section must be at least as large as the drain alongside the road, for any restriction will cause a decrease in velocity and the deposition of sediment. When the road surface and the side drains are maintained by smoothing runs with a grader the mitre drains are likely to be blocked by soil from the grader blade. The solution is either to use a gang of labourers to open the ends of the mitre drains again by hand work, or for the grader to continue its blading action while it turns into the mitre drain. It then has to back out and start again where it left the roadside drain. Mitre drains can only be used when the discharged water will flow naturally away from the road. In the case of a road diagonally down the hill side (figure 13.2.A) any water discharged from mitre drains on the uphill side would only return to the road lower down the slope.

For roads on gentle gradients open side drains are required only on the upper side, and these should be designed on the same principles as vegetated stormwater drains as discussed in section 8.2. There is no point in having a drain on the lower side, for any unnecessary collection and concentration is undesirable.

The main reason for avoiding roads running diagonally down a hillside is the difficulty of draining them. It is easy to design and maintain vegetation-lined open ditches on gradients up to about 1 in 50, but anything steeper is not suitable for earth channels. This means either lining the drains or passing the water under the road at frequent intervals by culverts. Either of these measures add disproportionately to the cost of simple low-cost roads.

If a design specification was requested for open drains at the sides of roads it could be very simply expressed as 'make them mowable'. A wide shallow cross-section with gently sloping sides will provide the best hydraulic design, and regular mowing of an established close-growing cover grass has been shown to be the most effective and the cheapest maintenance.

When simple earth or gravel roads are maintained by periodic grading with a self-propelled road grader problems can arise from the shape of drains which develop. The grader takes a small slice from the nearly vertical face of the drain and spreads it on the road, leaving a V-shaped ditch which is the shape most vulnerable to erosion (figure 13.3). Flat-bottomed drains are preferable, especially if a suitable grass can be established and then maintained by mowing. Even if the drain is kept clear of vegetation by an out-of-date road engineer who insists on bare drains, the risk of erosion is still reduced.

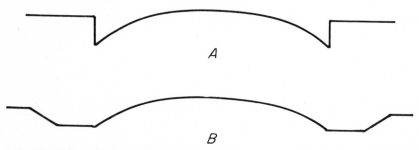

FIGURE 13.3   *The shape of graded road drains*
A with V-shaped drains is undesirable
B with mowable drains is preferable

Mechanical structures in the drains are highly undesirable. They are expensive to install, they require regular care and maintenance, and worst of all they seldom do their intended job of stopping erosion. With good choice of alignment, and properly designed open drains they can usually be avoided. The exception is at the entrance to culverts taking run-off under the road, where drop-inlet structures are usually desirable. (Figure 13.4.) They give better entry conditions to the culvert, perhaps allowing the use of a smaller pipe, they lower the effective gradient in the drain, and they reduce the depth of excavation necessary in the drain.

13.3.3   Stabilization of banks and cuttings

Steeply sloping earth banks are liable to land-slides and the key to the control of this form of erosion lies with drainage. Wet soil has both a greater weight and a reduced resistance to deformation, so a bank which is stable when dry can become unstable when wet. As with all drainage, the first principle is to intercept and divert as much water as possible before it arrives at the point where it becomes a nuisance. When a road has been cut into the side of a hill, giving a steep bank on the hill side of the road, it is most probable that above the bank there is more hillside from which surface run-off comes down towards the road. This should be diverted by stormwater drains, designed as the diversion drains to protect arable land (section 8.2). The diversion drain should be sited at some distance uphill from the edge of the embankment. If the drain is close to the edge there is the danger that when flowing full it will add to the weight, and also seepage from the drain may aggravate the very problem it is trying to solve. To avoid this the drain is sometimes built as a bank only, ie, without any excavated channel.

Drainage of the sloping face of the bank is usually carried out by rubble drains, that is drains excavated to a rectangular section of about 300 to 500 mm square and backfilled with rocks. The drains may be laid out straight up and down the slope of the bank, or on a herringbone pattern. If a vertical retaining wall is built at the foot of the slope it is important that it should have weep-holes to allow drainage. A free-draining material is usually placed behind the foot of the wall so that water can move laterally along to the weep-holes.

The other erosion hazard, that of surface erosion of the bank, is best controlled by vegetation, but the difficulty lies in establishing a dense vegetation on a steeply sloping bank of usually infertile subsoil. The

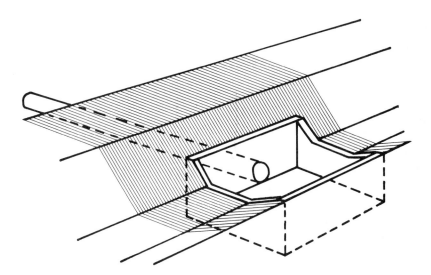

FIGURE 13.4 *Drop inlets improve road culverts*

planting techniques to help establish vegetation are the same as those used in gully control (section 12.4.2), that is replacing the top soil when this is practical, or planting in pockets of good soil, and the use of fertilizer and mulches.

Straw and hay are the most commonly used mulching materials, but any organic material will serve provided it can be finely divided and evenly spread. In the United States successful use has been made of *excelsior* which is fine curled wood shavings originally produced as a packing material (DUFFY and MCCLURKIN 1967). The difficulty with mulches is that although they are very effective aids to establishing the vegetation they are easily washed off steep slopes, and usually require some form of fastening down on slopes steeper than about 2 to 1. Several types of netting are manufactured specially for this purpose in the United States, some being woven from twisted kraft paper yarns, and others from jute yarns. To use these, the slope is smoothed, seeded and fertilized, then the layer of mulch is spread, and the netting unrolled over the mulch and anchored by wire staples rather like an oversized version of those used to fasten papers together. The netting which is intended only to anchor a straw mulch is very light with a loose open weave. Others, more closely woven from coarser yarns, can themselves serve as the mulch and are stapled directly to the soil after seeding and fertilizing. Some examples of the netting and its use are shown in plates 13.2 and 13.3. Transport costs make the use of the American

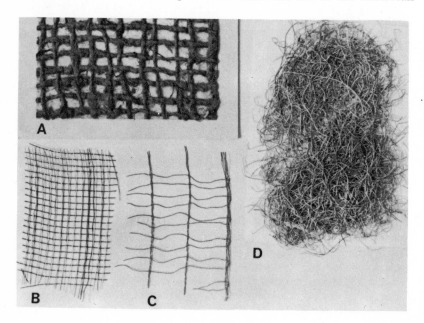

PLATE 13.2 *Some materials used to assist the stabilization of slopes. A 'Jute-net', B 'Erosionet', C 'Mulch-net', D 'Excelsior'*

PLATE 13.3 *'Erosionet' used to control erosion during establishment of grass in the central reservation of a 2-lane highway in the United States*

nettings uneconomical in most other countries, but where a fibre industry is already established the manufacture of a cheap local substitute
may be possible.

Another technique which is finding increasing favour for accelerating
the establishment of vegetation on slopes is the *spray-on* method. A
mixture of water, grass seed, fertilizer, and a filler is sprayed through a
high-pressure hose to form a thin film on the soil surface. One material
used as the filler is finely ground cellulose fibres, and this has the effect
of both forming a thin protective mulch against rain erosion, and also
providing enough moisture for the seed to germinate if no rain falls for
a few days after application. Since the mulch is a layer of unconnected
particles it is not resistant to surface flow and so this technique is only
suitable for gentle slopes (KILL and FOOTE 1969). Mineral fillers based
on gypsum, or perlite, or vermiculite are also used.

Alternatively, instead of a filler to bulk up the mixture, there may be
added a water-based emulsion, and examples in use are oil, bitumen
and latex. This kind of mixture sprays a thin surface layer which in
effect sticks down the soil particles, while not restricting germination,
indeed often improving it. For some of these emulsion mixtures the
recommended procedure is to first prepare a seed bed, apply the seed
and fertilizer, and then spray the mixture on top. In other cases the
seed and fertilizer may be added to the sprayed mixture.

A technique for combining the bulk of a straw mulch with the fixing
power of bitumen is also available. Two nozzles are used, one spraying
chopped straw blown by air, the other spraying a bitumen emulsion in
water. The streams of material from the two nozzles intermingle before
landing on the soil surface.

Yet another method uses a synthetic material—glass fibre. A continuous thread of glass fibre is sprayed out of a special high-pressure air
nozzle, and the air unravels the thread to form a light foam-like mulch
over the soil surface. The operator carries a 10 kgm roll of the glass
fibre thread in a shoulder container. Although more expensive than
organic mulches which are usually waste material, glass fibre has the
advantage of being not subject to decomposition. On steep slopes the
mulch can be anchored by spot applications of bitumen.

The spray-on methods are all fairly expensive either because of the
materials or high labour costs. They therefore find little application in
the control of erosion on farm land, but are being increasingly used for
the control of roadside erosion where the cost is justified by the need
to establish vegetation quickly.

13.4 RECLAMATION OF ERODED AREAS

Some land is destined by nature to be barren and subject to severe
erosion and it would be impractical and uneconomic to try to convert it
to productive farmland. But other land has slipped into a poor state
through mis-use or neglect and it is here that reclamation measures are

justified. I like to divide the problem quite arbitrarily into rejuvenation —that is when all that is required is a helping hand to improve a potentially stable situation (like aspirin for a healthy body temporarily out of sorts), and restoration, that is when there is something organically wrong which must be cured before the patient can recover.

13.4.1 Rejuvenation

To continue the medical simile, the symptoms of land requiring rejuvenation are easily recognized—sparse vegetation, high run-off, low infiltration, high rates of soil erosion—but which is the cause, and which the effect? The poor cover leads to the high run-off/low infiltration water balance, which in turn prevents better vegetation. The problem is how to turn this downward spiral into a rising spiral of better cover giving more available moisture, producing better cover. The corrective technique is to try to identify the limiting factor and improve it. Perhaps the problem is the rainfall/run-off relationship—there is sufficient rainfall for a better growth, but too much is lost as surface run-off. Some mechanically constructed storage like furrows, listing, or one of the other methods discussed in section 13.2 may increase the available moisture enough to change the whole pattern.

Alternatively the basic limitation may be an inherent lack of fertility, or a chemical imbalance which inhibits plant growth. Application of chemical amendments or of manures, or of artificial fertilizer may be the solution. Or perhaps the present vegetation is unable to make the best use of the ingredients for plant growth which are already available, and an improved variety or a different species could profitably be introduced. In the United States some dramatic improvements of range land have been achieved by replacing the indigenous scrub vegetation with improved grass varieties.

13.4.2 Restoration

When the situation is so bad that major remedial measures are required, an attack on the water balance is frequently made by ripping or subsoiling in an attempt to improve the infiltration. This can be very effective if it is directed towards a particular problem such as breaking up a plough pan or a naturally occurring obstacle to percolation like a layer of laterite. However if the primary purpose is to improve infiltration at the surface, then ripping is an expensive way of achieving what might be done equally well by a cheap surface-scarifying operation with a disc harrow or spike-tooth harrow. Many reclamation experiments with subsoiling show after a few years an improved vegetative growth along the lines of ripping, but no trace of the vegetation spreading to the ground between. If, as is often the case, the problem is poor surface infiltration, then instead of ripping to perhaps half a metre in depth at spacing of a metre or so, a better result would be achieved more efficiently and cheaply by an all-over discing operation. Considerable success is reported from Australia in the reclamation of what are locally known as *scald* areas (JONES 1966) and in South Africa in the restoration and improvement of the *veld*, the unimproved grazing lands. (SCOTT 1967.)

13.5 CONTROL OF STREAMBANK EROSION

In terms of the area affected, streambank erosion is a small problem, but its significance increases when other factors are considered. Land subject to surface erosion is only partly damaged, but land lost by bank erosion is completely and irretrievably lost, and what is more, the bottom lands of valley floors are nearly always valuable and highly productive. Bank erosion may also threaten roads and bridges with much more serious economic consequences than the value of the lost land. Considered as a source of sediment polluting the stream, bank erosion is important because all the soil goes directly into the stream with no possibility of any of it being trapped or filtered out.

13.5.1 Choice of control methods

On large rivers the main damaging action is the scour of the river flow, undermining the banks and causing their collapse. The regulation and control of the size of the flood is outside the scope of this book, and the practical issue is how to minimize the damage done by the existing floods. One of the factors to be considered is the variation in the level of the river or stream. A river whose flood height is several metres above the normal level of flow is going to require much more extensive bank protection than one whose flood rise is small.

Although most damage to the banks results from scour by the stream flow, another cause is surface run-off over the edges of the bank, and this aspect is more important in the case of smaller streams. Particularly vulnerable points are where man-made concentrations of water are discharged into the stream such as from drains and from mechanical protection works.

The risk of damage is increased when cultivation takes place right up to the edge of the stream or watercourse. If the natural vegetation is left undisturbed along the edge, this both slows down the surface run-off on its way into the stream, and also the stream in flood has its edges flowing over ground protected by vegetation, not over ploughed land. In Rhodesia there is legislation which prohibits all cultivation or disturbance of the natural vegetation within 30 metres of the·flood level of any stream or river.

Another example of streambank damage being affected by agricultural use is the cultivation of vegetable gardens in the bed of seasonally dry rivers (plate 13.4). The apparently dry sand deposits in the river bed often contain plenty of water not far below the surface. This allows the production of dry-season vegetables in small gardens temporarily cultivated well below the rainy season level of the stream. Shallow wells dug in the sand also provide water for domestic use and for cattle. The result is the disturbance or removal of the natural vegetation in the stream bed and on the banks, and much traffic up and down the banks, so that when the seasonal floods arrive the rate of stream bank erosion is increased. There is no easy solution to this problem for to restrict the use of ground below flood level would be to eliminate a useful source of food production.

Attempts to prevent or reduce streambank erosion fall into two groups—those directed towards making the floods less damaging, and

PLATE 13.4 *Vegetable gardens can make use of the water below the surface of the dry stream bed, but the next floods will carry away vast amounts of soil*

those directed towards making the banks more resistant, and these will each be considered in turn.

13.5.2   Controlling the streamflow

The principle is either to deflect the water away from vulnerable points, or to slow it down so that it is less erosive. Slowing the water may result in the deposition of sediment load, and this can further help protect vulnerable places. To deflect the flow away from the banks, jetties or groynes are built out from the bank, either at right angles or with a downstream deflection. Vertical timber piling is often used in deep water, or stone or concrete blocks. The use of *gabions* or wire baskets filled with rocks was described in section 12.5.2. on gully control, and these are also very effective for building groynes. The main advantage is that they have enough flexibility to readjust to localized scour when a rigid structure might crack.

An alternative approach is to build retards or permeable spurs, which stick out into the stream like jetties, but slow down the stream rather than divert it. Timber is the usual material, although prefabricated metal frames have been used in America. To save the laborious and expensive driving of piles into the river bed to anchor the retard it is common practice to hold it against the force of the water by wire cables fastened from the bank to the outer end of the structure. Illustrations and diagrams of the methods used in America are shown in AYRES (1936) and BENNETT (1939).

13.5.3   Protecting the bank

Instead of controlling the streamflow, or perhaps in addition to such measures, the approach may be to protect the bank against erosion. Vegetation is unlikely to be successful on its own for the deeper fast-flowing turbulent flow of a stream is much more erosive than the shallow smooth flow which can be kept to non-scouring velocities in a grassed waterway. However when unstable banks are shaped to a gentler slope they require vegetation to protect them from rain erosion and surface run-off, and some protection against scour by the stream may also be obtained. The requirements of such vegetation are rapid growth and a dense shallow rooting system. Willows (*Salix*) are very suitable and can be used in several ways. Complete rooted bushes may be planted, or cuttings will strike easily in moist soil. A technique reported by AYRES (1936) as having been introduced by a Mr Scheifele is to bury willow poles in shallow trenches extending from just below low water level and extending up the slope to the top of the bank. With the butts in water the poles develop a spreading root system, and send up shoots at every joint. The trenches are spaced about a metre apart, so a uniform cover soon develops.

But vegetation alone is seldom sufficient protection against the scour of the stream, so mechanical protection is usually necessary. One of the simpler methods is mats woven from flexible tree or bush cuttings, and willows are also commonly used for this purpose. The banks are shaped to a smooth slope of 1 in 2 or flatter, and the mats are secured on the banks by wiring them down onto stakes driven through the mats. The mats are continued down below the water line, and the underwater parts are weighted down by large rocks or concrete slabs.

Other materials for permanent protection works on sloping banks are masonry and concrete, both effective but expensive. The disadvantage of concrete, its lack of flexibility, can be overcome by using concrete panels joined together by flexible couplings. Dry walling built of selected undressed stones is called *rip-rap* in America. A cement grout can be brushed in if required. Gabions have been mentioned for gully control (section 12.5.2) and for jetties (section 13.5.2), and they can also be used to build vertical or stepped walls. For protecting sloping banks a variation is used called the *Reno Mattress*. This is the same kind of wire mesh basket filled in situ with stones and rock, but is wider and thinner. Each unit is 6 m long, by 2 m wide, with a choice of 170, 230 or 290 mm depth. Each unit is divided internally into 10 separate compartments each 0·6 m long, and this prevents the stone slipping down to the lower end (plate 13.5).

PLATE 13.5 *The 'Reno mattress' is a wide and shallow form of gabion used to give protection to sloping banks*

Yet another variation is the *sack gabion* which can be used on steeply sloping banks requiring protection above and below the water level. The empty gabions, shaped like huge sausages, are hung over the edge of the bank for ease of filling, and when full are lifted by crane and lowered into position in the water (plate 13.6).

PLATE 13.6   *Sack gabions are used to protect banks in deep water. They are filled in the vertical position while hanging down the bank, then lowered into position by crane*

References

AYRES, Q. C. 1936 *Soil Erosion and Its Control.* McGraw-Hill, New York and London

BENNETT, H. H. 1939 *Soil Conservation.* McGraw-Hill, New York and London

CHAPMAN, G. 1948 Size of Raindrops and their Striking Force on the Soil Surface in a Red Pine Plantation. *Transactions of the American Geophysical Union* 29, 664

CUSKELLY, S. L. 1969 Erosion-Control Problems and Practices on National Forest Lands. *Transactions of the American Society of Agricultural Engineers* 12, 1, 69–70, 85

DISEKER, E. G. and E. C. RICHARDSON 1962 Erosion Rates and Control Methods on Highway Cuts. *Transactions of the American Society of Agricultural Engineers* 5, 2, 153–155

DUFFY, P. D. and D. C. McCLURKIN 1967 Stabilizing Gully Banks with Excelsior Mulch and Lobolly Pine. *Journal of Soil and Water Conservation* 22, 2, 70

HUGGARD, E. R. 1958 *Forest Engineering Handbook*, Hefer, Cambridge

JOHNSON, A. W. 1961 Highway Erosion Control. *Transactions of the American Society of Agricultural Engineers* 4, 1, 144–152

JONES, R. M. 1966 Scald reclamation Studies in the Hay District
Part I Natural Reclamation of Scalds
Part II Reclamation by Ploughing
Part III Reclamation by Ponding Banks
Part IV Scald soils: Their Properties and Changes with Reclamation
Journal of the Soil Conservation Service of New South Wales
Part I 22, 3, 147–158; Part II 22, 4, 213–230; Part III 23, 1, 57–64 (1967); Part IV 25, 1, 104–120 (1969)

KILL, D. L. and L. E. FOOTE, 1969 Comparisons of Long and Short Fibred Mulches. Paper 69–703 presented to 1969 *Winter Meeting of American Society of Agricultural Engineers*

RENNER, F. G. and B. W. ALLRED, 1962 Classifying Rangeland for Conservation. *Agricultural Handbook* 235, *United States Department of Agriculture, Soil Conservation Service*

SCOTT, J. D. 1967 Advances in Pasture Work in South Africa Part I— Veld. *Herbage Abstracts*, 37, 1, 1–9

SEESTROM, W. R. 1966 Highway Routes in Undeveloped Areas. *Photogrammetric Engineering*, 32, 1, 121–125

TURNER, A. K. 1963 The Control of Roadside Erosion. *Overseas Bulletin* 17, *Road Research Laboratory*

VINCENT, V. 1962 The Planning Procedures of the Federal Department of Conservation and Extension—Ranch Planning, *African Soils*, 7, 7–17

Chapter 14　Wind erosion and its control

14.1　FACTORS AFFECTING WIND EROSION

In Chapter 1 the opinion was expressed that considered on a world scale the erosion caused by rainfall is more serious than that caused by wind, and that is one reason why this book concentrates much more on water erosion. But this does not mean that wind erosion is less serious everywhere, and there are areas where wind erosion is just as calamitous as the worst water erosion.

The point was also made that on a continental scale wind erosion is mainly confined to the arid and semi-arid climates. But this does not alter the fact that very serious local wind erosion can occur in humid areas. When a moderate total of annual rainfall is concentrated into part of the year, the remainder may be completely dry and so vulnerable to wind erosion. This situation may also result in water erosion and wind erosion both being major problems in the same area, although the more usual situation is of either one or the other occurring, but not both together.

Another reason for localized high rates of wind erosion in climates and regions where it is not widespread is the particular vulnerability to wind erosion of some soil types. One example is dry structureless sands in coastal areas which are subject to stronger winds than inland areas, and also have little cohesion to resist movement. Another example is light organic soil such as the fen soils in the eastern parts of England. Again these are liable to be subjected to above average winds, and have low resistance to movement, in this case because of their low weight.

Ignoring these localized special cases the factors which in general affect the likelihood of wind erosion are the soil conditions, the rainfall, and the vegetation.

The physical nature of the soil will affect the ease with which particles are dislodged, but far more important than these is the fact that only dry soil blows, and any soil will be unmoved by wind while its surface is moist. Climate therefore has a big influence on wind erosion, particularly the extent to which the soil will be dried by hot winds and low humidity, and also the rainfall. Wind erosion is more frequent when the mean annual rainfall is low, and as a rough guide areas most affected are those with less than about 300 mm, and those with higher rainfall but long dry periods. The third factor is the vegetation, for soil is almost immune to wind erosion when covered with a carpet of vegetation. This physically prevents the wind coming into direct contact with the soil in the same way that a good cover of vegetation reduces splash erosion.

For any given soil conditions the amount of soil which will be blown depends on two factors, the wind velocity and the roughness of the soil surface. Naturally a high wind velocity can move more particles and larger particles than a slower wind, in the same way that the sediment carrying capacity of flowing water increases with velocity. An empirical formula suggested by SCHWAB *et al* (1966) for this relationship is

$$S \propto (V - V_0)^3 \, d^{0.5}$$

where S is the quantity of soil moved

V is the wind velocity

V_0 is the minimum wind velocity which can move particles of this size

d is the diameter of the particles.

The roughness of the soil surface determines the frictional effect which it exerts on the wind, and so affects the wind gradient, that is the variation of velocity with height above the surface. The different wind gradients over a smooth soil and a rough cloddy surface are shown in figure 14.1. The considerable difference in the velocities at about 0·3 metres above the surface is important because it will be shown later that most soil movement occurs below that depth.

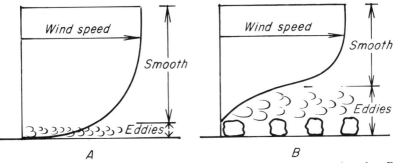

FIGURE 14.1   *Wind gradients over a smooth surface A, and over a rough surface B*

Since wind erosion is restricted to dry soils, and the amount is dependent upon wind velocity and ground roughness, we shall find that control measures are directed towards changing one or more of these factors, that is by maintaining soil moisture, reducing the wind velocity, or increasing soil roughness.

14.2   SOIL MOVEMENT BY WIND

14.2.1   Types of movement

Three distinct kinds of movement occur, depending upon the size of the soil particles.

Suspension is the movement of very fine particles, mainly less than 0·1 mm diameter. Stokes' law relates the speed of a body falling through a fluid to the square of the particle diameter, and the falling speed of such small particles is so low that once lifted they can remain suspended for long periods of time by the turbulence and eddy currents of the air. Dust storms are fine particles in suspension and can result in large amounts of soil being moved long distances.

Creep is the movement of particles at the other end of the size scale and which are rolled along the surface of the ground, pushed by the force of the wind and other particles moving with the wind. Theoretically there is no upper limit to the size of particle which could be rolled, but in practice most rolling particles are found to be in the size range 0·5 mm to 1 or 2 mm diameter.

Saltation is by far the most important of the three forms of movement. For one thing more soil is moved in this way than either of the other two, and also neither creep nor suspension occur without there being saltation. The movement is by a series of low bounces over the surface, and it occurs among the middle size of particles, light enough to be sometimes lifted off the surface, but too large to go into suspension. The size range of particles which may move in saltation is from 0·05 mm to 0·5 mm diameter, with most movement among particles 0·1 to 0·15 mm diameter. The kind of movement of a soil particle is thus determined by its size, as shown in figure 14.2. The dividing lines are naturally not very precise, with some overlap. The form of this bouncing movement is shown in figure 14.3 and starts with a particle rising into the airstream under the action of forces discussed shortly. The vertical speed falls off under the action of gravity, and at the same time the particle picks up lateral velocity from the wind. After rising to a peak which is only a few centimetres high it starts to fall, but continues to accelerate laterally under the force of the wind, and so returns to the soil in a long flat glide path, striking the soil with high energy.

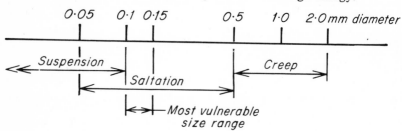

FIGURE 14.2   *The form of movement by wind is a function of particle size*

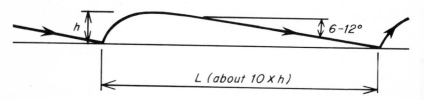

FIGURE 14.3   *The path of a particle moving in saltation*

Sometimes rotating particles have a very rapid spinning motion in flight, but it is not clear how often this happens. CHEPIL (1963) shows high speed photographs of wind tunnel experiments in which the majority of the particles are clearly seen to be spinning rapidly. From the exposure time, the speed of rotation can be calculated as between 1 200 and 60 000 revolutions per minute. On the other hand, photographs of other wind tunnel experiments by BAGNOLD (1953) show only isolated particles spinning, and Bagnold's comment is that 'rotation does not seem to be the rule'.

There are several possible causes which separately or in combination may cause the initial upward movement of a particle going into saltation. In the collisions between grains rolling and bumping over the surface one may easily be bounced up into the air. A factor which helps this upward movement, although it is not strong enough to start it, is the pressure effect of wind flowing over the sand grains. An increase in the velocity of a fluid results in a decrease in pressure, known as the *Venturi effect*, which is used in the carburettor of a petrol engine to assist the flow of petrol into the airstream going to the combustion chamber. A closer example is the flow of air over the wing of an aircraft (figure 14.4). We may loosely think in terms of the thrust of the air against the lower surface of the wing, but what really happens is that the air flows over the curved upper surface faster than over the lower surface. The downward pressure of the air on the top surface is less than the upward pressure on the lower surface, so there is a net upward force which is the lift which keeps the aircraft up. Similarly there is a net upward force as the wind blows over sand particles

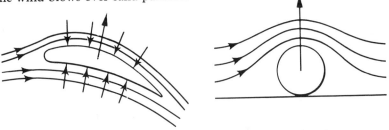

FIGURE 14.4 *Airflow over a curved surface results in a net upward force*

A third factor which can help start the saltation process is the vibration energy which a moving fluid can impart to bodies in its path. Examples are the low-frequency oscillation of water weeds in a fast-flowing stream, and the higher frequency vibration of a kite string or a telephone wire in a high wind. Dry sand grains can also pick up a very high frequency vibration energy from the wind, and cases are known of this reaching such a point that the sand emits a sound. In a chapter entitled *Singing Sands* BAGNOLD (1953) discusses a number of examples, and the conditions for this phenomenon to occur. The connexion with saltation is that when two rapidly vibrating particles touch, one may be flipped up into the air.

Finally, once any particle has gone into saltation for any of the reasons discussed, it returns to the ground with sufficient energy picked up from the wind to bounce many more particles into the air. This high energy impact of saltating particles is also a powerful force on the large grains rolling along the surface as part of the creep process.

14.2.2   The effects of wind erosion

Wind erosion, like gully erosion, is very much a case of prevention being better than cure, for like gully erosion the process is self-generating and once started becomes progressively more difficult to stop. This trend starts right at the initiation of soil movement. Just as starting friction is greater than sliding friction, so the velocity necessary to start the first particle moving (what Bagnold called the *Fluid Threshold Velocity*) is greater than the velocity required to sustain the movement (Bagnold's *Impact Threshold Velocity*). Again, once saltation has started, each moving particle picks up from the wind enough energy to start several particles moving so the effect snowballs rapidly.

This progressive acceleration of wind erosion takes place with respect to both time and space. In time, as we have just seen, the amount of soil movement increases, and there is another progressive effect in that as the finer soil particles are blown away into suspension, there is less to hold the remaining soil together. The arid zone soils most vulnerable to wind erosion tend to be poor, sandy, low in organic and colloidal matter. The loss of the finest particles reduces even further both their physical state and their fertility.

The soil movement also accelerates in space because the more soil is moving the greater is its power to move yet more soil. This effect is clearly seen in large arable fields where erosion starts in isolated spots, each of which grows rapidly in the downwind direction. Emergency tillage is a technique used to control this progression and is discussed in section 14.3.3.

An interesting point is that although the general relationship is that the rougher the surface the less the erosion (or conversely the smoother the surface the greater the erosion), yet at the limits this no longer holds. A smooth surface of very fine particles is in fact able to withstand high velocities without movement. In wind tunnel experiments cement powder was not moved at wind speeds fast enough to move pebbles of 4·6 mm diameter (BAGNOLD 1937). The reason is that smooth laminar flow occurs over the surface, and the particles are not dislodged. When the velocity necessary to start movement (fluid threshold velocity) is plotted against grain diameter, it falls to a minimum value of about 150 mm/sec for grains just less than 0·1 mm diameter, rising for grains greater or smaller than this.

All soil particles which start moving must be deposited eventually, and the form of deposition is, like the form of movement, dictated by the particle size. The large particles rolling along the surface just stop where they are as soon as there is any reduction in velocity. The medium sized particles in saltation are deposited in large amounts wherever local barriers or obstructions slow the wind. The large deposits against fences, hedges, and ditches are mainly the result of soil moving in saltation. The small particles in suspension are carried long distances in the upper atmosphere, but the principle still holds that deposition occurs when the velocity and turbulence decrease. The very large-scale deposits of loess soils in the mid-west of America, and in China, are the result of wind erosion, with the movement taking place in suspension.

In America an interesting case is reported where because wind-born soil was deposited on top of snow in Iowa it was possible to collect it separately and determine both the amount deposited (450 kgm per hectare) and also its source of origin in Texas 800 km away. Analysis of both the parent material and the deposited soil showed that the dust contained more than three times as much organic matter and nitrogen as the parent soil (BENNETT 1939).

14.2.3 Quantities of soil moved

Very large amounts of soil are moved by wind, although direct measurements are difficult and much reliance has to be placed on estimates based on extrapolation from laboratory experiments. The proportions of soil moved by the three different actions were studied in wind-tunnel experiments by CHEPIL (1945), who found that saltation accounts for the greatest part, from 55 to 72 per cent of the total, while from 3 to 38 per cent moved in suspension, and from 7 to 25 per cent by surface creep. However, it is not easy to differentiate between creep and saltation, for many particles alternate between the two movements. What is clear is that the main part of the movement takes place close to the ground, and Chepil found 50 per cent of the movement within 50 mm of the surface, and 90 per cent within 300 mm. In desert areas where the small particles have been blown away by past wind storms, the upper air may remain clear while surface movement occurs. BAGNOLD (1953) describes the curious sight of peoples' heads and shoulders projecting from a surface cloud as from the water of a swimming-bath, while their legs and bodies are invisible in the moving sand cloud near the surface.

Wind tunnel experiments have shown that very large amounts of sand are moved close to the surface, and that the amount increases rapidly with increased velocity (CHEPIL 1945). The soil moved over a strip 300 mm wide and a metre high was 222·5 kg/hour at a wind speed of 29 km/hour (490 lb/hour at 18 miles/hour), and 450 kg/hour at a wind speed of 40 km/hour (990 lb/hour at 25 miles/hour). This suggests that the movement is approximately proportional to the square of the velocity. To illustrate how big this movement is, the higher rate is equivalent to movement across the edge of a square hectare at a rate of 150 tons per hour. This movement per hour is the same order of magnitude as the movement per year by rainfall erosion.

Since soil in suspension may be up to one third of the total, the amount moved in dust storms is also very large. A much quoted estimate of the maximum probable load is 27 300 ton/km^3 (126 000 ton/mi^3), corresponding to a density of airborne material of 27·3 g/m^3, but this figure has been taken too seriously for it originated from some ingenious but not very scientific guesswork in 1896 by A. J. Udden who said of it 'It is not believed that the data presented justify any great claims for exactness for a general estimate, which is made here in the absence of a better one'. A better estimate, quoted by BENNETT (1939) is that a storm covering 13 000 km^2 (5 000 mi^2) to a height of 3 050 metres (10 000 ft) could carry 7 million tons of soil. This corresponds with a density of about 0·2 g/m^3. Estimates of the amount of dust deposited are probably more reliable, though difficult to measure except when the deposit can be collected, as from snow or ice. Reported estimates range up to 35 g/m^2 (100 ton/mi^2), and this suggests that only a very small proportion of the suspended load is deposited in one place. If all the load were instantaneously dropped, then even at the lower estimate of 0·2 g/m^3 this would amount to 600 g/m^2. In fact the dust settles slowly over a wide area as the wind becomes still, and wind-deposited loess soils are always found to occur over large areas.

14.2.4   Estimating soil loss by wind

Attempts have been made to quantify the factors which influence wind erosion in order to combine them into a numerical equation which will allow the prediction of the amount of wind erosion in given conditions. This method successfully produced the Universal Soil-Loss Equation for rain erosion (section 10.1), but in that case there was a vast amount of experimental data from field plots which allowed the calculation of the values of the empirical constants. Much less comparable data for wind erosion is available, so extrapolation from wind tunnel experiments was necessary for some factors, such as the relative erodibility of different soil types.

The equation was developed by W. S. Chepil who devoted a lifetime to the study of wind erosion and whose writings dominate the literature on the subject. Its purposes are defined by him as

1 to serve as a tool for determining the potential amount of wind erosion under existing local conditions, and
2 as a guide for determining the management conditions necessary to control wind erosion in those conditions (CHEPIL and WOODRUFF 1963).

The equation is of the form:

$$E = f(I, C, K, L, V)$$

where E is the soil loss by wind erosion
   I is the erodibility, ie, vulnerability to wind erosion
   C is a factor representing the local wind conditions
   K is the soil surface roughness

L is the width of the field in the direction of the prevailing wind
and

V is a measure of the vegetative cover.

The mathematical relationships between the factors are complicated by inter-actions, and unlike the Universal Soil-Loss Equation, they cannot simply be multiplied together to give the answer. Graphical and tabular solutions are therefore required, and were first developed for the Great Plains (WOODRUFF and SIDDOWAY 1965) and later extended to the rest of the United States (SKIDMORE and WOODRUFF 1968). Computer solutions have recently been developed (SKIDMORE *et al* 1971). While originally developed for the Great Plains, the equation has been applied in other regions, for example in New Jersey (HAYES 1965) and in the south-east (CARREKER 1966).

14.3 THE CONTROL OF WIND EROSION ON AGRICULTURAL LAND

This aspect of wind erosion is very well reviewed in great detail in other texts and so this discussion will be limited to the general principles. Readers seeking more information are recommended to see Chapter 13 of STALLINGS (1957) for control by agricultural management, and *Agricultural Development Paper* 71 (FAO 1960) for a review of the machinery used.

14.3.1 Land management

Wind erosion of serious economic consequence is mainly limited to agricultural land, for sand movement in desert areas is a geological process which only occasionally interferes with man's activities. The fundamental principle in controlling man-made accelerated wind erosion is correct land use. When the cause is improper or unsuitable land use no control by expedient will be successful without the restoration of an ecologically acceptable use of the land. The classic example of wind erosion caused by unsuitable land use was the *Dust Bowl* in the central plains of America in the 1930s. The natural vegetation, resulting from the climate of generally low rainfall with periodic severe droughts, is open prairie grassland, but the settlers from the east, accustomed to better rainfall, ploughed the prairie and planted wheat. Sometimes there would be good rains and good crops, but a period of drought years would bring crop failure and dust storms. The history of the area is of recurrent cycles of development, when the plains were ploughed and farmouses built, followed by their being abandoned a few years later when the next drought struck. As well as the variations in rainfall, there were economic pressures which were sometimes the cause and sometimes the effect of labour migrations and price fluctuations (DASSMAN 1959). Eventually after the catastrophic dust storms of 1934 and 1935 which gave the area the name *dust bowl* it was realized that most of the area is just not capable of arable production, and government financial and technical assistance were turned to the job of putting the land back into grass. On the whole the problem has now been brought under control but the Soil Conservation Service is reported to have estimated that 5·6 million hectares (14 million acres) of land under cultivation should be returned to grass (DASSMAN 1959), so perhaps even now the lesson has not been fully learned.

14.3.2   Crop management

Assuming that the form of agriculture is right for the ecological conditions, much can be done to reduce wind erosion by the choice of crop management practices, some examples of which may be briefly described.

Since soil only blows when it is dry, anything which conserves soil moisture is beneficial. Partial cropping may help by reducing the evaporation. This is done by cropping the same ground alternate years (hoping there will be build up of moisture during the fallow year) or by cropping part of the land in strips, leaving the remainder in fallow. Another approach to moisture conservation is mulching the soil surface, which both increases infiltration and reduces surface evaporation.

The maintaining of a protective cover on the surface of the soil is the key to management for wind control just as it is for control of rain erosion. In addition to the beneficial effects on moisture it also slows down the wind in the critical area close to the soil surface. Much can be achieved by the careful planning of rotations, especially if there are annual periods particularly liable to strong winds, like the great plains area where the danger periods are autumn and early spring. In the areas with sufficient rain for continuous cropping a rotation of spring wheat and autumn rye is used, each crop being seeded through the stubble of the previous crop, so that the soil is not left bare and vulnerable at the danger times.

In situations when drought has caused crop failure and so left the soil unprotected it may be appropriate to grow a crop solely for its cover effect without any expectation of obtaining a harvestable crop.

Vegetative cover is cheap and effective and so used more often than not, but other materials can be used, usually in the form of a protective film sprayed on the surface like those used for roadside stabilization and described in Chapter 13. Materials used include water-based emulsions of resin, asphalt, starch, latex, or oil. They are most likely to be cheap enough to use for this purpose when available as a by-product from a local industrial process. An example is a resinous by-product from the wood-pulp industry in Washington and Oregon, which is used on the light erodible soils of the Columbia Basin Project in the non-irrigation season. The control of wind erosion by the use of additives is more common in the cases of stabilizing sand dunes, beach sands, or mine dumps, but this is outside the scope of the present discussion.

The inclusion of periods of grass in rotations is beneficial. In addition to the grass cover ensuring good infiltration and restricting soil movement, it also leaves an improved physical structure and increased organic matter for the grain crops which follow.

Harvesting methods which leave the maximum amount of crop residue are now commonplace. A standing stubble is more effective than when it is chopped and spread on the surface, and the taller the stubble the better. Hybrid varieties with very uniform growth make it possible to set the combine harvesters high to take very little of the stalk with the heads.

Conventional methods of land preparation and weed control aim to invert the soil and bury the surface vegetation. Since this is just what is not required for wind erosion control, special tillage practices and implements are often used. Chisel ploughs can be used instead of discs or mouldboards, and subsurface tillage gives weed control without disturbing the surface. Two implements used for this purpose are the rod-weeder and the duck-foot cultivator (figure 14.5). The rod-weeder is a square bar which revolves as it is drawn through the soil 50 to 100 mm below the surface, loosening weed roots without disturbing the surface mulch. The duck foot cultivator achieves a similar effect with flat V-shaped sweeps.

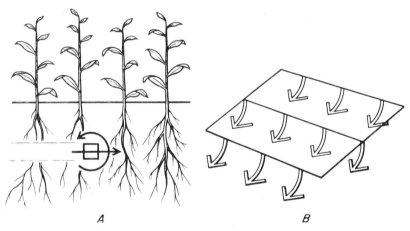

FIGURE 14.5   *Two implements for subsurface cultivation*
A Rod weeder   B Duck-foot cultivator

Another approach to reducing wind erosion is to slow down the wind by physical barriers. These may be in the form of an increased roughness of the soil surface or by planted vegetative barriers. Ordinarily in arable farming the objective is to create as fine and smooth a seedbed as possible, but when wind erosion is likely the opposite is the case. The surface should be as rough and cloddy as is compatible with being able to seed the crop. For row crops the roughness may be further increased

by ridges about 200–300 mm high (8–12 in.) spaced about twice this
distance apart. The furrows prevent surface movement by saltation or
creep and the tops of the ridges are rough and cloddy, so resistant to
erosion. Obviously the ridges must run at right angles to the prevailing
wind direction.

Vegetative barriers may be created by strip-cropping with alternate
bands of tall and short crops. For example, strips of tall sorghum
stubble can be left standing through the winter to give protection to
wheat when it is small and vulnerable the following spring. Another
example is the rotation wheat, sorghum, fallow, when strips of each
progress across the land. When the land is to be ploughed, leaving unploughed strips of stubble has the same effect—anything which breaks
the flat even regularity is helpful.

Windbreaks and shelter belts are the other way of creating physical
barriers, and they are efficient and successful in areas like the Great
Plains which are marginal for crop production with a rainfall of up to
400 or 500 mm. However in many areas where wind erosion is pre-
valent the low rainfall is unlikely to be sufficient for good tree growth.
This matters because the effect of windbreaks is a function of their
height. For example the wind velocity is reduced to 40% of the open
velocity at a distance downwind of 4 times the height of the windbreak.
Low windbreaks will therefore only be effective if they are so closely
spaced that they interfere with farming operations. The effect, and the
selection, establishment, and management of windbreaks are thoroughly
discussed by READ (1964).

14.3.3 Tillage techniques and implements

When wind erosion is likely, the objectives of tillage are to keep the soil
as rough as is compatible with growing the crop. In general terms, any
implement or operation which roughens is desirable, and any which
pulverizes and smooths is undesirable. A convenient way of describing
the implements used is therefore under these headings.

The main group of implements whose roughening is desirable are
ploughs, ridgers, and cultivators. Among the types of plough, mouldboards find least favour for they bury more crop residues and have a
higher draft. Discs have lighter draft, and are better in rough or stony
conditions, or working through a heavy mulch, but they partly bury
the residues. Chisel ploughs are very suitable, whether the rigid tine
or spring-shank type. The *stump-jump* chisel plough used in Australia
and Africa prevents shock load damage on striking boulders or tree
stumps.

Ridgers, called *listers* in America, are like ploughs with two opposed
mouldboards, the most common size being 360 mm (14 in.) across the
wings. They are usually mounted on a tool bar so the spacing between
ridges is adjustable.

The duck-foot cultivator was mentioned earlier for sub-surface weed
control, but it is also widely used for seed bed preparation. Many

different shapes of shank and of working points are used in different conditions, and the choice of these and the speed of operation will give different effects. But the main point is that the action is of bursting through and stirring the soil, of roughening it and bringing up clods, not pulverizing or smoothing.

A second group of implements are useful in particular situations. The one-way disc is something between a disc plough and a disc harrow, with large discs up to 610 mm (24 in.) diameter. It is useful in the system called *trash farming* when large amounts of crop residues are broken up and partly buried in the plough layer.

Shallow cultivations by small duck-foot sweeps have been mentioned for seed-bed preparation and for weed control, and a similar implement with much larger V-shaped sweeps is used at greater depth as a primary tillage tool when crop residues are on the surface. The blades are usually from 760 mm to over 2 metres in width (30 in. to 7 ft), and a rolling coulter cuts residues ahead of the shank (figure 14.6). The depth of operation is up to 200 mm (8 in.). Like all sub-surface tillage implements it can only be operated in soils free from stones, boulders, and tree stumps and roots.

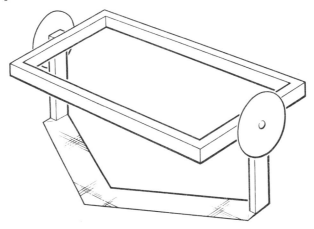

FIGURE 14.6   *The large V-sweep used for primary tillage*

Another tool with a special purpose use is the rotary cultivator or rotary weeder. This is the implement shown in figure 14.7 and not to be confused with the power driven *Rotavator* or *Rotary Hoe*. This implement was originally designed for high-speed shallow tillage to control small weeds in maize lands. It is sometimes called a *culti-packer* or *skew-treader* and can be drawn in either direction. When drawn one way the tines penetrate up to 75 mm (3 in.) for cultivation, and the other way they pack the soil, with negligible penetration. In wind erosion control its use is in large gangs at high speed to spread evenly over the surface any crop residues left in rows by harvesting or cultivating machinery.

The implements to be avoided in wind erosion areas are those which break down the soil, and leave it smooth and vulnerable. All harrows fall in this category, with disc-harrows and spike-tooth harrows being the least desirable. Spring-tooth harrows are less damaging, but chisel cultivators will do a similar job with less pulverization. Power-driven rotary hoes of the conventional type should be avoided, for they give a well-aerated finely-divided seed bed which may be ideal for germination but is the condition most vulnerable to wind erosion. However the introduction of slow-speed machines, sometimes called rotary spaders, which turn up large clods may present this method of tillage in a much more favourable light.

Planting equipment suitable for wind erosion conditions is as important as tillage equipment. Desirable features are the ability to seed through a surface mulch and to leave the surface rough. A very successful type is the deep-furrow drill which works well in heavy residues, pushing up a ridge on either side and planting in the furrow between.

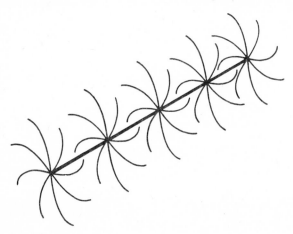

FIGURE 14.7   *The rotary weeder, useful for spreading mulches*

14.3.4   Emergency tillage

In dry areas which are marginal for crop production a lot of farming is speculative, that is a gamble on the seasonal rainfall being adequate, and the hope that the successes of the good years will pay for the failures of the droughts. It is usually done on a large scale with a minimum investment in production costs. In this situation when the soil starts to blow and it is obvious that left unchecked it will worsen until the crop is ruined, then it is economic to sacrifice part of the crop if by so doing the remainder can be saved. Emergency tillage is the ripping of rough strips through the field at right-angles to the wind in order to temporarily halt the surface movement by saltation and creep. In serious cases the ridger is used but the chisel plough is quicker and cheaper, and may give sufficient protection in less serious situations. Control is more easily achieved in medium textured soils because it is easier to throw up clods than in sandy soils. Emergency tillage is essentially a temporary measure to obtain control until more permanent solutions can be applied.

References

BAGNOLD, R. A. 1937 The Transport of Sand by Wind. *Geographical Journal*, 89, 409–438

BAGNOLD, R. A. 1941 *The Physics of Blown Sand and Desert Dunes.* Methuen, London

BENNETT, H. H. 1939 *Soil Conservation.* McGraw-Hill, New York and London

CARREKER, J. R. 1966 Wind Erosion in the South-east. *Journal of Soil and Water Conservation*, 21, 3, 86–88

CHEPIL, W. S. 1945 Dynamics of Wind Erosion (Parts I to V). *Soil Science* 60, 305–320, 397–411, 475–480 (1945), 61, 167–177, 257–263 (1946)

CHEPIL, W. S. 1950 Properties of Soil which Influence Wind Erosion (Parts I to V). *Soil Science* 69, 149–162, 403–414 (1950), 71, 141–153 (1951), 72, 387–401, 465–478 (1951)

CHEPIL, W. S. and N. P. WOODRUFF 1963 The Physics of Wind Erosion and its Control. *Advances in Agronomy* 15, 211–302

DASMANN, R. F. 1959 *Environmental Conservation.* Wiley, New York

HAYES, W. A. 1965 Wind Erosion Equation useful in Designing North Eastern Crop Protection. *Journal of Soil Water Conservation*, 20, 4, 153–155

READ, R. A. 1964 Tree Windbreaks for the Central Great Plains, *Agricultural Handbook* 250, *Forest Service, United States Department of Agriculture*

FAO 1960 Soil Erosion by Wind and Measures for its Control. *Agricultural Development Paper* 71, FAO

SCHWAB, G. O., R. K. FREVERT, T. W. EDMINSTER and K. K. BARNES 1966 *Soil and Water Conservation Engineering* (2nd Edition), Wiley, New York

SKIDMORE, E. L. and N. P. WOODRUFF 1968 Wind Erosion Forces in the United States and their Use in Predicting Soil Loss. *Agricultural Handbook* 346. *Agricultural Research Service, United States Department of Agriculture*

SKIDMORE, E. L., P. S. FISHER and N. P. WOODRUFF 1971 *Wind Erosion Equation: Computer Solution and Application. Proceedings of the Soil Science Society of America*, 35

STALLINGS, J. H. 1957 *Soil Conservation.* Prentice-Hall, Englewood Cliffs, New Jersey

UDDEN, J. A. 1896 Dust and Sand Storms in the West. *Popular Science Monthly*, 49, 655–664

WOODRUFF, N. P. and F. H. SIDDOWAY 1965 A Wind Erosion Equation. *Proceedings of the Soil Science Society of America*, 29, 5, 602–608

Chapter 15   Erosion research methods

15.1   The purpose of erosion research

15.1.1   The need for research

A national programme of soil conservation needs to be based on factual information about rates and quantities of erosion. For example some land obviously needs to be protected by mechanical works such as channel terraces, some land equally obviously does not, and a great deal of land lies somewhere between the two extremes. At some point the terraces become unnecessary or uneconomic but a logical decision on where to draw the line can only be made if data is available on how much soil erosion is occurring, and how much it would be reduced by terraces. Similarly, the effect of channel terraces should be compared with the effect of alternative measures, and the effect should also be measured on the different soils and crops which are likely to be encountered. A great deal of research on these subjects has already been carried out, particularly in the last twenty years, at first almost entirely in the United States but increasingly in other countries. Much of the resulting information can be usefully applied in countries other than where the research was done, or the results can be thought of as a pilot experiment to show which factors should be studied locally. Often it is sufficient to measure how local conditions compare with other conditions which have already been investigated. For example, if it can be shown that the soils and rainfall of a region are similar to those of some part of the United States then a store of useful information becomes available. Even when local conditions of climate, soil, or land use are so different that the search for information has to start from the beginning, the techniques and apparatus already developed will still be helpful.

15.1.2   Defining the objectives

Before deciding on a research programme it is important to define very clearly the objectives. If the purpose is to obtain a practical answer to a practical problem, such as which of two popular rotations is more subject to erosion, then the experimental procedures will be very different from those required to establish long-term fundamentals like the erosive power of the local rainfall. The scale of the experiments also needs to be considered, for analytical studies of detailed points might be done on small plots or in the laboratory, but practical farming operations can only be tested on plots large enough for farm-scale practices. The required accuracy must be agreed, for a precise and accurate technique will be wasted if the question is simply 'which of two alternatives is better?'

The use of statistics in the design of experiments and the treatment of results is a difficult problem. HAYWARD (1968) has looked closely at the results of many field plot experiments and come to the conclusion that few of them have been scientifically tested. On the other hand the approach commonly taken by the practical conservation research worker is that he is 'measuring differences so large that they don't need statistics to explain them'—a most unscientific opinion although it has great appeal to the field worker. In most situations a compromise somewhere between the extreme positions will give the best results. It is important to avoid collecting a great mass of information which is of little value because its reliability is questionable. On the other hand practical conservation policies are not going to be influenced by the value of the third decimal place. If conservation research is to be effective, the results must at some point be translated into action on the ground.

15.2 RECONNAISSANCE STUDIES OF EROSION

15.2.1 The accuracy of measurements

Quantitative measurements of erosion are most frequently and most accurately obtained from permanent plots, but this method is not always suitable. For example exploratory trials to establish the order of magnitude of the loss do not warrant fixed plots. Another case is measuring localized erosion which cannot be fitted onto a plot, like erosion in gullies, or on roads, or caused by overgrazing. In such cases the order of accuracy required may be very different from that which is suitable for measuring the soil loss from different crop rotations. If all the soil eroded from a field plot is collected in tanks and weighed, then even a coarse measurement of the weight gives an accurate estimation of the soil loss. For example if the soil lost from a plot of 100 m² is measured to the nearest 0·1 kg this corresponds to an estimate of soil loss to the nearest 10 kg/ha. By comparison a direct measurement of the level of the soil surface is a very crude estimate. If the change were measured to the nearest millimetre this corresponds with an estimate of the soil loss to the nearest 15 000 kgm/ha, ie, the accuracy is about 1 500 times less! (In imperial units the soil loss from a plot of 1/50 acre, measured to the nearest $\frac{1}{4}$ lb, corresponds to 1/200 ton/acre. Measuring the change in height to $\frac{1}{25}$ in. corresponds to 7 tons/acre, ie, the accuracy is 1 400 times less.)

15.2.2 Measuring changes in surface level

For losses from arable land, estimates to the nearest 15 tons/ha (7 tons/acre) would be unacceptable, but if the losses are known to be very high, or if the loss is concentrated in small areas, a quick estimate based on change in surface level may suffice. Several methods for providing a datum for measuring the surface level are described by

GLEASON (1957). One idea is to drive into the ground 'spikes' or galvanized iron nails about 300 mm long. Measurements of the distance from the top of the spike to ground level will show changes in surface level. When cycles of erosion and deposition are likely, as often happens in gully erosion, the nail is passed through a galvanized-iron washer and driven in flush with the surface. When erosion takes place the washer descends with the soil surface but any subsequent deposition goes on top of the washer, so that it shows the lowest position and the depth of deposition.

Another simple way to record the original level is to press bottle tops into the soil surface. The depth of subsequent erosion is shown by the height of the pedestals where the soil is protected by the bottle top. Large soil movements in river beds and gullies can be assessed by spraying a collar of paint round rocks and tree roots at soil level. Erosion reveals an unpainted band below the paint line, indicating the depth of soil removed.

The direct measurement of changes in soil level is most suitable in the case of localized erosion where the rates are high and the position of the erosion can be predicted. For example the soil loss from a badly eroding road can be studied by taking an accurate cross-section of levels between two fixed bench marks one on either side of the road. Measuring the levels with sufficient accuracy is fairly easy, the problem is locating the point on the ground so that subsequent measurements can be taken at exactly the same place. Anything in the form of permanent marker posts is likely to interfere with the surface run-off and the erosion pattern. In the case of measuring erosion on grazing lands, the animals habits are easily influenced by the introduction of anything alien to them. Sometimes they will shy away from a marker so the traffic is less than normal, sometimes curiosity leads to a concentration round a bench mark. To overcome this problem a device to measure surface levels accurately on grazing land was developed by the author (HUDSON 1964a). Metal pegs were set unobtrusively at ground level in concrete blocks at intervals of 2 m (6 ft). A light aluminium girder could be fitted onto any two adjacent pegs and this gave a firm datum from which the level to the soil surface could be accurately measured at marked positions. Between readings the girder was removed so that there was no interference with cattle movement. It was possible to measure to the nearest millimetre (0·05 in.), which allowed annual changes to be clearly recognized.

15.2.3 Measuring gully erosion

When the progress of gully erosion is being studied, measurements are needed of the horizontal spread of the gully as well as vertical changes. One method is to put in a line of pegs at a fixed distance from the gully, another is to lay out a rectangular grid of pegs. In either case measurements from the datum are repeated at regular intervals to establish the rate at which the edge of the gully is moving. For this type of survey a photographic record is also useful, and quantitative estimates can be made provided the photographs are taken accurately. Markers should be established so that subsequent photographs can be taken from precisely the same point and direction, and the photograph must include some means of measuring the scale.

15.3 FIELD EXPERIMENTS

The lead in the design and operation of experimental plots for the measurement of soil and water losses has unquestionably come from the United States. The first experiments were started by the Forest Service in Utah in 1915, followed by those of Professor Miller in Missouri in 1917. Today there are many experimental sites throughout the country. The Soil Conservation Service was at one time operating 44 experiment stations, and very many others are operated by the Forest Service and other Federal Government Agencies, and by State Extension Services, Universities, and Colleges. When a centralized data handling centre was set up at Purdue University in 1954 it was able to put on punch cards the results of 65 000 storms, and 8 250 plot-years of records, and 2 500 watershed-years (WISCHMEIER 1955). Experiments have also been made in many other countries so there is no lack of information on the design and operation of field plots. Plate 15.1 shows part of the author's field experiments in Africa.

15.3.1 Plot size

A convenient way of grouping the different kinds of experiments is according to size of plot since this reflects both the object of the experiment and the nature of the data collection.

The smallest size, often called a micro-plot, is about one or two square metres. It is cheap to manufacture and instal, and so is particularly useful when large numbers are required for preliminary investigations. The example in plate 15.2 was used in Malawi to establish the order of magnitude of the difference in run-off from land with or without a surface mulch when the ground is planted to young tea bushes. The accuracy is not great, but quite sufficient for simple comparisons such as the yes-no mulch treatment. A cheap simple plot in large numbers is also suitable for a project such as establishing for the first time the relative erodibility of different soil types, but the method is not suitable for sampling the soil loss from larger catchments (HAYWARD 1969).

When it is necessary to also measure surface run-off, then longer plots are required so that the cumulative effect of the run-off increasing down the slope is reproduced, but for simple treatment the width of

PLATE 15.1   *Experimental plots at Henderson Research Station, Mazoe*

PLATE 15.2 *Micro-plots are useful for establishing the order of magnitude of the difference in run-off and erosion between simple treatments—in this case with and without a surface mulch. The stump in the centre of each plot is a newly planted tea bush*

plot can be quite narrow. One size has been used so often in America that it serves as the standard against which others are compared. The width chosen was 6 ft (approximately 2 metres), and then to give a plot size of 0·01 acre (0·004 hectare) the length of the plot was made 72·6 ft (about 22 metres). This is about the largest size of plot from which it is practical to collect the whole of the run-off, for larger plot sizes need some device to divide the run-off into fractions so that the collected portion is of manageable size. Even for plots of this size some fractioning device may be necessary in areas of high run-off. Plots of this size are suitable for cropping or rotation experiments provided that it is acceptable for the tillage operations to be carried out by hand.

Where field-scale farming operations are an essential part of the treatments under test, larger plots are used from 0·02 hectare upwards. Details of construction are given by HUDSON (1957) and MUTCHLER (1963). Unless very large storage tanks are provided, plots of this size will require some mechanical division of the run-off, and some common types of divisor are described in section 15.3.4. The more complicated equipment required for larger plots makes them expensive. Even if the cost is reduced by economies in construction (GARCIA *et al* 1963) there still remains the high labour cost of operation.

In addition to the size of the plot there is also the question of its shape, and particularly its length. It is quite clear that the length of the plot affects not only the total soil loss but also the soil loss per unit area. The relationship was discussed in section 10.5.1 and is of the form

$$E \propto L^x$$

where E is the erosion per unit area
L is the length of the slope
x is a constant with a typical value of about 0·5.

However the value of x varies for different soils, slopes, and crops, so it is not easy to adjust the results from one plot length to what they would have been from another length. Where length of slope is one of the variables in the experiment this will decide the plot lengths, but for all other cases there are two alternative approaches. One is to adopt a standard length arbitrarily chosen, like the 72·6 ft used in the United States. The alternative is appropriate when it is probable that the land will be protected by mechanical works such as channel terraces, for then the research problem is to measure the soil loss which will occur after the land has been protected. In this case the length of the plots should be the same as the distance between the terraces, and this will be determined by a formula which takes account of slope, soil, and climate, as discussed in section 8.3.1.

15.3.2 Plot boundaries

It is necessary to isolate the plot run-off from that of the surrounding area. The plot boundaries should prevent the passage into or out of the plot both above ground and below. The upslope edge of the plot particularly needs protection from water running downhill. The boundaries may be made from strips of metal, wood, or asbestos-cement set on edge in the soil, or earth ridges may be built up. A disadvantage of earth ridges is that in the process of scooping up the earth a channel is left, and this invites the concentration of run-off and the attendant danger of scour. If tractor tillage operations are part of the treatment it is convenient for the borders to be removeable as shown in plate 15.3.

At the bottom edge of the plot, the water and soil is collected in a sunken trough running the width of the plot. Any permanent materials are suitable, and brickwork, concrete, and sheet metal have all been used. Seepage underneath the collecting trough should be guarded against. If large amounts of soil are eroded, the ground level of the plot will be lowered, but the fixed lip of the collecting trough may act as a constraint reducing the erosion at that point. To overcome this problem some installations have provided for the sill to be lowered (HUDSON 1957) but this refinement is only necessary for high rates of soil loss.

PLATE 15.3   *Removable plot boundaries are necessary if tractor tillage is part of the plot treatment. In this case planks of asbestos-cement are set in the ground*

The collecting trough is usually built with a steep gradient to avoid any deposition of the eroded soil. When accurate measurements of run-off are required it is usual to provide covers since the 100% run-off from the impervious surfaces is significant when compared with the plot run-off. From the collecting trough the run-off is led through pipes or channels to the storage tanks.

15.3.3   Flumes and recorders

When a hydrograph of the rate of run-off is required, a measuring flume is installed at the outlet from the plot. For large plots the quantity of run-off is also obtained from this record by summing the rates of flow over the time duration. For smaller plots with storage tanks it is easier to obtain the quantity of run-off by measuring the volume in the tanks, and the flow recorder only provides data on rates of flow.

A range of flumes particularly suitable for this kind of work has been designed by the United States Soil Conservation Service, and full working drawings are published (USDA 1962). These are known as 'H' flumes, and the capacity ranges from 0.0028 m^3/s (0.1 cusec) to 3.08 m^3/s (110 cusecs). Plate 15.4 shows an H flume used to record the

PLATE 15.4 *An H-type flume recording run-off from the maize plot behind, which is 2 hectares (4½ acres)*

run-off from a plot of 2 hectares (4½ acres). The shape of the notch gives the desirable combination of sensitivity at low flows at the same time as large capacity at high flows. The backward slope makes the flume unlikely to be blocked by floating debris, and the floor is non-silting. If carefully manufactured to the prescribed tolerances, the calibration charts provided can be used and it is not necessary to calibrate each flume. A free fall from the outlet side of the flume is preferable, but when the available head is limited, the flume can be installed to flow with partial submergence, and calibration corrections for this are also provided up to 85% submergence. The rate of flow through the flume is a function of the depth of flow, and this is measured in a well-chamber connected to the wall of the flume. Spot measurements of depth can be made with a hook-gauge, but it is usual to instal a float-operated liquid-level recorder.

Another well-tested flow-measuring device is the Parshall flume, and construction details and rating tables are available for flumes catering for a wide range of flows (PARSHALL 1950). This flume, like the H flume, can be operated either with free flow or with partial submergence, but in the latter case measurements of the depth of flow are required at two points in the flume.

PLATE 15.5 *A divisor which takes a one-tenth sample by collecting the flow from one of ten V-notches. An HS flume (right back) measures the rate of run-off into the tanks*

PLATE 15.6 *This divisor takes a one-fifteenth sample by collecting the flow through one of fifteen vertical rows of holes drilled in a stainless steel plate*

15.3.4 Tanks and divisors

In the case of small plots all the run-off is led into a collecting tank, where it is stored until it can be measured, sampled, and recorded. For larger plots, or when large amounts of run-off are expected, it is impractical to store the whole of the run-off, and some device is used to divide it accurately so that a known fraction can be separated off and stored. A device widely used in America is the Geib divisor, which consists of a number of equal rectangular slots. The water passing through the central slot is collected and stored, while that through all the other slots runs to waste. Manufacturing instructions are published (USDA 1962) but it needs to be made to a high standard of accuracy. Several alternatives have been suggested as more appropriate to the manufacturing skills found in developing countries, and these include running the water through a number of pipes (SHERRY 1953), or through V-notches, or through holes drilled in a plate (HUDSON 1957). Some examples are shown in plates 15.5 and 15.6.

Divisors with moving parts are usually considered to be unsatisfactory because of the risk of something going wrong or getting stuck, and the only moving sampler which has achieved much success is the Coshocton revolving wheel sampler (USDA 1962). This is installed under the discharge from a flume, such as an H flume, and the force of the water turns a wheel mounted on a vertical axis. A narrow slot in the wheel passes under the stream of water on each revolution, taking a small sample each time. One disadvantage is that the size of the sample is not constant at all rates of flow.

Another sampler designed for use with an H flume, and which does attempt to adjust the size of the sample according to the flow was used by KOHNKE (1944). This consisted of a series of holes drilled in the side of the H flume, with the holes increasing in size from bottom to top, so that the sample taken at higher flow was greater in volume but therefore more nearly a constant proportion.

15.3.5 Emptying and recording

Having collected in the storage tanks a mixture of the soil and water lost from the plot (or a known proportion of it) the mixture must next be separated so the soil and water may each be measured. In fact the amount of water displaced by the soil in the mixture is so small that the volume of the run-off can be taken as the volume of the mixture. Measuring the weight of soil is more difficult. The simplest approach is to weigh a given volume of the mixture and hence determine its density. Knowing the average specific gravity of the soil particles it is possible to calculate the concentration of soil in the muddy run-off. This technique has been used (BARNETT and HOLLADAY 1965), but JACKSON (1964) showed that the accuracy is low, and developed a more accurate and reliable method. This consists of adding flocculating agents so that the soil settles quickly and firmly to the bottom. The clear supernatant water can be poured off and measured, and the thick sludge of soil is sampled for gravimetric analysis by drying and weighing. Mass-production techniques were developed so that this procedure could be used for the daily recording of the soil loss from a large number of plots. The speed of the measuring procedure is important now that the erosivity can be calculated from rainfall records for individual storms. Much more information can be obtained from experimental plots provided the losses can be measured after every storm.

15.4 RAINFALL SIMULATORS

15.4.1 The advantages and objectives

Field plot experiments depend upon natural rainfall, which is always unpredictable and frequently perverse. For many years research workers have sought to be independent by using a man-made artificial simulation of rainfall. This has two main advantages, both very important. The speed of research is greatly accelerated since the results are no longer dependent upon waiting for the right kind of rain to come at the right time, and also the efficiency of the research is increased by control of one of the most important variables. It is no longer necessary to interpolate or extrapolate the results from the storm which most nearly matched the requirements—the same storm can be created over and over until the results have been tested and confirmed. These advantages naturally only accrue from the use of an efficient simulator, and this might be defined as one which can reproduce, accurately and repeatedly, artificial rain which will have precisely the same effect on the soil as natural rain. The design objectives of simulators have therefore changed with better knowledge of the features of rainfall which cause erosion.

The earliest designers of simulators sought only to apply a given quantity of water, then the next stage was concern to apply it at intensities comparable with real rain. From about 1940 on the size of raindrops was known, so the design objective became to reproduce the drop size distribution of natural rain. Around 1950 it was shown that erosivity is linked with kinetic energy, and so the ideal simulator was expected also to reproduce this characteristic. This steady increase in knowledge of what the rainfall simulator should be trying to do, has made them increasingly effective. Today there are a number of really efficient models available to the conservation research worker, and they form one of his most valuable tools. The development of simulator studies has been reviewed elsewhere (HUDSON 1964(b), MUTCHLER 1965), so this account is concerned more with a practical description of the principles and the machines which would be of interest to anyone starting a programme of erosion research.

15.4.2 Non-pressurized droppers

Many early simulators worked by water dripping off the ends of pieces of cotton thread. The number of threads determined the amount of rain, and some control of the size of the drops was obtained by varying the size of the thread. The original design on this principle was due to Ellison in the 1940s, and was intended for laboratory use, although larger versions were also built for field studies.

When Laws' classic work established the range of drop sizes, and the relation between distribution of drop size and intensity (described in Chapter 3), more variation in drop size was required than could be achieved by thread droppers. One solution used in many designs is to use small diameter tubes or nozzles which produce drops of constant size. Glass tubing is often used, and also stainless-steel hypodermic needles. The smallest drops are produced by blowing them off the ends of nozzles before they have reached full size. Like the thread droppers, the main use of nozzle droppers has been for laboratory studies, but field models have also been made.

The basic disadvantage of both thread and nozzle droppers is that the drops can only achieve terminal velocity if they fall from a considerable height. For the largest size of drops (about 5 mm diameter) the required height is about 12 metres, and this is too high for convenient operation of a simulator, either in the laboratory or in the field.

15.4.3 Spraying simulators

The alternative to individual drop formers is pressurized spraying nozzles. Many types of nozzle have been used, some designed originally for other purposes such as irrigation or firefighting, others designed specially for imitating rainfall. The first design which set out to reproduce both the drop size distribution and the intensity of natural rain was the Type F nozzle (WILM 1943), and this was the basis of many simulators until about 1955. Then the significance of kinetic energy was appreciated (as discussed in Chapter 4) and the type F was seen to produce only about half the energy of natural rain (MEYER 1965). The main reason for this was that the nozzle sprayed upwards, and even when installed several feet above the ground the drops reached the soil surface at velocities well below terminal velocity. Once the prime importance of kinetic energy was recognized there arose a new generation of simulators with downward sprays so that drops leaving the nozzle under pressure have a better chance of accelerating to terminal velocity.

The most important breakthrough was the simulator developed by MEYER at Purdue University and called by him the *rainulator* (MEYER and McCUNE 1958). This machine was enormously complicated and expensive because the design specification called for an instrument which could be used on field plots up to 3 metres wide by 25 metres

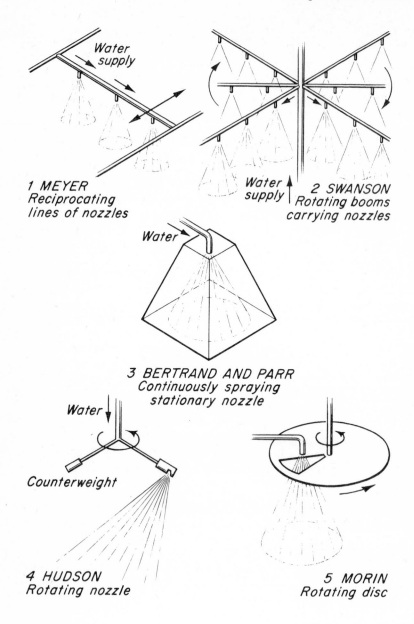

FIGURE 15.1   *The working principle of some rainfall simulators*

long (14 ft by 75 ft). Its vital feature was that it was the first simulator which was designed to reproduce a given kinetic energy, and all subsequent simulators owe something to this design. In particular the nozzles, selected after much investigation, have been adopted by most subsequent research workers.

A major difficulty with spraying simulators is that if the spray is to include drops of the largest size which occur in natural rain, then the nozzle opening has to be large—about 3 mm diameter. But even with low water pressures the intensity produced from nozzles of this size is much higher than natural rain. It is therefore necessary to have some kind of interruption of the spray to reduce the intensity to that of natural rain. In MEYER'S *rainulator* two methods were used. The spray nozzles were mounted on an overhead carriage which traversed backward and forward across the plot, and also the flow of water to the nozzles was switched on and off by solenoid valves.

This simulator was very efficient, but because it was designed for use on large plots it was complicated and expensive. Most of the subsequent developments have therefore been concerned with designing simpler or smaller machines. A disadvantage of the rainulator was the labour required to assemble it in position over the test plots, and SWANSON designed a machine to overcome this while still being suitable for plots up to 5 metres by 25 metres (SWANSON 1965). The basis of this simulator is a commercial rotating-boom irrigation machine. Ten booms, each 8 metres long are supported on a central stem which also carries the water supply to 30 nozzles on the booms (plate 15.7). The nozzles spray continuously from a height of 3 m while the machine rotates at 4 revolutions/minute, and are spaced so that even distribution is obtained over the circular area being rained on. The machine is installed at the side of the plot, so the booms can rotate over it. If two plots can be arranged side by side, with a gap between for the machine to stand in, the rain can be applied simultaneously to both plots. Plot lengths up to 15 m can be rained on by one machine, or for longer plots two machines can be used.

Large simulators like those of MEYER and of SWANSON are necessary for use on plots where field-scale farming operations are carried out, but for laboratory work or on small test plots in the field, much smaller machines are sufficient. A convenient and simple design is to use a single nozzle spraying downwards, but the difficulty is always that the kinetic energy is lower than natural rain of the same intensity. Machines of this type are suitable for studies of infiltration, such as the successful *Purdue Sprinkling Infiltrometer* (BERTRAND and PARR 1961), but with a kinetic energy of less than half that of natural rain it does not reproduce the damaging effect of rain on the soil. Even on small machines if realistic kinetic energy values are to be achieved it is necessary to reduce the intensity by intermittent application, and a small simulator which does this is shown in plate 15.8. A specially designed nozzle was fixed to an upside-down irrigation sprinkler so that it was driven

PLATE 15.7   *Swanson's rotating-boom simulator, made from a modified irrigation machine*

round by the reaction of the jets like the rotary sprinklers used to water lawns. The nozzle produced a fan-shaped spray which rotated over a hexagonal test plot. The machine was designed to be light and portable so that it could be taken to remote areas with poor road access. After the machine is set up in position it can be moved round and positioned in turn over each of the 6 hexagonal plots which are arranged in circular pattern around the supporting mast. Six replications of each test can thus be made without moving the machine (HUDSON 1965).

A completely novel approach to the problem of reducing the intensity was introduced by Morin and his co-workers (MORIN *et al* 1967). In their simulator a fixed nozzle sprays continuously, but the soil is intermittently shielded from the spray. The nozzle is directed vertically downwards, and just below it is a metal disc which rotates in the horizontal plane. A radial slot is cut in the disc, and each time this passes under the nozzle a short burst of rain passes through towards the plot below. The proportion of the spray which passes is determined by the angle of the slot, for example a 20 degree slot passes $\frac{20}{360}$ or $\frac{1}{18}$ of the total flow. This design therefore allows the use of large nozzles which give the right drop size distribution and kinetic energy, but which are not possible in other designs because of the excessive volume. In figure 15.1 the principle of this simulator is compared with that of the others which have been discussed.

PLATE 15.8 *A small circulating simulator. The inverted Y rotates under the reaction of the jets. Tests can be carried out on each of the hexagonal plots, giving 6 replications at each test site*

The frequency of the bursts of rain is controlled by the speed of rotation of the disc. A much faster rate of stopping and starting is possible than in the simulators where the nozzle moves, and so the effect is much more like continuous rain. The speed of rotation has to be limited because at high speeds the edge of the slot chops up any drops which it strikes, and so disturbs the drop size distribution. Speeds up to 200 revolutions per minute are satisfactory, and this means the bursts of rain strike the soil at a little faster than three per second, and at this rate the effect on the soil cannot be distinguished from the effect of continuous rain.

Further developments of Morin's simulator have been made at the

National College of Agricultural Engineering and include a slot which can be changed during operation so that the intensity can be varied during the simulated storm (FORREST 1970). Another variation is to cut several slots in the disc so that the frequency of the bursts of rain can be increased while keeping the speed of revolution low (BOYD 1971). Although early applications of this kind of simulator have been limited to small plots, it is very promising, and further developments may well include multiple sprayers for larger field plots.

References

BARNETT, A. P. and J. H. HOLLADAY 1965 To Weigh Dry Soil in Sludge—Fast. *Agricultural Engineering* 46, 8, 451–452

BERTRAND, A. R. and J. F. PARR 1961 Design and Operation of the Purdue Sprinkling Infiltrometer. *Research Bulletin 763, Agriculture Experiment Station*, Purdue University

BOYD, J. E. L. 1971 *The Effect of Management Practices on the Erodobility of some African Soils*, M.Phil. Thesis, University of Reading

FORREST, P. M. 1970 *The Development of Two Field Instruments to measure erosivity: A simple rainfall intensity meter, and an acoustic rainfall recorder tested with a rotating disc simulator.* B.Sc.(Hons.) dissertation, National College of Agricultural Engineering

GARCIA, G., W. C. HICKEY and E. J. DORTIGNAC 1963 An Inexpensive Run-off Plot. *Research Note RM12, Forest Service, United States Department of Agriculture*

GLEASON, C. H. 1957 Reconnaissance Methods of Measuring Erosion. *Journal of Soil and Water Conservation* 12, 3, 105–107

HAYWARD, J. A. 1968 The Measurement of Soil Loss from fractional acre plots. *Lincoln Papers in Water Resources, 5, New Zealand Agricultural Engineering Institute, Lincoln College*

HAYWARD, J. A. 1969 The Use of Fractional Acre Plots to Predict Soil Loss from Mountain Catchments. *Lincoln Papers in Water Resources, 7, New Zealand Agricultural Engineering Institute, Lincoln College*

HUDSON, N. W. 1957 The Design of Field Experiments on Soil Erosion. *Journal of Agricultural Engineering Research* 2, 1, 56–67

HUDSON, N. W. 1964a Field Measurements of Accelerated Soil Erosion in Localized Areas. *Rhodesia Agricultural Journal* 31, 3, 46–48

HUDSON, N. W. 1964b A Review of Artificial Rainfall Simulators. *Research Bulletin 7, Department of Conservation and Extension, Rhodesia*

HUDSON, N. W. 1965 *The Influence of Rainfall on the Mechanics of Soil Erosion.* M.Sc. Thesis, University of Cape Town

JACKSON, D. C. 1964 Sludge Sampling Techniques for Soil Erosion Research. *Research Bulletin 12, Department of Conservation and Extension, Salisbury, Rhodesia*

KOHNKE, H., and R. B. HICKOK 1944 An Automatic Aliquot Run-off Sampler. *Proceedings of the Soil Science Society of America,* 8, 444–447

MEYER, L. D., and D. L. McCUNE 1958 Rainfall Simulator for Run-off Plots. *Agricultural Engineering* 39, 10, 644–648

MEYER, L. D. 1965 Simulation of Rainfall for Erosion Control Research. *Transactions of the American Society of Agricultural Engineering,* 8, 1, 63–65

MORIN, J., D. GOLDBERG, and I. SEGINER 1967 A Rainfall Simulator with a Rotating Disc. *Transactions of the American Society of Agricultural Engineering* 10, 1, 74–77, 79

MUTCHLER, C. K. 1963 Run-off Plot design and installation for Soil Erosion Studies. *Agricultural Research Service* 41–79, *United States Department of Agriculture*

MUTCHLER, C. K. and L. F. HERMSMEIER 1965 A Review of Rainfall Simulators. *Transactions of the American Society of Agricultural Engineering,* 8, 1, 67–68

PARSHALL, R. L. 1950 Measuring Water in Irrigation Channels with Parshall Flumes and Small Weirs. *Circular* 843, *United States Department of Agriculture, Soil Conservation Service*

SHERRY, S. P. 1953 The effect of different methods of brushwood disposal upon site conditions in Wattle Plantations. Experimental layout and apparatus designed for the measurement of run-off and soil loss. *Wattle Research Institute Report for* 1952–1953

SWANSON, N. P. 1965 Rotating-Boom Rainfall Simulator. *Transactions of the American Society of Agricultural Engineering* 8, 1, 71–72

UNITED STATES DEPARTMENT OF AGRICULTURE 1962 Field Manual for Research in Agricultural Hydrology. *Agricultural Handbook* 224

WILM, H. G. 1943 The Application and Measurement of Artificial Rainfall in Types FA and F Infiltrometers. *Transactions of the American Geophysical Union* 24, 480–487

WISCHMEIER, W. H. 1955 Punch Cards Record Run-off and Soil Loss Data. *Agricultural Engineering,* 36, 664–666.

Chapter 16   Pollution and soil erosion

16.1   Erosion as a source of pollution

When discussing in section 2.2.5 the relative importance of different forms of erosion the point was made that the problem may be either the reduced capacity for agricultural production or the nuisance of the products of erosion. The greater part of this book has been concerned with the aspect of the loss of production, but because of the present surge of public concern about damage to the environment, we should also consider the relation between soil erosion and pollution. In fact erosion is a very small part of the overall pollution problem, but the soil conservationist gladly accepts the prevention of pollution as another reason for better soil conservation.

In the current concern about present-day pollution there is sometimes a tendency to over-emphasize it as a product of modern technology. Certainly we have recently acquired some new and most undesirable pollutants, but comparisons with the past should be made carefully and accurately. The River Thames in London is today heavily polluted by every kind of contamination—but it is only the nature of the pollution which has changed not the basic problem. Over a hundred years ago it was just as filthy, but then the main problem was crude sewage. That problem was reduced by the provision of sewage treatment plants, and today's pollution problems are also capable of solution as soon as we are prepared to pay the price.

Pollution by industrial waste is not new either, but is now happening on a larger scale. Many rivers in industrial areas of Europe have been polluted for a century. Some, like the Trent which drains from the industrial centre of England, are being steadily improved by better treatment of industrial wastes.

The ramifications of pollution are endless, and so arbitrary boundaries must be set for the discussion in this chapter. No attempt will be made to discuss pollution outside the areas where it is directly and significantly linked with soil erosion. There are some other important agricultural aspects of pollution, especially the discharge of organic wastes. The effluent from livestock buildings, the drainage from silage, and the waste water from crop processing, all present particular problems but they are not connected with soil conservation. Neither will air pollution be considered, for dust storms and wind erosion have been discussed in chapter 14, and the other problem, contamination from aerial spraying of pesticides is outside the scope of this book.

The three topics related to erosion which will be discussed are the problems resulting from the soil which is eroded, from plant nutrients in surface run-off, and from the contamination of run-off by pesticides.

SEDIMENT POLLUTION

16.2.1   The problems caused by sediment

The effects of the soil particles carried off in surface run-off are many and varied. Some have direct and calculable costs such as the increased cost of treatment of water supplies for domestic, industrial, or agricultural use. Others are less obvious and may be difficult to assess in economic terms, for example the lower penetration of sunlight in turbid water resulting in reduced photosynthesis in the aquatic plant life. There may even be beneficial effects of sediment. The most frequently quoted example of this aspect is the contribution to fertility from the silt deposited by the flood waters of the River Nile, although the real value of this has recently been questioned (KEIM 1969). In other circumstances the deposition of sediment on productive land may impair its productivity. Deposition within the river can cause many problems like the blanketing of fish spawning grounds or the blocking of outlets or inlets. A change in sediment load can upset a stable river system. The most common example is that when a silt-laden river deposits its silt in a storage dam, the silt-free stream below the dam adjusts to the new regime by scouring the channel, and may undermine the foundations of bridges or dams.

As well as the costs incurred by the purification of silty water, there are likely to be costs arising from using the untreated water. It adds to the wear of mechanical plant like pumps, distribution systems, and irrigation sprinklers, and when applied to the land it may interfere with infiltration rates, and can only complicate irrigation and drainage practices (ASCE 1969).

In a summary of the river pollution problem ROBINSON (1971) suggests that sediment is certainly the greatest pollutant in terms of volume, but that other sources such as industrial discharges can be as significant and may well be more difficult to correct. The soil conservation works described in previous chapters are on the whole effective, and certainly the obvious problem of sedimentation of reservoirs can be greatly reduced by the application of known techniques. STALL (1962) estimated that deposition in 9 reservoirs in Illinois could be reduced by 43 to 92 per cent by watershed conservation, a figure in accord with a more recent estimate by HAYES (1970) who suggest that soil conservation practices on cropland can reduce soil erosion by more than 90 per cent.

16.2.2   From the land to the reservoir

Not all the soil which is eroded from agricultural land becomes sediment in reservoirs. Some is held in conservation works and some by vegetation, or in pools and hollows. Of the soil which does get into the streams and rivers, only a part is deposited in the reservoir, and some is carried over the spillway. This can be expressed in the form of an equation.

$$\text{Reservoir Sedimentation} =$$
$$\text{Gross erosion} \times \text{delivery ratio} \times \text{trap efficiency.}$$

Gross erosion is the total amount of soil movement within the catchment, including all forms of wash and rill erosion from agricultural land, gully and stream bank erosion, and erosion from non-agricultural sources such as highway construction, or building development.

Delivery ratio is the ratio of the amount of silt arriving in the stream compared with the gross movement of soil from its original place, ie it allows for the soil which moves but is trapped before it gets to the stream. Naturally the delivery ratio of soil eroded from gullies is very high since it falls directly into the stream, but with soil lost from grazing land or arable land there is more opportunity for it to be intercepted.

Trap efficiency is the ratio of sediment caught in the reservoir compared with the total load in the stream, ie it measures how much is deposited in the reservoir and how much is carried over the spillway when the reservoir is full. The amount trapped in the reservoir depends mainly on the proportion of the flow which is stored. A reservoir storing the whole flow has no outflow and a 100% trap efficiency, while a small storage reservoir on a large river will pass most of the flood water and so also pass on a lot of the sediment. The size of the reservoir also affects the amount trapped. Two studies of American data give guides on how to estimate the trap efficiency. DENDY ET AL (1967) use the *C/W ratio*, which is the ratio of the capacity in acre-feet to the catchment area (in American terminology the watershed area) in square miles. Table 16.1, from DENDY, shows the average annual percentage depletion of storage.

TABLE 16.1 *Average annual depletion of storage (percent)*
(from DENDY ET AL 1967)

Capacity (acre-feet)	C/W Ratio				
	1	*1–10*	*10–100*	*100–1 000*	*1 000*
0–10	7·2	4·0	2·2	3·7	0
10–100	50·5	7·2	2·4	2·1	0·3
100–1 000	0·5	1·8	1·5	0·6	0·2
1 000–10 000	0	1·6	1·2	0·5	0·1
10 000–100 000	0	1·0	0·8	0·3	0·1
100 000–1 000 000	0	0	0·5	0·2	0·1
over 1 000 000	0	0	0·1	0·2	0·1

The other approach, preferred by BRUNE (1953) uses the ratio of capacity to inflow, the *C/I ratio*, which is the C/W ratio (acre-feet of storage per square mile of drainage area) divided by the average annual inflow (acre-feet of run-off per square mile of drainage area). BRUNE'S results are shown approximately in figure 16.1.

16.2.3 Sources of sediment

The term gross erosion was used to include all forms of erosion within

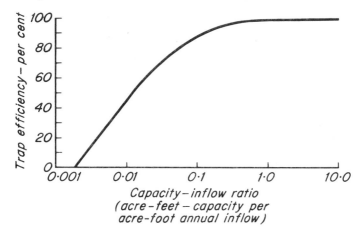

FIGURE 16.1 *The trap efficiency of reservoirs (from* BRUNE *1953)*

the catchment, but some will be more important than others as producers of silt. In terms of loss of productivity, the loss of top soil by splash and wash and rill erosion is most important, and the loss of land from gully erosion is relatively unimportant. However, in terms of the production of sediment in streams and rivers, the soil coming from the collapse of gully walls is important because it all goes directly into the stream flow. The proportion of sediment due to sheet erosion in the United States was analysed by GLYMPH (1957) who found that sheet erosion was 'clearly the dominant source' and accounted for between 11 and 100% of the total sediment. However, there are several reasons for caution in using this result to predict what may happen in other countries. If the proportion of arable land is small, as is the case in many developing countries, there may be much more opportunity for the sheet-eroded soil to be stopped on its way to the rivers. The soil type is also important, and the fine-grained silt loams and loess soils of the American Mid-west will be much more easily carried to the streams than, for example, the coarse-grained granite sands of southern Africa. A third reason why GLYMPH's result in America may not apply elsewhere is that variations in rainfall erosivity may also influence the kind of erosion. A rainfall regime where much of the erosion damage is caused by infrequent severe storms could be expected to give rise to more erosion of the dramatic or gully-cutting type, than when the main effect is wash erosion from evenly spread rain. This concept is in line with the thought developed in section 4.5.3 that the proportion of damage caused by isolated storms may well be higher in tropical Africa than in the United States.

There certainly seem to be large and significant variations in the sediment yields of the major rivers of different continents. Table 16.2 shows the summarized data from many surveys reviewed by HOLEMAN

(1968) who concluded that Asia yields something like 80% of the sediment reaching the oceans annually.

TABLE 16.2   *Summary of annual sediment yields*
             (from HOLEMAN *1968)*

Continent	Measured annual sediment yields of rivers to oceans		Total sediment yield to oceans extrapolated from measured data	
	Measured drainage area (square miles)	*Annual suspended sediment discharge (tons per square mile)*	*Total area draining to oceans (square miles)*	*Total annual suspended sediment discharge (10^9 tons)*
North America	2 464 649	245	8 000 000	1·96
South America	3 820 370	160	7 500 000	1·20
Africa	3 146 680	70	7 700 000	0·54
Australia	414 610	115	2 000 000	0·23
Europe	1 357 357	90	3 600 000	0·32
Asia	4 212 830	1 530	10 400 000	15·91
Total	15 416 496	Average 520	39 200 000	20·16

Non-agricultural activities can result in high rates of sediment production from small areas. The drastic disturbance of vegetation and top soil necessarily associated with highway construction or urban housing development is bound to put the soil in a highly erodible condition, even if this is only a temporary situation. DAWDY (1967) draws attention to the 'drastic effects' of urbanization on sediment yield during the construction period, and studies of the erosion effects of residential development in Maryland are reported by GUY (1963) and of suburban highway construction by VICE ET AL (1969). In the State of Maryland recent legislation makes it compulsory to apply approved conservation practices to development sites (HAWKINS 1971). The problems of erosion associated with roads and highways were discussed in section 13.3.

16.2.4   Factors affecting Sediment Yield

Soil type and land use

In chapter 10 the Universal Soil-Loss Equation showed that on arable land the effect of management far outweighed differences in soil type. But soil type becomes more important when we consider how much of the eroded soil actually reaches the stream, and the larger the catchment of the stream or river the less does the silt load depend on management, and the more it becomes a function of soil and climate.

Catchment size

There is an association between rates of sediment production and size of catchment. This is far from saying that the two are correlated or that sediment can be predicted from catchment area, but if the data from a large number of rivers is plotted as sediment yield against size of catchment then it is possible to draw an envelope which encloses a chosen percentage of the plotted points. An example is shown in figure 16.2 but this technique must be used with care because so many other factors also affect the issue.

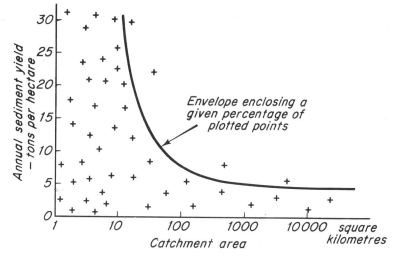

FIGURE 16.2   *The form of the relationship between sediment production and catchment area*

Climate and rainfall

The relationship between sediment production and mean annual rainfall has been investigated on a world scale by FOURNIER (1969) and in the United States by LANGBEIN and SCHUMM (1958). The general relationship is shown in figure 16.3 and is similar to that between erosion and rainfall in figure 1.3, that is in very dry conditions there is no surface run-off and no sediment movement and in high rainfall the vegetation prevents erosion, so there is a peak at medium values of rainfall. In the south-west of the United States the peak observed by LANGBEIN and SCHUMM was at about 300 mm of rain, but this could well vary if the soil, climate, topography, and land use were different.

The relative part played by the infrequent heavy storm, compared with the smaller storm which happens more often, was discussed in section 4.5.3 in the context of damage to arable land, and in section 16.2.3 in the context of sheet erosion compared with other forms. When considered in terms of sediment production the balance moves slightly towards a greater contribution from the large storm. This is logical for in large storms the interception of run-off and silt load between the source and the river is likely to be a smaller proportion than in small storms, that is the delivery ratio will be higher in the large storms. PIEST (1963) summarizes the position found in reservoirs in the United States as more than half the total sediment coming from storms with a return period of more than one year.

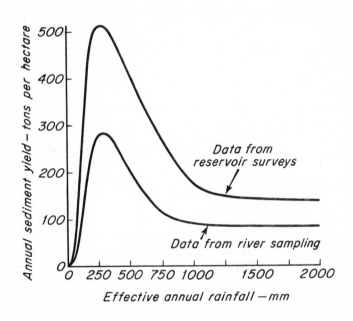

FIGURE 16.3   *The effect of rainfall on sediment yield (from* LANGBEIN AND SCHUMM *1958). Effective rainfall is the annual rainfall adjusted for the effect of annual temperature*

16.2.5   Control of sedimentation

The best and simplest way of reducing sedimentation is to prevent or control the erosion at its source. Other approaches are to intercept the sediment before it gets into the reservoir, or to minimize the amount which remains in the reservoir. Permanent interception by dams or basins designed as silt traps is effective, but this is usually found to be either temporary or expensive. Small cheap silt trap dams soon fill up, and there may not be suitable sites for a second generation. Silt traps with large capacity are likely to be expensive because being upstream they are likely to be on steeper watercourses. The storage capacity achieved per unit construction cost is often lower for the silt traps than the main reservoir, and in that case it may well be cheaper to raise the height of the main dam and store the silt there.

In the case of reservoirs where the outflow and water level are controlled it may be possible to reduce the sediment by selecting the least sediment-laden floodwater to fill the dam. The concentration of sediment usually reaches a peak ahead of the hydrograph peak as shown in figure 16.4 and it may be possible to leave the floodgates open allowing the muddiest flow to pass downstream, and then to store the later flood. This technique requires sufficient knowledge to predict the river's behaviour in order to decide the optimum time to start filling the reservoir.

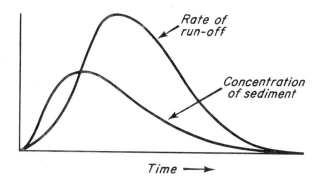

FIGURE 16.4 *The timing of peak rates of run-off and of sediment concentration*

Emptying out the sediment from the reservoir basin would seem to be a fairly obvious solution, but is disappointingly ineffective. In special situations dredging or siphoning sludge over the dam wall may be practical, but the direct removal by standard earthmoving techniques such as bulldozers and carry-alls is usually too expensive. If the deposit is usable as gravel or sand, or as construction fill, it may be economic to remove it, but it is more often just mud, hard to handle and difficult to dispose of, and in this case it may be cheaper to build new capacity.

16.3 CHEMICAL POLLUTION FROM FERTILIZERS

A point sometimes overlooked by those who point an accusing finger is that plant nutrients are highly desirable on the land, where they are applied at considerable expense, so the farmer wishes more than anyone to stop them leaving his land. The problem is therefore very different from that of industrial wastes, where the factory is trying to get rid of an undesirable as cheaply as possible.

16.3.1   The problems of plant nutrient pollution

The most important problem arising from the movement of plant nutrients is the loss of fertility. In economic terms this far outweighs the nuisance caused by the chemicals in the run-off.

The question of whether contamination from fertilizers is important depends on the use of the water. For irrigation water, nitrogen and phosphate in the water could well be an advantage, while industrial uses are not likely to be adversely affected at the concentrations usually found. On the other hand contamination of domestic supplies may be a problem. There is no cheap effective treatment for the removal of phosphates, nitrates or chlorides, and there may be direct health hazards—for example nitrates can produce a condition in infants known as *methemoglobinemia*.

The most frequently occurring problem arising from pollution by plant nutrients is the effect on the biological balance in streams, rivers, and lakes. The natural balance between aquatic life and its environment seem to be particularly vulnerable to outside disturbances in lakes. Young lakes tend to have low levels of plant nutrients and are called *oligotrophic* (few nutrients). The natural process is for the level to increase as surface run-off brings in fresh supplies of nutrients, until the lake becomes *mesotrophic* (of intermediate nutrient status), and finally *eutrophic* (high nutrients).

Eutrophication is the term given to the acceleration of the normal process when there is an increased inflow of nutrients. When a lake goes eutrophic there is a rapid, often spectacular, growth in algae, called the algae *bloom* by water engineers, and a number of consequential problems. The algae can add undesirable taste or odour to drinking water, can cause problems with the clogging of filters, and can lower the available oxygen so that fish and other aquatic life is affected.

16.3.2   Sources of plant nutrients

The two elements which are the main problems are nitrogen and phosphorous, and these come from many sources, but the proportion coming from agricultural land is usually a large part of the total. Three main studies are worth quoting. One of the earliest detailed studies was carried out on a group of lakes in Wisconsin by SAWYER (1947) who found that treated sewage effluents formed 15% of the inflow, but contributed 75% of the nitrogen and 88% of the phosphate, the remainder coming from agricultural run-off. A study in England on the Great Ouse River (OWENS and WOOD 1968) also showed a high proportion of phosphate coming from sewage (80%), but less than 20% of the nitrogen from sewage with the remainder coming from agricultural land. However, these results may be influenced by unusually high proportions of sewage discharge and the overall assessment by the Task Force of the

American Water Works Association (McCARTY 1967) is rather different. Their conclusion was that run-off from agricultural land is by far the greatest contributor of both nitrogen and phosphate, as shown in table 16.3.

TABLE 16.3 *Estimate of nutrient contributions from various sources (from McCARTY 1967)*

Source	Nitrogen (millions of lb/year)	Phosphorus (millions of lb/year)
Domestic waste	1 100–1 600	200–500
Industrial waste	> 1 000	*
Rural run-off:		
Agricultural land	1 500–15 000	120–1 200
Non-agricultural land	400–1 900	150–750
Farm animal waste	> 1 000	*
Urban run-off	110–1 100	11–170
Rainfall	30–590	3–9

* Insufficient data available to make estimate

16.3.3 The extent of chemical pollution

When erosion takes place from arable land, the eroded soil nearly always has a higher concentration than the soil left. This is partly because the nutrients are likely to be greater in the top layers of soil, and partly because the finer fractions are more easily washed away, and the nutrients, particularly phosphorous, are adsorbed on to the particle surface, and so more common in fine particles with a greater surface area. The ratio of plant nutrients in the eroded soil to those in the parent material is called the enrichment ratio and some values are shown in table 16.4. The general pattern is that while total loss of

TABLE 16.4 *Enrichment ratios (from HUDSON AND JACKSON 1959)*

Plant nutrients	Extreme values		Majority values	
	Low	High	Low	High
Nitrogen	1·35	4·20	1·90	2·30
Organic carbon	1·35	4·20	1·80	2·20
Phosphorus	1·15	5·56	2·20	2·60

nutrients increases with total loss of solids, a dilution effect accompanies higher soil loss and the concentration (and hence enrichment ratio) decreases. Similar enrichment ratios have been reported by FIPPIN (1945), and by MASSEY and JACKSON (1952). A general review of plant nutrient losses is given by BARROWS and KILMER (1963).

Soluble nutrients, like nitrate nitrogen, will be mainly linked with run-off and phosphate will be mainly linked with the solids of erosion. The interchange of phosphate between the two has been studied recently by LATTERELL ET AL (1971), who showed that sediment has a high capacity to remove ortho-phosphate from solution, but subsequent release will only occur when the concentration in the water is low. In other words the fear need not be taken too seriously that sediment might act as a storage bank of pollution which could be subsequently released into the water.

16.3.4   Control of chemical pollution

Theoretically it should be possible to adjust the application of fertilizer so that all is taken up by the plants, leaving no surplus to be leached out and form a pollution problem. In practice there will always be some leaching losses, although this is not at all the farmer's wish or intention. In areas of high rainfall the surplus will be removed by surface or subsurface drainage, and this is bound to contain soluble nutrients. The only practical solutions are to minimize surface run-off and surface erosion and thus reduce the supply of nutrients to surface waters.

16.4   POLLUTION BY PESTICIDES

16.4.1   The extent of the problem

The wider issues of the pollution of the environment by pesticides have been given prominent attention since the publication of the emotive and prejudiced, but brilliantly successful *Silent Spring* by RACHEL CARSON. This drew attention to the alarming extent to which the long-lasting pesticides were building up in the soil, in natural waters, in wild life and domestic animals, and even in man. This is a huge subject worthy of much detailed discussion and argument, but our present purpose must be limited to considering only those aspects which are directly linked to erosion because of the pesticides used in agriculture and contained in surface run-off and eroded soil. As in the case of chemical pollution from fertilizers, the problems relate mainly to the contamination of water supplies, and like the simpler chemicals, one part of the problem is that simple, cheap, and effective methods are not available for removing the pollutants. There are the same problems of odour and taste, but the most important is the health hazard. All pesticides are used because of their destructive action on some living organism, and they all too frequently also affect other living things. One particularly noticeable feature of pesticide pollution is the way in which harmless concentrations of a residual chemical can be built up through the food chain cycle, particularly those chemicals which like DDT are firmly held in body tissues. An example quoted by MELLANBY (1967) is an American lake with a concentration of DDD (a close relative of DDT) of 0·015 parts per million. The concentrations at successive stages in the food chain were, the plankton had 5 parts per million, small fish 10, large fish up to 100, and predatory fish-eating birds 1600 parts per million, which was fatal.

Residual pesticides are on the whole not readily soluble, and the transport mechanism is that, like phosphate, they are adsorbed on to the surface of fine soil particles and carried in suspension. Recent studies of the movement of pesticides from experimental plots showed that more than twice as much was carried by the eroded soil as by the run-off water (HAAN 1971).

Another feature is the persistence with which some of the residual pesticides are retained in the soil. Long-term experiments were established in 1949 at Beltsville, Maryland, and showed that after nearly 20 years up to 40% of some pesticides were still present. (NASH and WOOLSON 1967).

16.4.2 The sources of pesticide pollution

When assessing the desirability or undesirability of pesticides many factors should be considered—the cost, the effectiveness, the danger to operators, the available alternatives. In the context of pollution arising from soil erosion the vital question is their persistence, for chemicals which break down rapidly are less likely to be a pollution problem, while the almost indestructible ones can go on being a source of pollution from where they are applied and in all their subsequent movements down streams and rivers to lakes or oceans. A convenient way of looking at them is according to their purpose, ie, whether used as herbicides, fungicides, or insecticides.

Herbicides

Pollution problems do not arise solely from the use of new chemicals, for copper salts and arsenical compounds have been used as herbicides for a very long time, and because they are long lasting they can build up over the years. Small amounts of copper may be deliberately added to reservoirs to control algae, but fish are also susceptible and copper poisoning of fish has been reported from run-off from orchards or vineyards.

The *Dinitro* compounds discovered in the 1930s such as *DNOC* and *Dinoseb* are extremely dangerous to mammals, but they break down rapidly, and anyway have been largely replaced by less dangerous compounds. The next development was the so-called *hormone weed killers*, more properly *auxin type growth regulators*, such as *MCPA* and *2-4-D*.

Cases of fish poisoning by run-off are reported, but again the rapid breakdown of these substances in the soil, within a few weeks of application, makes them not a serious source of pollution.

The latest generation of herbicides are the synthetic organic group, used mainly as non-selective destroyers of all vegetation. Of these *Simazine* and *Monuron* are long-lasting and need to be used carefully, but there is usually no need for them since others are equally effective but less persistent. *Dalapon* lasts 6 or 8 weeks, but is unlikely to be a run-off contaminant, indeed it is frequently used for the control of weeds in and near streams and rivers with no apparent ill effects. *Paraquat* is even shorter lived being neutralized almost at once on contact with the soil. On the whole herbicides do not appear to play a significant part in pollution resulting from erosion.

Fungicides

Fungicides could well be pollutants if it were not for the fact that they are used in limited quantities on limited areas, for they are nearly all long-lasting. *Bordeaux* mixture, based on copper sulphate, and other *sulphur* formulations are widely used to control blight on fruit trees and potatoes. When high concentrations have built up in the soil, local contamination from run-off can harm fish, but dilution soon reduces the concentration to harmless levels. Fungicide dressings applied to seeds are often based on organo-mercury compounds and these too are very persistent. Attention has recently been drawn to dangerously high levels of mercury found in tuna fish in many parts of the world, and there is little doubt that one of the original sources of the mercury is seed dressings. The problem arises because mercury, like DDT, is absorbed by living tissues, and can be concentrated by the food chain from insignificant amounts to dangerous levels.

Insecticides

Of the old-fashioned simple insecticides *arsenic* is long lasting and potentially dangerous in run-off, but is used sparingly and so is not a problem, and *nicotene, rotenone* (derris) and *pyrethrum* are quickly broken down. Starting in 1945 a large group of organo-phosphorous insecticides were produced, many of them so dangerously poisonous that it is questionable whether they should ever have been allowed to go into general use. However they do have the merit of quickly decomposing and so on the whole are not a serious pollution problem. The range includes *Parathion, Malathion, Menazon* and the systemic poisons *OMPA* or *Schradan*, and *Phosphamidon, Disulphaton* or *Phorate*, and *Dichlorvos.*

The organo-chlorines, or chlorinated hydrocarbons, are a very different matter, and most of the charges of pollution are quite rightly directed against this group. DDT is the prime example, an extraordinarily efficient insecticide which has produced almost incalculable benefits in the control of insect-carried diseases and of insect damage to food crops.

Its resistance to break down would be an added advantage as an insecticide if it were not combined with its affinity for fatty living tissues. A considerable proportion of DDT taken into living bodies is retained, resulting in a progressive accumulation which may be further accelerated by a food chain.

The other groups of chlorinated hydrocarbons have similar properties although they vary in their persistence and their toxicity. *Benzene hexachloride* or *BHC*, or *Lindane*, discovered in 1940, is both less stable than DDT, and less poisonous, but it is persistent, and can cause the same kind of problem as DDT. The *cyclodienes* are the latest group of chlorinated hydrocarbons developed since about 1948. The most familiar names are *Aldrin, Dieldrin, Heptachlor, Endosulfan*, and *Endrin*. They are very persistent, and poisonous to mammals in various degrees. Birds are particularly vulnerable and this has led to much of the public outcry against their use.

16.4.3   Control of pesticide pollution

A vast literature confirms the extent to which persistent pesticides are today present in the environment, a comprehensive recent review being that by EDWARDS (1970). There is a widespread appreciation of the seriousness of the problem, and government controls on the use of pesticides is spreading rapidly, with the lead coming from North America and Europe. Control is sometimes by direct legislation, sometimes by voluntary agreements with the manufacturers, and sometimes by recommendations to the users. There is some form of control or restriction on the use of chlorinated hydrocarbons in most States in America, and most countries in Europe, and the most usual targets are DDT, and the aldrin dieldrin group. However EDWARDS summarizes the situation by saying 'Thus it is likely that soil residues of persistent insecticides will begin to diminish, although even if no more persistent insecticides were used, there would certainly still be insecticide residues in soil for several decades to come'.

In Africa and Asia the position is very different, where there is a massive use of DDT, and a large use of aldrin and dieldrin. One might argue that in hungry developing countries *not* using these pesticides is a luxury which they cannot afford.

Apart from the issue of restricted use, the pollution associated with erosion will be effectively controlled if the erosion itself is controlled. Some of the pollutants are in solution, and conservation measures will only have a minor effect on these. Conservation works, and land and crop management often reduce the surface run-off and increase the infiltration, and in this case some solutes may be retained in the soil, but in other situations the increased infiltration could mean more leaching from the soil. On the whole dissolved pollutants are not likely to be much affected by conservation works, and anyway the problems from this kind of pollution are not very important.

The pollution associated with eroded soil is much more serious. There are the physical problems such as the siltation of reservoirs, and the problems caused by plant nutrient and pesticides which are mainly associated with soil movement because the chemicals are attached to the eroding soil particles. Effective control of the soil movement will therefore effectively control the pollution resulting from erosion.

References

AMERICAN SOCIETY OF CIVIL ENGINEERS 1969 Sedimentation Engineering Chapter VI, Economic Aspects of Sedimentation, Task Committee for Preparation of Manual on Sedimentation, *Proceedings of the American Society of Civil Engineers, Hydraulics Division* 95 HY1, 6334, 191–207

BARROWS, H. L. and V. J. KILMER 1963 Plant Nutrient Losses from Soils by Water Erosion, *Advances in Agronomy* 15, 303–316

BRUNE, G. M. 1953 Trap Efficiency of Reservoirs, *Transactions of the American Geophysical Union* 34, 3, 407–417

CARSON, R. 1963 *Silent Spring*, Hamilton, London

DAWDY, D. R. 1967 Knowledge of sedimentation in urban environments, *Proceedings of the American Society of Civil Engineers, Hydraulics Division* 93, HY6, 5595, 235–245

DENDY, F. E., J. A. SPRABERRY and W. A. CHAMPION 1967 Sediment deposition in Reservoirs in the United States, *United States Department of Agriculture*, ARS-41-137

EDWARDS, C. A. 1970 *Persistent pesticides in the environment*, Butterworths, London

FIPPIN, E. O. 1945 Plant Nutrient Losses in Silt and Water in the Tennessee River System, *Soil Science* 60, 223–239

FOURNIER, F. 1969 Suspended Load Transport by Streamflows, *Bulletin of the International Association of Scientific Hydrology* 14, 3, 7–49

GLYMPH, L. M. 1957 Importance of Sheet Erosion as a source of sediment. *Transactions of the American Geophysical Union* 38, 6, 903–907

GUY, H. P. 1963 Residential construction and sedimentation at Kensington, Maryland, *Proceedings of Federal Inter-Agency Sedimentation Conference, United States Department of Agriculture, Miscellaneous Publication* ARS-970, 30–37

HAAN, C. T. 1971 Movement of Pesticides by Run-off and Erosion, *Agricultural Engineering* 52, 1, 25

HAWKINS, A. C. 1971 Maryland's Sediment Control Law, *Journal of Soil and Water Conservation* 26, 1, 28–30

HAYES, W. A. 1970 Less pollution with improved erosion control, *American Society of Agricultural Engineers*, Paper 70–702

HOLEMAN, J. N. 1968 The Sediment Yield of Major Rivers of the World, *Water Resources Research* 4, 737–747

HUDSON, N. W. and D. C. JACKSON 1959 Results achieved in the measurement of erosion and run-off in Southern Rhodesia, *Proceedings 3rd Inter-African Soils Conference*, Dalaba, 1959

KEIM, P. F. 1969 Discussion on 'Economic Aspects of Sedimentation', *Proceedings of the American Society of Civil Engineers, Hydraulics Division*, 95, HY6, 6866, 2165–2166

LATTERELL, J. J., R. F. HOLT and D. R. TIMMONS 1971 Phosphate availability in Lake Sediments, *Journal of Soil and Water Conservation* 26, 1, 21–25

LANGBEIN, W. B. and S. A. SCHUMM 1958 Yield of Sediment in Relation to Mean Annual Precipitation, *Transactions of the American Geophysical Union*, 39, 1076–1084

MASSEY, H. F. and M. L. JACKSON 1952 Selective Erosion of Soil Fertility Constituents, *Soil Science Society of American Proceedings* 16, 4

MCCARTY, P. L. (Chairman) 1967 Sources of Nitrogen and Phosphorous in Water Supplies, Report of Task Group 2610P, *Journal of American Water Works Association* 59, 344–366

MELLANBY, K. 1967 *Pesticides and Pollution*, Collins, London

NASH, R. G. and E. A. WOOLSON 1967 Persistence of Chlorinated Hydrocarbon Insecticides in Soil, *Science*, 157, 924

OWENS, M. and G. WOOD 1968 Some aspects of the eutrophication of water, *Water Research* 2, 151

PIEST, R. F. 1963 The role of the large storm as a sediment contributor, *Federal Inter-Agency Sedimentation Conference, United States Department of Agriculture, Miscellaneous Publication* 970

ROBINSON, A. R. 1971 Sediment, Our Greatest Pollutant, *Agricultural Engineering* 52, 1, 26

SAWYER, C. N. 1947 Fertilization of Lakes by Agricultural and Urban Drainage, *New England Water Works Association* LX1, 2, 109–127

STALL, J. B. 1962 Soil Conservation can reduce reservoir sedimentation, *Public Works Magazine*, September, 1962

VICE, R. B., H. P. GUY and G. E. FERGUSON 1969 Sediment Movement in an area of Suburban Highway Construction, Scott Run Basin, Fairfax County, Virginia, 1961–64, *United States Geological Survey Water Supply Paper* 1591-E, 41

Appendix 1

SOME CONVERSION FACTORS FROM METRIC OR SI UNITS TO IMPERIAL UNITS

Linear measure

1 kilometre	= 0·6214 mile		1 mile	= 1·609 kilometre
1 metre	= $\begin{cases} 39\cdot37 \text{ inches} \\ 3\cdot2808 \text{ feet} \end{cases}$		1 yard	= 0·9144 metre
			1 foot	= 0·3048 metre
1 millimetre	= 0·03937 inch		1 inch	= 25·4 millimetres

Square measure

1 square kilometre	= 0·3861 square mile	= 247·1 acres
1 hectare	= 2·471 acre	= 107640 square feet
1 square metre	= 10·764 square feet	= 1·196 square yard
1 square centimetre	= 0·155 square inch	
1 square millimetre	= 0·00155 square inch	
1 square mile	= 2·5899 square kilometres	
1 acre	= 0·4047 hectare	
1 square yard	= 0·836 square metre	
1 square foot	= 0·0929 square metre	
1 square inch	= 645·2 square millimetres	

Cubic measure

1 cubic metre	= 35·314 cubic feet	= 1·308 cubic yard
1 cubic yard	= 0·7645 cubic metre	
1 cubic foot	= 0·02832 cubic metre	= 28·317 litres
1 cubic inch	= 16·38716 cubic centimetres	

Weight

1 metric ton	= 0·9842 ton (of 2240 pounds)	= 2204·6 pounds
	= 1·1023 ton (of 2000 pounds)	
1 kilogram	= 2·2046 pounds	= 35·274 ounces
1 ton (of 2240 pounds)	= 1·016 metric ton	= 1016 kilograms
1 pound	= 0·4536 kilogram	= 453·6 grams

Measures of Soil Loss

1 metric ton/km^2 = 0·00446 tons/acre (2000 lb)

                                = 0·004 tons/acre (2240 lb)

1 kilogram/hectare   = 0·895 lb/acre

Appendix 2

COMMON AND BOTANICAL NAMES OF SOME GRASSES AND
PLANTS COMMONLY USED IN SOIL CONSERVATION

A Grasses used for lining channels and waterways

Buffalo grass in Australia (and sometimes in America) (Also called St Augustine grass in West Africa and Crab grass in Jamaica)	*Stenotaphrum secundatum*
But Buffalo grass in America can also mean	*Buchloë dactyloides*
Bermuda grass in America	*Cynodon dactylon*
Star grass in Africa	
Couch grass	
Quick grass	*Cynodon* spp
Kentucky bluegrass or	
Smooth-stalked meadow grass	*Poa pratensis*
Smooth brome grass	*Bromus inermis*
Blue grama	*Bouteloua gracilis*
Tall fescue	*Festuca elatior* (or *Arundinacea*)
Wheatgrass	*Agropyron* spp
Centipede grass	*Eremochloa ophiuroides*
Weeping love grass	*Eragrostis curvula*
Swaziland finger grass	*Digitaria Swazilandensis*
Pangola grass	*Digitaria decumbens*
Kikuyu grass	*Pennisetum clandestinum*
Canary grass	*Phalaris canariensis*
Guinea grass	*Panicum maximum*
Bahia grass	*Paspalum notatum*

B Some plants used in gully control

Kudzu vine	*Pueraria thunbergiana*
Tropical Kudzu	*Pueraria phaseolides*
Taiwan Kudzu	*Pueraria tonkinensis*
Centrosema	*Centrosema pubescens*
Reed canary grass	*Phalaris arundinacea*
Common reed	*Phragmytes* spp
Lespedezah	*Lespedeza sericea* *Lespedeza juncea*
Grama grasses	*Bouteloua* spp
Bluestem grasses	*Andropogon* spp
Saltbush	*Atriplex* spp
Sand-bar willow	*Salix exigua*

Indexes

Subject index

Index of names